WOBURN COLLEGIATE INSTITUTE

2222 ELLESMERE RD. — S ARBOROUGH, ONT.

Date Rec'd	NAME	Class	Date Ret'd
	HELEN KIM	5K	SEP 5 89.
	Alison Herron	5F	
	Vincent Cooney	OACF	01/02

| LOAN BOOK NUMBER | 88 - 34 |

ALGEBRA & GEOMETRY

Series General Editor
Ronald G. Dunkley

Text General Editor
William J. Gilbert

Authors
Edwin Anderson   Peter W.D. Crippin   Larry Davidson   Frank J. Rachich
Frank A. Zorzitto

Holt, Rinehart and Winston of Canada, Limited

Series General Editor

Ronald G. Dunkley
University of Waterloo
Waterloo, Ontario

Text General Editor

William J. Gilbert
University of Waterloo
Waterloo, Ontario

Authors

Edwin Anderson
University of Waterloo
Waterloo, Ontario

Peter W.D. Crippin
Woburn Collegiate
Scarborough Board
of Education, Ontario

Larry Davidson
University of Waterloo
Waterloo, Ontario

Frank J. Rachich
Ingersoll District Collegiate
Oxford County Board of
Education, Ontario

Frank A. Zorzitto
University of Waterloo
Waterloo, Ontario

Reviewing Consultants

Bruce Dancy
Martingrove Collegiate
Etobicoke Board of Education
Etobicoke, Ontario

Leslie Khan
Saint Paul High School
Welland County RCSSB
Niagara Falls, Ontario

Fred Kurban
Lester B. Pearson Collegiate
Scarborough Board of Education
Scarborough, Ontario

Andy Patterson
Saunders Secondary School
London Board of Education
London, Ontario

Production Coordinator
Francine Geraci

Graphic Design, Art, and Assembly
Blue Line Productions Inc.

Cover Photo by
Henry Reis/Masterfile

Executive Editor
Ken Leland

Content Editor
Santo D'Agostino

Copy Editor
Freya Godard

Canadian Cataloguing in Publication Data

Main entry under title:

Algebra and geometry

Includes index.
ISBN 0-03-922048-6

1. Algebra. 2. Geometry. I. Anderson, Edwin.
II. Gilbert, William J., 1941–

QA154.2.A62 1988   512'.12   C88-093060-8

The metric usage in this text conforms to the standards established by the Canadian General Standards Board.

Printed in Canada
1 2 3 4 5 92 91 90 89 88

Table of Contents

Foreword

The ordering of the topics could be changed, and the chapter on complex numbers could follow Chapter 4. Various sections are optional and are marked as such.

Even the best of mathematicians make mistakes. However, they usually discover most of them by checking their results. Students should get into the habit of checking their answers wherever possible (before they turn to the answer in the back of the book). We have given some indication of checks that can be performed at the end of many of the examples. For example, the computation of a cross product is prone to error and should always be checked by using the dot product. A check does not have to be infallible to be useful; even a rough estimate of an answer can often catch mistakes.

The exercises at the end of each section are mainly routine applications of the material in that section, whereas the problems are more challenging and may require the use of other mathematical ideas or approaches.

Answers involving square roots are normally left in that form. When we have to make approximations, we normally calculate numbers to two decimal places, and angles in degrees to the nearest degree.

Table of Symbols

Symbol	Meaning
$\boldsymbol{R}$	Real numbers
$\boldsymbol{R}^2$	2-space, $\{(a, b) \mid a, b \in \boldsymbol{R}\}$
$\boldsymbol{R}^3$	3-space, $\{(a, b, c) \mid a, b, c \in \boldsymbol{R}\}$
$\boldsymbol{R}^n$	n-space, $\{(a_1, a_2, a_3, \ldots, a_n) \mid a_i \in \boldsymbol{R}\}$
$\overrightarrow{AB}$	Vector from A to B
$\vec{n}$	Vector
$\vec{i}, \vec{j}, \vec{k}$	Standard basis vectors in $\boldsymbol{R}^3$
$|\vec{n}|$	Length of the vector $\vec{n}$
$\vec{n} \cdot \vec{m}$	Dot product of the vectors $\vec{n}$ and $\vec{m}$
$\vec{n} \times \vec{m}$	Cross product of the vectors $\vec{n}$ and $\vec{m}$
$A \sim B$	Row equivalence of the matrices A and B
A^t	Transpose of the matrix A
A^{-1}	Inverse of the matrix A
$\det A$	Determinant of the matrix A
$|A|$	Determinant of the matrix A
R_θ	Matrix of the rotation through θ
$T: \boldsymbol{R}^n \to \boldsymbol{R}^m$	Transformation from $\boldsymbol{R}^n$ to $\boldsymbol{R}^m$
$P \to Q$	P is mapped to Q
$\sum$	Summation symbol
$n!$	n factorial, $n(n - 1)(n - 2) \cdots (3)(2)(1)$
$\binom{n}{r}$	n choose r, $\dfrac{n!}{r!(n - r)!}$
$\mathbb{Z}$	Integers, $\{\ldots, -3, -2, -1, 0, 1, 2, 3, \ldots\}$
$\mathbb{C}$	Complex numbers, $\{x + yi \mid x, y \in \boldsymbol{R}\}$
i	Square root of -1
$\operatorname{Re} z$	Real part of the complex number z
$\operatorname{Im} z$	Imaginary part of the complex number z
$|z|$	Modulus or absolute value of z
$\bar{z}$	Conjugate of z
$\operatorname{cis} \theta$	$\cos \theta + i \sin \theta$
$e^{i\theta}$	$\cos \theta + i \sin \theta$
$\square$	End of proof or example
	Computer problem

Wind velocity is an example of a vector quantity.

Vectors

A great deal of the mathematics we study in high school traces its roots back many centuries, often to the ancient Greeks. However, the development of vectors is a fairly recent episode in the history of mathematics. The origin of vectors can be traced back to the mid-nineteenth-century work of the great mathematician and physicist, William Rowan Hamilton (1805-1865). Hamilton lived in Dublin, Ireland, and like many other great scientists, he excelled in a number of fields. For example, by the time he was five, he had mastered Latin, Greek, and Hebrew, and by the age of thirteen, he had learned half a dozen more languages.

Hamilton spent 15 years searching for a generalization of complex numbers in the plane to three dimensions. He finally succeeded, in 1843, in discovering a four-dimensional generalization that he called the quaternions. These quaternions had many of the properties of complex numbers, but their multiplication was not commutative. However, it turned out that a by-product of this discovery was more important for mathematics; this was his concept of a three-dimensional **vector** as being a single mathematical object with three components.

In the 1880s, many of Hamilton's ideas were extended, simplified, and applied to mathematical physics and engineering by J. Willard Gibbs (1839-1903) and Oliver Heaviside (1850-1925). Gibbs was instrumental in developing vector analysis for use in statistical mechanics. Much of his work was later used in developing other branches of physics, including quantum theory.

It was well into this century before mathematicians appreciated vectors. Nowadays, vectors are applied not only to problems in mathematics and physics but are also used extensively in the social sciences.

In this book we shall concentrate on vectors in two and three dimensions. These are easier to visualize and are more useful in physical applications, because the simplest mathematical models of the world are three-dimensional. However, most of the ideas developed in this book can be generalized to higher dimensions, where they can be applied to more advanced problems.

1.1 Vectors and Scalars

Many physical quantities, such as length, mass, time, and temperature, can be completely specified by a single real number describing its size or magnitude. Other quantities, such as force, velocity, and acceleration, require a magnitude **and** a direction to describe them. For example, the wind velocity may be 20 km/h coming from the southeast, and the force exerted by gravity on a one-kilogram mass may be 10 newtons in a downward direction. Quantities that have both magnitude and direction are called **vectors**. Quantities that can be described by a single number are called **scalars**.

A **vector** is a quantity that has both magnitude and direction.

Vectors can be represented either geometrically or algebraically. Geometrically, a vector can be represented as a **directed line segment**, which is an arrow running between two points. Its important quantities are its magnitude (or length) and its direction.

Examples of quantities that can be described by vectors are forces, velocities, and electromagnetic fields, because their direction and magnitude must always be specified. On the other hand, quantities such as age, speed, length, and area are described by scalars because their direction is not specified.

If A and B are two points, then the vector represented by the directed line segment from A to B is denoted by $\overrightarrow{AB}$. We may also denote it by a single letter such as $\vec{v}$. The **magnitude or length** of this vector is denoted by $|\overrightarrow{AB}|$ or $|\vec{v}|$ and is the non-negative distance from A to B.

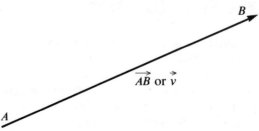

The vector with zero magnitude is called the **zero vector** and is denoted by $\vec{0}$; its direction is undefined.

The word 'vector' is derived from the Latin word "vectus," meaning carried. For example, if one is carried by an airplane or car from point A to point B, the journey can be represented by the vector $\overrightarrow{AB}$.

The vector represented by the directed line segment from B to A is denoted by $\overrightarrow{BA}$ and is called the **opposite** of $\overrightarrow{AB}$; both $\overrightarrow{AB}$ and $\overrightarrow{BA}$ have the same magnitude, but their directions are opposite.

Consider the example of an airplane flying at 500 km/h in a northeasterly direction. We can represent its velocity in a diagram by the vector $\overrightarrow{AB}$ of length 5 cm pointing to the northeast (1 cm represents 100 km/h). In mathematics, 'velocity' is always a vector quantity, whereas 'speed' is the magnitude of the velocity and is a scalar. In this case, the speed of the plane is 500 km/h and its velocity is 500 km/h northeast.

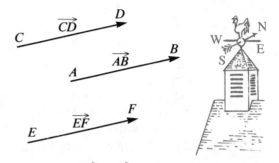

We could also have represented the velocity by the vectors $\overrightarrow{CD}$ or $\overrightarrow{EF}$. The three line segments, from A to B, from C to D, and from E to F, are parallel, have the same length, and point in the same direction.

Equality of Vectors

Two vectors, $\overrightarrow{AB}$ and $\overrightarrow{CD}$, are equal if and only if
1. $\overrightarrow{AB}$ is parallel to $\overrightarrow{CD}$
2. $\overrightarrow{AB}$ has the same length as $\overrightarrow{CD}$ (i.e., $|\overrightarrow{AB}| = |\overrightarrow{CD}|$)
3. the direction from A to B is the same as from C to D

The vectors $\overrightarrow{AB}$ and $\overrightarrow{CD}$ are equal if and only if the directed line segment $\overrightarrow{CD}$ is a translation of the line segment $\overrightarrow{AB}$. This is also equivalent to saying that $ABDC$ is a parallelogram. Every vector can be represented by an infinite number of equivalent directed line segments, provided that they meet the conditions summarized in the box.

We shall see in section 1.5 that vectors can also be characterized algebraically as ordered pairs, ordered triples, etc.

To obtain the algebraic representation of a vector, translate the vector until its initial point is at the origin. The coordinates of its end point is its algebraic description. For example, in the diagram, the end point of $\overrightarrow{OA}$ is (3, 4), so we say that $\overrightarrow{OA}$ = (3, 4).

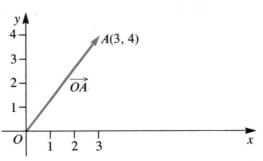

In general, an *n*-tuple of numbers $(x_1, x_2, \ldots, x_n)$ can be considered to be the algebraic representation of the line segment that joins the origin to the point $(x_1, x_2, \ldots, x_n)$ in Euclidean *n*-dimensional space $\boldsymbol{R}^n$.

Exercises 1.1

1. Explain, in your own words, the difference between a vector and a scalar.

2. Explain whether each quantity is a vector or a scalar.

    a. age ˢ   **b.** volume ˢ   **c.** translation √   **d.** momentum √
    e. mass ˢ   **f.** weight √   **g.** frequency ˢ   **h.** magnetic force √
    i. energy ˢ   **j.** density ˢ   **k.** friction √   **l.** temperature ˢ

3. A car is travelling around a circular track at a constant speed. The velocity of the car at the position *A* is along the tangent and is represented by $\overrightarrow{AB}$ in the diagram (1 cm represents 10 km/h). The velocity at *C* is represented by $\overrightarrow{CD}$.

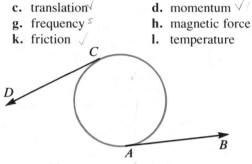

    a. In common-sense terms, state why it is reasonable to represent velocity as a tangent vector.

    b. Explain why $\overrightarrow{AB}$ and $\overrightarrow{CD}$ are usually not equal vectors.

    c. When will the two vectors be equal?

    d. When will their magnitudes be equal?

    e. When will the two vectors be opposite?

    f. At what points will the two vectors be perpendicular to each other?

    g. An occupant of the car can feel acceleration as a force acting upon his or her body. In which direction do you think the acceleration vector lies? (Compare the feelings you get when accelerating quickly on a straight road and in going around a sharp curve.)

Problems 1.1

1. The directed line segments shown are all equivalent and represent the same vector. Find the coordinates of *D*, *F*, *G*, *H*, *I*, and *J*.

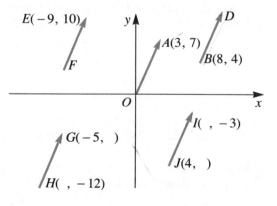

2. The fraction $\frac{3}{4}$ can be represented in many ways, such as $\frac{6}{8}$, $\frac{9}{12}$, or $\frac{30}{40}$. The precise way to define the fraction $\frac{3}{4}$ is as the equivalence class $\left\{\frac{3}{4},\ \frac{6}{8},\ \frac{9}{12},\ \ldots\right\}$ consisting of all ratios representing $\frac{3}{4}$. Under what conditions do the two ratios $\frac{a}{b}$ and $\frac{c}{d}$ represent the same fraction? Similarly, the precise way to define a vector is as an equivalence class of directed line segments. Give such a definition for a vector.

1.2 Vector Addition

In many physical applications of vectors we need to find the combined effect of two vectors. For example, what is the combined effect of two forces acting on an object? How do we find the velocity of an airplane relative to the ground if we know its velocity in the air and the velocity of the wind?

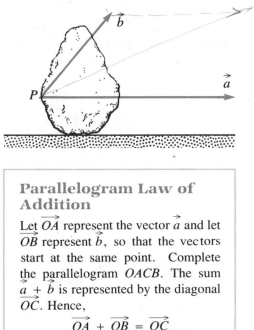

To imagine what the sum of two vectors should be, consider two people trying to move a rock by pushing it with forces $\vec{a}$ and $\vec{b}$. Let us assume that they are both pushing at a point P. The sum of the vectors $\vec{a} + \vec{b}$ is the combined effect of these forces. Their resultant force is represented by the diagonal of the parallelogram with sides along $\vec{a}$ and $\vec{b}$.

Parallelogram Law of Addition

Let $\overrightarrow{OA}$ represent the vector $\vec{a}$ and let $\overrightarrow{OB}$ represent $\vec{b}$, so that the vectors start at the same point. Complete the parallelogram $OACB$. The sum $\vec{a} + \vec{b}$ is represented by the diagonal $\overrightarrow{OC}$. Hence,

$$\overrightarrow{OA} + \overrightarrow{OB} = \overrightarrow{OC}$$

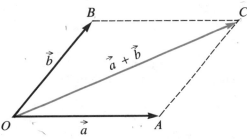

The sum $\vec{a} + \vec{b}$ is also called the **resultant** of $\vec{a}$ and $\vec{b}$. Notice that the magnitude, or length, of $\vec{a} + \vec{b}$ is less than or equal to the combined magnitudes of $\vec{a}$ and $\vec{b}$; that is,

$$|\vec{a} + \vec{b}| \le |\vec{a}| + |\vec{b}|$$

Therefore, when two people try to push the rock as in the example, the effect will be less than the sum of the individual effects. If however, they were to push in the same direction, the magnitude of the resultant would be equal to the sum of the two magnitudes.

In general, if we wish to add the vectors $\vec{a}$ and $\vec{b}$, we have to choose representative line segments $\overrightarrow{OA}$ and $\overrightarrow{OB}$ that start at the same point O. Note, that in the parallelogram $OACB$, $\vec{b} = \overrightarrow{OB} = \overrightarrow{AC}$, so that the sum of $\vec{a}$ and $\vec{b}$ can also be computed by using the triangle OAC.

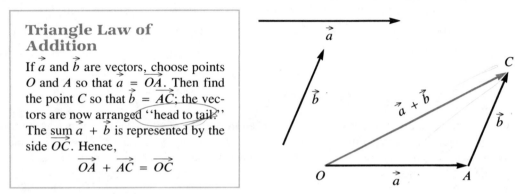

Triangle Law of Addition

If $\vec{a}$ and $\vec{b}$ are vectors, choose points O and A so that $\vec{a} = \overrightarrow{OA}$. Then find the point C so that $\vec{b} = \overrightarrow{AC}$; the vectors are now arranged "head to tail." The sum $\vec{a} + \vec{b}$ is represented by the side $\overrightarrow{OC}$. Hence,

$$\overrightarrow{OA} + \overrightarrow{AC} = \overrightarrow{OC}$$

The Triangle Law can be thought of as follows. Suppose you walk from O to A; you have then moved along the vector $\vec{a} = \overrightarrow{OA}$. If you now walk from A to C, you have moved along $\vec{b} = \overrightarrow{AC}$; your final position would have been the same if you would have walked along the vector $\vec{a} + \vec{b} = \overrightarrow{OC}$.

Example 1. Given the vectors $\vec{a}$, $\vec{b}$, and $\vec{c}$, sketch $\vec{a} + \vec{b}$ and $(\vec{a} + \vec{b}) + \vec{c}$.

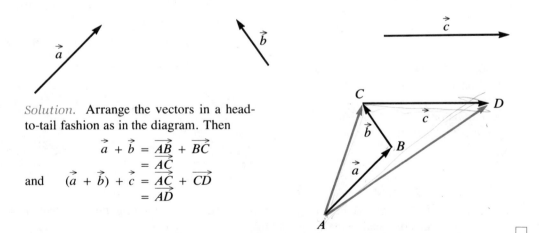

Solution. Arrange the vectors in a head-to-tail fashion as in the diagram. Then

$$\vec{a} + \vec{b} = \overrightarrow{AB} + \overrightarrow{BC}$$
$$= \overrightarrow{AC}$$
and $\quad (\vec{a} + \vec{b}) + \vec{c} = \overrightarrow{AC} + \overrightarrow{CD}$
$$= \overrightarrow{AD}$$

Velocity must always be measured relative to some object or frame of reference. For example, when you walk up the aisle of an airplane, your velocity relative to the plane may be 5 km/h towards the front of the plane, but your velocity relative to the ground will be quite different. On a boat, the speedometer will measure the speed of the boat relative to the water.

Example 2. A sailboat is heading due south, and its speed through the water is 6 knots. If there is a 3 knot current flowing due east, find the velocity of the boat relative to the land.

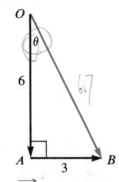

Solution. Since velocity is a vector, we have to find the speed of the boat, relative to the land, and the direction of motion relative to the land. Represent the velocity of the boat relative to the water by $\overrightarrow{OA}$ and the current velocity by $\overrightarrow{AB}$ in a head-to-tail fashion. Then the velocity of the boat, relative to the land, is the resultant

$$\overrightarrow{OA} + \overrightarrow{AB} = \overrightarrow{OB}$$

The speed of the boat relative to the land is the magnitude $|\overrightarrow{OB}|$; by Pythagoras' Theorem the speed is

$$\sqrt{6^2 + 3^2} = 3\sqrt{5}$$
$$\approx 6.7$$

The angle θ satisfies $\tan \theta = \frac{3}{6} = 0.5$ so that θ is approximately $27°$. Hence, the velocity of the boat relative to the land is 6.7 knots in a direction $27°$ east of south. $\square$

Parallel vectors are sometimes called **collinear vectors** because they can be translated so that they lie along a straight line. If a and b are parallel vectors, they can be represented by $\overrightarrow{AB}$ and $\overrightarrow{BC}$, where A, B, and C are collinear points.

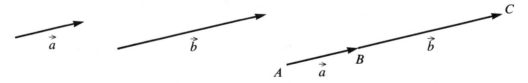

The vectors $\overrightarrow{AB}$ and $\overrightarrow{BA}$ are always parallel, but they point in the opposite direction. Their sum is $\overrightarrow{AB} + \overrightarrow{BA} = \overrightarrow{AA}$, which is the zero vector. The **zero vector** has zero magnitude and undefined direction and is denoted by $\vec{0}$. Hence, $\overrightarrow{AB} + \overrightarrow{BA} = \vec{0}$, and we write $\overrightarrow{BA} = -\overrightarrow{AB}$ for opposite vectors.

To find the difference of two vectors, $\vec{a} - \vec{b}$, add $\vec{a}$ to the opposite of $\vec{b}$. In the diagram, $-\vec{b} = \overrightarrow{OD}$, so by the Parallelogram Law,

$$\vec{a} - \vec{b} = \vec{a} + (-\vec{b})$$
$$= \overrightarrow{OA} + \overrightarrow{OD}$$
$$= \overrightarrow{OE}$$

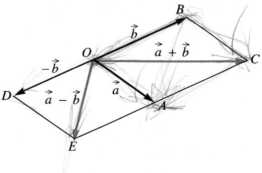

Notice that the diagonal of one parallelogram represents $\vec{a} + \vec{b}$ and the diagonal of the other parallelogram represents $\vec{a} - \vec{b}$.

Alternatively, we could use the Triangle Law to obtain

$$\begin{aligned} \vec{a} - \vec{b} &= \overrightarrow{OA} - \overrightarrow{OB} \\ &= \overrightarrow{OA} + \overrightarrow{BO} \\ &= \overrightarrow{BC} + \overrightarrow{CA} \\ &= \overrightarrow{BA} \\ &= \overrightarrow{OE} \end{aligned}$$

Exercises 1.2

1. Given the forces, $\vec{a}$, $\vec{b}$, and $\vec{c}$, sketch the sums $\vec{a} + \vec{b}$ and $(\vec{a} + \vec{b}) + \vec{c}$.

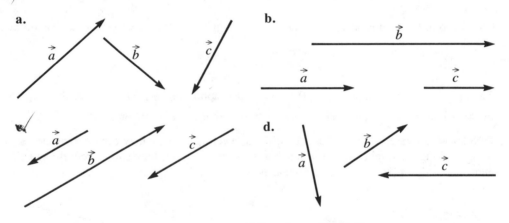

a.

b.

c.

d.

2. Consider the parallelogram $PQRS$, where $\overrightarrow{QP} = \vec{a}$ and $\overrightarrow{PS} = \vec{b}$. Find representatives of the following vectors.

   a. $\vec{a} + \vec{b}$ **b.** $\vec{b} + \vec{a}$ **c.** $\vec{a} - \vec{b}$ **d.** $\vec{b} - \vec{a}$

3. Given the three vectors $\vec{a}$, $\vec{b}$, and $\vec{c}$, construct the following vectors.

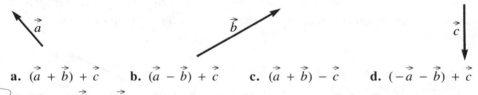

   a. $(\vec{a} + \vec{b}) + \vec{c}$ **b.** $(\vec{a} - \vec{b}) + \vec{c}$ **c.** $(\vec{a} + \vec{b}) - \vec{c}$ **d.** $(-\vec{a} - \vec{b}) + \vec{c}$

4. Two forces, $\vec{F}_1$ and $\vec{F}_2$, acting in the same direction, are applied at P to move a rock.

   a. What is the magnitude of the resultant of these forces?

   b. What force, $\vec{F}$, would keep the rock from moving?

   c. If the force $\vec{F}_1$ is changed to point in the opposite direction and $\vec{F}_2$ is unchanged, describe the new situation in terms of the forces involved.

5. Two forces, $\vec{F}_1$ and $\vec{F}_2$, are applied at the point P to move a rock. The angle between the vectors $\vec{F}_1$ and $\vec{F}_2$ is θ.

a. Draw a diagram to represent the combined effect of the two forces.

b. Calculate the magnitude of the resultant in terms of the magnitudes of $\vec{F}_1$ and $\vec{F}_2$.

c. Copy the diagram and draw the force $\vec{F}_3$ that if applied to P, would prevent the rock from moving.

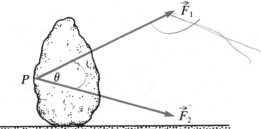

6. An airplane is heading due north with an air speed of 650 km/h. There is a wind blowing directly from the east, and the navigator calculates that they are heading $3°$ west of north over the ground. What is the wind speed?

7. In the rectangular prism, find a vector expression, in terms of $\vec{s}$, $\vec{t}$, and $\vec{u}$, for each vector.

a. $\overrightarrow{GH}$ **b.** $\overrightarrow{JE}$

c. $\overrightarrow{HI}$ **d.** $\overrightarrow{FK}$

e. $\overrightarrow{KH}$ **f.** $\overrightarrow{HK}$

g. $\overrightarrow{EL}$ **h.** $\overrightarrow{HG}$

i. $\overrightarrow{JH}$ **j.** $\overrightarrow{JK}$

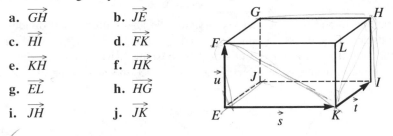

8. Given any vectors $\vec{x}$, $\vec{y}$, and $\vec{z}$, show graphically that
$$(\vec{x} + \vec{y}) + \vec{z} = \vec{x} + (\vec{y} + \vec{z})$$

What property of vectors does this illustrate?

9. By drawing a diagram and choosing appropriate representations, express each sum as a single vector.

a. $\overrightarrow{QT} + \overrightarrow{TX} + \overrightarrow{XY}$ **b.** $\overrightarrow{XY} - \overrightarrow{XT} + \overrightarrow{YX}$

10. Express each sum as a single vector.

a. $\overrightarrow{CA} + \overrightarrow{TC} - \overrightarrow{RC} + \overrightarrow{RT}$ **b.** $\overrightarrow{AB} - \overrightarrow{CB} - \overrightarrow{AD} + \overrightarrow{CD}$

11. If $\vec{a}$ is parallel to $\vec{b}$, but in the opposite direction, express the magnitude of $\vec{a} + \vec{b}$ in terms of the magnitudes of $\vec{a}$ and $\vec{b}$.

12. Show geometrically that the following inequalities are true for any vectors $\vec{a}$ and $\vec{b}$. Under what conditions does each equality hold?

a. $|\vec{a} + \vec{b}| \le |\vec{a}| + |\vec{b}|$ **b.** $|\vec{a} + \vec{b}| \ge ||\vec{a}| - |\vec{b}||$

13. The diagonals of a parallelogram $ABCD$ meet at the point E. Show that

$$\overrightarrow{EA} + \overrightarrow{EB} + \overrightarrow{EC} + \overrightarrow{ED} = \vec{0}$$

14. If K is the midpoint of AB and P is the midpoint of CD, show that

$$\overrightarrow{PK} + \overrightarrow{PK} = \overrightarrow{CA} + \overrightarrow{DB}$$

Problems 1.2

1. Recall that the three medians of a triangle ABC intersect in a point G and that G divides each median in a 2:1 ratio. Show that

$$\overrightarrow{GA} + \overrightarrow{GB} + \overrightarrow{GC} = \vec{0}$$

2. Two non-zero vectors $\vec{u}$ and $\vec{v}$ are such that $|\vec{u} + \vec{v}| = |\vec{u} - \vec{v}|$. Show that $\vec{u}$ and $\vec{v}$ must be perpendicular.

1.3 Scalar Multiplication

In addition to being able to add and subtract vectors, we can also multiply and divide vectors by scalars. Consider the situation in which we apply a force, $\vec{F}$, to a rock but the rock does not move. We then decide to double our effort by pushing twice as hard in the same direction. The new force is in the same direction and has twice the magnitude of $\vec{F}$ and is denoted by $2\vec{F}$.

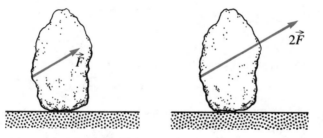

The vector $2\vec{F}$ is called a scalar multiple of the vector $\vec{F}$. If a vector is multiplied by a scalar, the resulting vector is collinear to the original. If the scalar is negative, then the vector points in the opposite direction to the original. If the scalar is zero, we obtain the zero vector, $\vec{0}$, which is also considered to be collinear with the original vector.

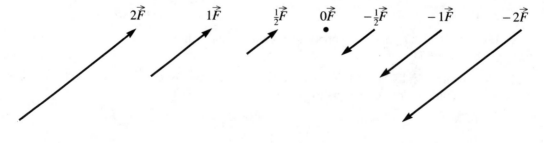

Scalar Multiplication

If $\vec{v}$ is a vector and k is a real number, then $k\vec{v}$ is also a vector such that
1. $|k\vec{v}| = |k||\vec{v}|$
2. the directions of $\vec{v}$ and $k\vec{v}$ are the same if $k > 0$ and opposite if $k < 0$

Note that $1\vec{F}$ is just $\vec{F}$ and that $-1\vec{F}$ is the opposite vector to $\vec{F}$. Division of vectors by non-zero scalars is equivalent to scalar multiplication. For example, dividing $\vec{F}$ by 2 is the same as multiplying $\vec{F}$ by $\frac{1}{2}$.

A **unit vector** is a vector that has a magnitude of one unit. We can find a unit vector in the direction of any vector by dividing the original vector by its magnitude.

Unit Vector

If $\vec{a}$ is a non-zero vector, then $\vec{b} = \dfrac{1}{|\vec{a}|}\vec{a}$ is a unit vector in the direction of $\vec{a}$.

Proof. Since $|\vec{b}| = \dfrac{1}{|\vec{a}|}|\vec{a}| = 1$, $\vec{b}$ is a unit vector. Since $\dfrac{1}{|\vec{a}|} > 0$, $\vec{b}$ is in the same direction as $\vec{a}$. $\qquad\square$

Example 1. Two unit vectors, $\vec{a}$ and $\vec{b}$, make an angle of 60° with each other. Construct $2\vec{a} + 3\vec{b}$ and calculate its magnitude.

Solution. Construct $2\vec{a} + 3\vec{b}$ as shown in the diagram. The vectors $\overrightarrow{PQ} = 2\vec{a}$ and $\overrightarrow{QR} = 3\vec{b}$ are placed head to tail so that $\angle PQR = 120°$, since it is the supplement of 60°.

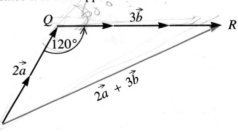

By the Triangle Law of Addition, $\overrightarrow{PR}$ represents $2\vec{a} + 3\vec{b}$. By the Cosine Law,

$$|2\vec{a} + 3\vec{b}|^2 = 2^2 + 3^2 - 2(2)(3)\cos 120°$$
$$= 4 + 9 + 2(2)(3)\tfrac{1}{2}$$
$$= 19$$

Hence, $|2\vec{a} + 3\vec{b}| = \sqrt{19} \approx 4.36.$ $\qquad\square$

YOU MUST KNOW THIS THOROUGHLY!!

Example 2. Three unit vectors, $\vec{m}$, $\vec{n}$, and $\vec{p}$, all lie in the same plane and are such that the angle between $\vec{m}$ and $\vec{n}$ is $60°$, the angle between $\vec{m}$ and $\vec{p}$ is $30°$, and $\vec{n}$ and $\vec{p}$ are perpendicular. Construct the vector $\vec{a} = \vec{m} + 2\vec{n} - 3\vec{p}$ graphically and determine its magnitude.

Solution. Construct $\vec{a}$ as shown in the diagram. Notice that
$\theta + \phi = \angle ABC = 180° - 60° = 120°$.

Join B to D. Since $\angle BCD = 90°$, it follows from Pythagoras' Theorem that

$$|\vec{BD}| = \sqrt{2^2 + 3^2}$$
$$= \sqrt{13}$$

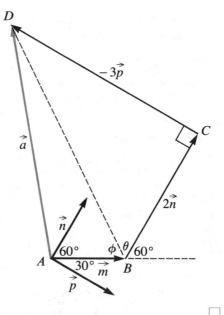

Also, $\tan \theta = \dfrac{|\vec{DC}|}{|\vec{BC}|} = \frac{3}{2}$, so $\theta \approx 56.3°$.

Hence, $\phi = 120° - \theta \approx 63.7°$. By the Cosine Law in triangle ABD,

$$|\vec{AD}|^2 = |\vec{AB}|^2 + |\vec{BD}|^2 - 2|\vec{AB}||\vec{BD}| \cos \phi$$
$$\approx 1^2 + (\sqrt{13})^2 - 2(1)(\sqrt{13}) \cos 63.7°$$
$$\approx 10.80$$

Hence, $|\vec{a}| \approx 3.29$.

Exercises 1.3

1. If $\vec{a}$ and $\vec{b}$ are the vectors shown, is there a scalar k such that $\vec{a} = k\vec{b}$? Explain your answer.

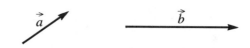

2. Sketch each vector, using $\vec{a}$ and $\vec{b}$ from Exercise 1.

   a. $-\frac{1}{2}\vec{a}$ **b.** $2\vec{b}$ **c.** $0\vec{a}$ **d.** $\vec{a} + \vec{b}$

   e. $2\vec{a} + 3\vec{b}$ **f.** $\sqrt{2}\vec{a} + 0.5\vec{b}$ **g.** $-\frac{3}{2}\vec{b} - \frac{2}{3}\vec{a}$ **h.** $\dfrac{\vec{a} + \vec{b}}{2}$

3. Find possible values for k if the length of the vector $\vec{x} = k\vec{y}$ is $3|\vec{y}|$.

4. Given two distinct unit vectors, $\vec{x}$ and $\vec{y}$, that make an angle of $30°$ with each other, calculate $|2\vec{x} - 3\vec{y}|$.

5. Consider three distinct unit vectors $\vec{a}$, $\vec{b}$, and $\vec{c}$, that lie in a plane. The angles between $\vec{a}$ and $\vec{b}$ and between $\vec{b}$ and $\vec{c}$ are 45°. Graphically construct the vector $\vec{a} - 2\vec{b} + 3\vec{c}$. Calculate the magnitude of this vector and use your diagram to verify that it is correct.

6. In the rectangle $OABC$, $\vec{i}$ and $\vec{j}$ are unit vectors, $|\overrightarrow{OA}| = 4$, and $|\overrightarrow{OC}| = 5$.

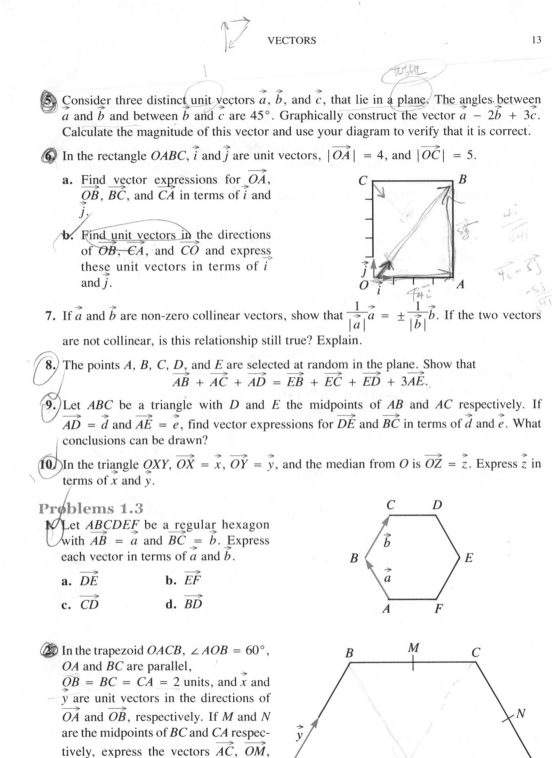

a. Find vector expressions for $\overrightarrow{OA}$, $\overrightarrow{OB}$, $\overrightarrow{BC}$, and $\overrightarrow{CA}$ in terms of $\vec{i}$ and $\vec{j}$.

b. Find unit vectors in the directions of $\overrightarrow{OB}$, $\overrightarrow{CA}$, and $\overrightarrow{CO}$ and express these unit vectors in terms of $\vec{i}$ and $\vec{j}$.

7. If $\vec{a}$ and $\vec{b}$ are non-zero collinear vectors, show that $\frac{1}{|\vec{a}|}\vec{a} = \pm\frac{1}{|\vec{b}|}\vec{b}$. If the two vectors are not collinear, is this relationship still true? Explain.

8. The points A, B, C, D, and E are selected at random in the plane. Show that
$$\overrightarrow{AB} + \overrightarrow{AC} + \overrightarrow{AD} = \overrightarrow{EB} + \overrightarrow{EC} + \overrightarrow{ED} + 3\overrightarrow{AE}.$$

9. Let ABC be a triangle with D and E the midpoints of AB and AC respectively. If $\overrightarrow{AD} = \vec{d}$ and $\overrightarrow{AE} = \vec{e}$, find vector expressions for $\overrightarrow{DE}$ and $\overrightarrow{BC}$ in terms of $\vec{d}$ and $\vec{e}$. What conclusions can be drawn?

10. In the triangle OXY, $\overrightarrow{OX} = \vec{x}$, $\overrightarrow{OY} = \vec{y}$, and the median from O is $\overrightarrow{OZ} = \vec{z}$. Express $\vec{z}$ in terms of $\vec{x}$ and $\vec{y}$.

Problems 1.3

1. Let $ABCDEF$ be a regular hexagon with $\overrightarrow{AB} = \vec{a}$ and $\overrightarrow{BC} = \vec{b}$. Express each vector in terms of $\vec{a}$ and $\vec{b}$.

   a. $\overrightarrow{DE}$ b. $\overrightarrow{EF}$

   c. $\overrightarrow{CD}$ d. $\overrightarrow{BD}$

2. In the trapezoid $OACB$, $\angle AOB = 60°$, OA and BC are parallel, $OB = BC = CA = 2$ units, and $\vec{x}$ and $\vec{y}$ are unit vectors in the directions of $\overrightarrow{OA}$ and $\overrightarrow{OB}$, respectively. If M and N are the midpoints of BC and CA respectively, express the vectors $\overrightarrow{AC}$, $\overrightarrow{OM}$, and $\overrightarrow{ON}$ in terms of $\vec{x}$ and $\vec{y}$.

1.4 Laws of Vector Algebra

In developing procedures for adding vectors and multiplying vectors by scalars, we have assumed basic properties, such as associativity and commutativity, without stating them directly. In this section we examine these properties explicitly and show that the basic laws of vector algebra are similar to those of arithmetic and elementary algebra. The following laws can be derived from the basic principles we have developed so far.

Properties of Vector Addition and Scalar Multiplication

If $\vec{a}$, $\vec{b}$, and $\vec{c}$ are vectors, $\vec{0}$ is the zero vector, and m and n are real numbers, then the following properties are valid.

- $\vec{a} + \vec{b} = \vec{b} + \vec{a}$ (Commutative Law)
- $(\vec{a} + \vec{b}) + \vec{c} = \vec{a} + (\vec{b} + \vec{c})$ (Associative Law)
- $\vec{a} + \vec{0} = \vec{a}$
- Each vector $\vec{a}$ has a negative, $-\vec{a}$, such that $\vec{a} + (-\vec{a}) = \vec{0}$
- $m(n\vec{a}) = (mn)\vec{a}$ (Associative Law)
- $m(\vec{a} + \vec{b}) = m\vec{a} + m\vec{b}$ (Distributive Law)
- $(m + n)\vec{a} = m\vec{a} + n\vec{a}$ (Distributive Law)
- $1\vec{a} = \vec{a}$

We shall prove some of these laws; the others can be proved in a similar way and are left as an exercise.

Proof of the Associative Law $(\vec{a} + \vec{b}) + \vec{c} = \vec{a} + (\vec{b} + \vec{c})$

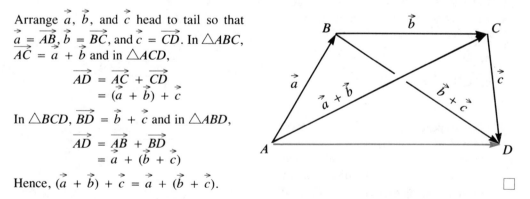

Arrange $\vec{a}$, $\vec{b}$, and $\vec{c}$ head to tail so that $\vec{a} = \overrightarrow{AB}$, $\vec{b} = \overrightarrow{BC}$, and $\vec{c} = \overrightarrow{CD}$. In $\triangle ABC$, $\overrightarrow{AC} = \vec{a} + \vec{b}$ and in $\triangle ACD$,

$$\overrightarrow{AD} = \overrightarrow{AC} + \overrightarrow{CD}$$
$$= (\vec{a} + \vec{b}) + \vec{c}$$

In $\triangle BCD$, $\overrightarrow{BD} = \vec{b} + \vec{c}$ and in $\triangle ABD$,

$$\overrightarrow{AD} = \overrightarrow{AB} + \overrightarrow{BD}$$
$$= \vec{a} + (\vec{b} + \vec{c})$$

Hence, $(\vec{a} + \vec{b}) + \vec{c} = \vec{a} + (\vec{b} + \vec{c})$. □

The associative law extends to any number of vectors, and so we may omit brackets without being ambiguous. For example, we write $\vec{a} + \vec{b} + \vec{c}$ for $(\vec{a} + \vec{b}) + \vec{c}$ or for $\vec{a} + (\vec{b} + \vec{c})$. Because addition is commutative, we may also change the order of the sum of vectors. For example, $\vec{a} + \vec{b} - \vec{c} + \vec{d} = \vec{d} - \vec{c} + \vec{a} + \vec{b}$.

Proof of the Distributive Law $\quad m(\vec{a} + \vec{b}) = m\vec{a} + m\vec{b}$

Consider the five cases: *Case I.* $\vec{a} = \vec{0}$ or $\vec{b} = \vec{0}$; *Case II.* $\vec{a} \| \vec{b}$; *Case III.* $m > 0$; *Case IV.* $m < 0$; *Case V.* $m = 0$.

Case I. Suppose that $\vec{a} = \vec{0}$. Then $\vec{0} + \vec{b} = \vec{b}$ and the left side is $m\vec{b}$. The length of $m\vec{a}$ is $m0 = 0$, and so $m\vec{a}$ is the zero vector and the right side is $m\vec{b}$. Hence, the law holds. If $\vec{b} = \vec{0}$, the argument is similar.

Case III. Suppose $m > 0$ and $\vec{a}$ and $\vec{b}$ are non-parallel vectors.

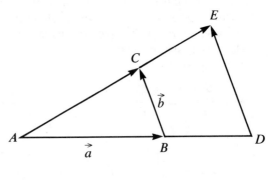

Let $\overrightarrow{AB} = \vec{a}$ and let $\overrightarrow{BC} = \vec{b}$, as in the diagram. Then, by the Triangle Law of Addition, $\overrightarrow{AC} = \vec{a} + \vec{b}$. Assuming $m > 1$, extend AB to D so that $\overrightarrow{AD} = m\overrightarrow{AB} = m\vec{a}$ and extend AC to E so that

$$\overrightarrow{AE} = m\overrightarrow{AC} = m(\vec{a} + \vec{b})$$

Since $\triangle ABC$ is similar to $\triangle ADE$, DE is parallel to BC and $\overrightarrow{DE} = m\overrightarrow{BC} = m\vec{b}$. By the Triangle Law in $\triangle ADE$,

$$\begin{aligned} m(\vec{a} + \vec{b}) &= \overrightarrow{AE} \\ &= \overrightarrow{AD} + \overrightarrow{DE} \\ &= m\vec{a} + m\vec{b} \end{aligned}$$

If $0 < m < 1$, the proof is the same, but the diagram is different.

The other cases are left as exercises.

Example. If $\vec{a} = 3\vec{x} - 5\vec{y}$ and $\vec{b} = -2\vec{x} + 9\vec{y}$, find $5\vec{a} - 9\vec{b}$.

Solution.

$$\begin{aligned} 5\vec{a} - 9\vec{b} &= 5(3\vec{x} - 5\vec{y}) - 9(-2\vec{x} + 9\vec{y}) \quad \text{(by substitution)} \\ &= 15\vec{x} - 25\vec{y} + 18\vec{x} - 81\vec{y} \quad \text{(by the Distributive Law)} \\ &= 15\vec{x} + 18\vec{x} - 25\vec{y} - 81\vec{y} \quad \text{(by the Commutative Law)} \\ &= (15 + 18)\vec{x} - (25 + 81)\vec{y} \quad \text{(by the Distributive Law)} \\ &= 33\vec{x} - 106\vec{y} \end{aligned}$$

In practice, it is not necessary to write out all the steps or to indicate which property you are using, as we have done in the above example.

Exercises 1.4

1. Use the diagram to show that

$$\vec{AB} = \vec{CB} + \vec{DC} + \vec{ED} + \vec{AE}$$

2. A parallelepiped is a box-like object in which opposite faces are congruent parallelograms. In the pictured parallelepiped, state a single vector that is equal to each sum.

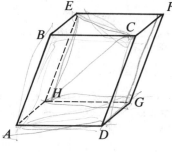

a. $\vec{AB} + \vec{BC} + \vec{CD} + \vec{DG}$

b. $\vec{AD} + \vec{AB} + \vec{CE} + \vec{EH}$

3. Let $\vec{a} = 2\vec{i} - 3\vec{j} + \vec{k}$, $\vec{b} = \vec{i} + \vec{j} + \vec{k}$, and $\vec{c} = 2\vec{i} - 3\vec{k}$. Find

     a. $\vec{a} + \vec{b} + \vec{c}$ **b.** $\vec{a} + 2\vec{b} - 3\vec{c}$ **c.** $2\vec{b} - 3\vec{c}$

4. If $\vec{a} = 3\vec{x} + 2\vec{y}$ and $\vec{b} = 5\vec{x} - 4\vec{y}$, find $\vec{x}$ and $\vec{y}$ in terms of $\vec{a}$ and $\vec{b}$.

5. Check each identity algebraically and with the use of a diagram.

     a. $\vec{x} + \dfrac{\vec{y} - \vec{x}}{2} = \dfrac{\vec{x} + \vec{y}}{2}$ **b.** $\vec{x} - \dfrac{\vec{x} + \vec{y}}{2} = \dfrac{\vec{x} - \vec{y}}{2}$

6. A cube is constructed from the three vectors, $\vec{OP} = \vec{p}$, $\vec{OQ} = \vec{q}$, and $\vec{OR} = \vec{r}$. Copy the diagram and draw the following vector diagonals.

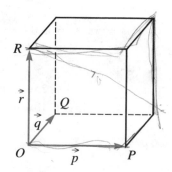

     a. $\vec{a} = \vec{p} + \vec{q} - \vec{r}$

     b. $\vec{b} = \vec{p} - \vec{q} + \vec{r}$

     c. $\vec{c} = \vec{p} - \vec{q} - \vec{r}$

     d. $\vec{d} = \vec{q} - \vec{p} - \vec{r}$

7. Use the diagram in the previous exercise to verify the commutative property by showing that

$$\vec{p} + \vec{q} - \vec{r} = \vec{p} - \vec{r} + \vec{q} = \vec{q} + \vec{p} - \vec{r} = \vec{q} - \vec{r} + \vec{p}$$

8. State a single vector in the square-based pyramid that is equivalent to each vector.

  a. $\overrightarrow{AE} + \overrightarrow{ED} + \overrightarrow{DC}$

  b. $\overrightarrow{AD} - \overrightarrow{AE}$

  c. $\overrightarrow{AC} + \overrightarrow{CB} + \overrightarrow{BE} + \overrightarrow{ED} + \overrightarrow{DA}$

  d. $\overrightarrow{AE} - \overrightarrow{AD}$

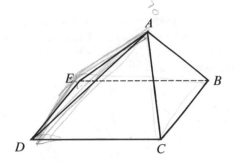

Problems 1.4

1. If $\overrightarrow{XQ} + \overrightarrow{XY} = (m - 1)\overrightarrow{YQ}$, what conclusions can you draw?

2. If $|\vec{x}| = 11$, $|\vec{y}| = 23$, and $|\vec{x} - \vec{y}| = 30$, find $|\vec{x} + \vec{y}|$.

3. Let $\vec{x}$, $\vec{y}$, and $\vec{z}$ be non-zero vectors, no two of which are collinear. Find their sum if $\vec{x} + \vec{y}$ is collinear with $\vec{z}$ and if $\vec{y} + \vec{z}$ is collinear with $\vec{x}$.

EXPLAIN THIS!

4. In the trapezoid $TXYZ$, $\overrightarrow{TX} = b\overrightarrow{ZY}$. If the diagonals meet at O, find an expression for $\overrightarrow{TO}$ in terms of $\overrightarrow{TX}$ and $\overrightarrow{TZ}$.

1.5 Coordinate Systems

In this section we shall show how vectors in one, two, and three dimensions can be represented algebraically by using coordinate systems. The geometric and algebraic approaches to vectors complement each other. The geometric definition, using directed line segments, aids in visualization, whereas the algebraic definition, using coordinates, aids in computation. We therefore need to develop skill in translating between the algebraic and geometric viewpoints.

Coordinate systems were first introduced by René Descartes (1576-1650), and the Cartesian coordinate systems are named in his honour. His great classic of literature and philosophy, entitled *Discours de la méthode pour bien conduire sa raison, et chercher la vérité dans les sciences*, was published in France in 1637. It contained three appendices, *La Géométrie, La Dioptrique*, and *Les Météores*.

La Géométrie was the only mathematical book that Descartes wrote, but it had a great influence on mathematics in the seventeenth century. His new idea was to introduce coordinates so that geometric problems could be solved by using algebraic methods. For example, geometric problems about plane conic sections correspond to algebraic problems involving quadratic equations in two variables.

Let us now consider vectors lying on the real line. Translate each vector so that its initial point coincides with the origin O. Then the final point A of each vector $\overrightarrow{OA}$ corresponds to a real number a, where a is the coordinate of the point A. Hence, the vector $\overrightarrow{OA}$ can be described by the single real number a.

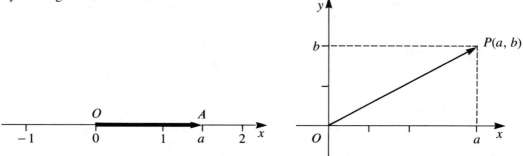

Now consider vectors in the plane. We shall use the conventional coordinate system; that is, we choose the positive directions of the x-axis and y-axis so that a 90° counterclockwise rotation about the origin takes the positive x-axis onto the positive y-axis. In this coordinate system, the points in the plane correspond to the set of ordered pairs of real numbers $\boldsymbol{R}^2$.

$$\boldsymbol{R}^2 = \boldsymbol{R} \times \boldsymbol{R} = \{(a, b) \mid a, b \in \boldsymbol{R}\}$$

That is, each point in the plane is described by one and only one pair of coordinates (a, b).

Any vector in the plane can be represented by $\overrightarrow{OP}$, a directed line segment starting at the origin. If necessary, the line segment representing the vector can be translated so that it does start at the origin. If the coordinates of P are (a, b), then $\overrightarrow{OP}$ is called the **position vector** of P and we write $\overrightarrow{OP} = (a, b)$. The numbers a and b are called the **components** of $\overrightarrow{OP}$. In this way every vector in the plane has a unique algebraic description as an ordered pair in $\boldsymbol{R}^2$.

The notation (a, b) now has two geometric meanings: it means either the point (a, b) or the vector from the origin to the point (a, b). It should be clear from the context whether it means a point or a vector, but be careful not to confuse the two meanings.

Let $\vec{i}$ and $\vec{j}$ be unit vectors in the positive directions of the x-axis and y-axis, respectively. If P is a point with coordinates (a, b), then the position vector of P is $\overrightarrow{OP} = (a, b)$. Drop the perpendicular from P to the x-axis and call its point of intersection with the x-axis A. Then $\overrightarrow{OA}$ is a units long in the x-direction and $\overrightarrow{AP}$ is b units long in the y-direction. Hence, $\overrightarrow{OA} = a\vec{i}$ and $\overrightarrow{AP} = b\vec{j}$ and, by the Triangle Law of Addition in triangle OAP, we obtain the following description of vectors in the plane.

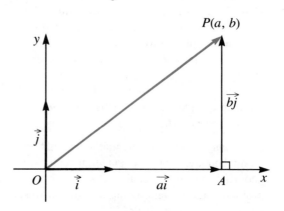

Vectors in the Plane

Every vector $\overrightarrow{OP}$ in $\mathbf{R}^2$ can be written in either of the equivalent forms

$$\overrightarrow{OP} = (a, b) \quad \text{or} \quad \overrightarrow{OP} = a\vec{i} + b\vec{j}$$

The vector $\vec{i}$ has the coordinates $(1, 0)$, and the vector $\vec{j}$ has the coordinates $(0, 1)$. This pair of vectors is called the **standard basis** for $\mathbf{R}^2$. Thus (a, b) and $a\vec{i} + b\vec{j}$ are two equivalent algebraic representations of the geometric vector $\overrightarrow{OP}$. The zero vector in two dimensions is $\vec{0} = (0, 0)$.

Just as points in two-dimensional space can be described by using ordered pairs of real numbers, points in three-dimensional space can be described by using ordered triples of real numbers. To do this, construct a **coordinate system in three dimensions** by choosing one point, O, as the origin and three mutually perpendicular lines through the origin, as axes. The three lines are labelled the x-axis, the y-axis, and the z-axis; these axes are all copies of the real number line.

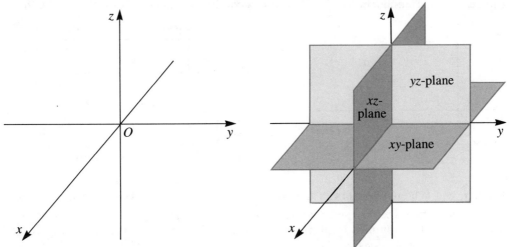

The plane through the origin, containing the x-axis and the y-axis, is called the xy-plane. The plane containing the y-axis and z-axis is called the yz-plane and the plane containing the x-axis and z-axis is called the xz-plane. These three planes are known as the **coordinate planes**.

There are essentially two different ways of choosing the positive directions of the three axes. Mathematicians usually use the right-hand convention, and we shall use that convention in this book. That is, if we look at the xy-plane from a point on the positive z-axis and rotate the x-axis through $90°$ to coincide with the y-axis, then the rotation appears to be counterclockwise; in the left-hand convention the rotation would appear to be clockwise.

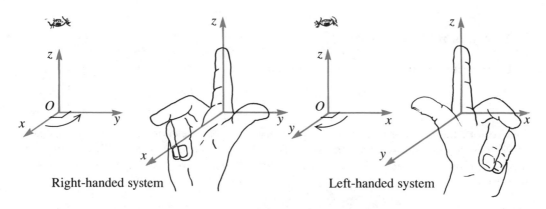

Right-handed system   Left-handed system

For each point P in three-dimensional space, assign the **coordinates** $(a, b, c) \in \mathbf{R}^3$ as follows. Drop the perpendicular from P to the xy-plane and call its point of intersection with the xy-plane N. Then drop the perpendicular from N onto the x-axis and call its point of intersection with the x-axis M. Let a, b, and c be the signed distances from O to M, M to N, and N to P, respectively; a coordinate is positive if its distance is pointing towards the positive side of the corresponding axis, and negative otherwise. Hence, to go from O to P we go a units in the x-direction, b units in the y-direction, and c units in the z-direction. The numbers a, b, and c are called the **components** of $\overrightarrow{OP}$. The zero vector in three dimensions is $\vec{0} = (0, 0, 0)$.

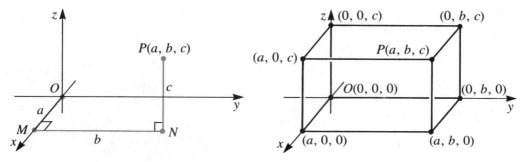

Let $\vec{i}$, $\vec{j}$, and $\vec{k}$ be unit vectors in the positive directions of the x-axis, y-axis, and z-axis, respectively. These vectors can be written as $\vec{i} = (1, 0, 0)$, $\vec{j} = (0, 1, 0)$, and $\vec{k} = (0, 0, 1)$ and are called the **standard basis vectors** in 3-space. As in two dimensions, we have the following description of vectors in 3-space.

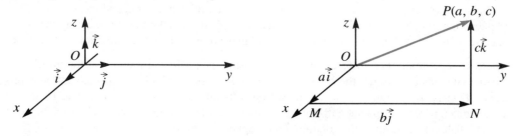

Vectors in 3-space

Every vector $\overrightarrow{OP}$ in $\boldsymbol{R}^3$ can be written in either of the equivalent forms

$$\overrightarrow{OP} = (a, b, c) \quad \text{or} \quad \overrightarrow{OP} = a\vec{i} + b\vec{j} + c\vec{k}$$

Example. Sketch the vector $\vec{v} = (3, 4, -1)$ in three dimensions.

Solution. If $\vec{v} = \overrightarrow{OP}$, then P has coordinates $(3, 4, -1)$. To reach P from O, we go 3 units in the x-direction, 4 units in the y-direction, and -1 unit in the z-direction; that is, we move 1 unit below the xy-plane.

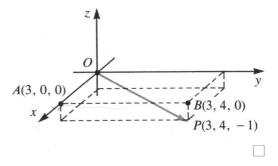

To summarize, we have the following equivalent ways of describing vectors in one, two, and three dimensions.

Vector	Geometric Form	Algebraic Form		
in $\boldsymbol{R}$	$\overrightarrow{OA}$	a	or	$a\vec{i}$
in $\boldsymbol{R}^2$	$\overrightarrow{OP}$	(a, b)	or	$a\vec{i} + b\vec{j}$
in $\boldsymbol{R}^3$	$\overrightarrow{OP}$	(a, b, c)	or	$a\vec{i} + b\vec{j} + c\vec{k}$

Mathematicians also consider vectors in higher dimensional spaces as n-tuples $(a_1, a_2, \ldots, a_n) \in \boldsymbol{R}^n$. It may not be possible to visualize such vectors, but they are widely applicable in the description of physical systems. For example, a solution to a system of equations in n variables is an n-dimensional vector.

Cubic Space Division, by M. C. Escher.

Exercises 1.5

1. Draw the x-axis, y-axis, and z-axis and accurately plot the points.

$A(1, 0, 0)$ $B(0, 1, 0)$ $C(0, 0, 1)$ $D(3, 2, 0)$

$E(-3, 2, 0)$ $F(2, 0, 1)$ $G(-2, 0, 1)$ $H(0, 2, -3)$

2. Express each vector in the form $a\vec{i} + b\vec{j} + c\vec{k}$.

    a. $(1, 3, 2)$ **b.** $(1, 0, 5)$ **c.** $(-6, -8, 11)$ **d.** $(9, -6, 2)$

3. Express each vector in the form (a, b, c).

    a. $3\vec{i} - 2\vec{j} + 7\vec{k}$ **b.** $-9\vec{i} + 3\vec{j} + 14\vec{k}$ **c.** $\vec{i} + \vec{j}$ **d.** $2\vec{i} - 9\vec{k}$

4. Calculate each expression.

    a. $(2\vec{i} + 3\vec{j}) + 4(\vec{i} - \vec{j})$ **b.** $3(\vec{i} - 2\vec{j} + 3\vec{k}) - 3(-\vec{i} + 4\vec{j} - 3\vec{k})$

    c. $-3(\vec{i} - \vec{k}) - (2\vec{i} + \vec{k})$ **d.** $5(9\vec{i} - 7\vec{j}) - 5(-9\vec{i} + 7\vec{k})$

5. Where are the following general points located?

    a. $A(x, y, 0)$ **b.** $B(x, 0, z)$ **c.** $C(0, y, z)$

6. Prove that if $a_1\vec{i} + b_1\vec{j} = a_2\vec{i} + b_2\vec{j}$, then $a_1 = a_2$ and $b_1 = b_2$; that is, each point in the plane has a unique expression in terms of $\vec{i}$ and $\vec{j}$.

Problems 1.5

1. The three coordinate planes divide three-dimensional space into eight regions, called octants. How can you tell which octant a given point lies in by looking at its coordinates? What reasonable symbols could you use for each of these octants?

2. Let $\vec{u}$ and $\vec{v}$ be any two non-collinear vectors in the plane. Such a pair of vectors is called **a basis** for the vectors in the plane. Show that any vector in the plane can be written uniquely as $a\vec{u} + b\vec{v}$, for some $a, b \in \mathbf{R}$.

1.6 Vector Addition Using Components

In this section we determine the rules for the addition, scalar multiplication, and magnitude of algebraic vectors in terms of their components. These rules will allow us to calculate with vectors more easily.

Vector Addition

In $\mathbf{R}^2$, $(a_1, b_1) + (a_2, b_2) = (a_1 + a_2, b_1 + b_2)$.

In $\mathbf{R}^3$, $(a_1, b_1, c_1) + (a_2, b_2, c_2) = (a_1 + a_2, b_1 + b_2, c_1 + c_2)$.

Proof. We shall prove the result in $\mathbf{R}^3$; the proof in $\mathbf{R}^2$ is similar. We have
$(a_1, b_1, c_1) = a_1\vec{i} + b_1\vec{j} + c_1\vec{k}$ and $(a_2, b_2, c_2) = a_2\vec{i} + b_2\vec{j} + c_2\vec{k}$, and so

$$(a_1, b_1, c_1) + (a_2, b_2, c_2) = a_1\vec{i} + b_1\vec{j} + c_1\vec{k} + a_2\vec{i} + b_2\vec{j} + c_2\vec{k}$$
$$= (a_1 + a_2)\vec{i} + (b_1 + b_2)\vec{j} + (c_1 + c_2)\vec{k}$$
$$= (a_1 + a_2, b_1 + b_2, c_1 + c_2)$$

Note that we used the commutative and distributive laws for vector addition and scalar multiplication in proving this result. Geometrically, this means that if P_1 and P_2 have coordinates (a_1, b_1, c_1) and (a_2, b_2, c_2) respectively, then in the parallelogram $OP_1 PP_2$, the vertex P has coordinates $(a_1 + a_2, b_1 + b_2, c_1 + c_2)$.

Scalar Multiplication

In $\mathbf{R}^2$, $m(a, b) = (ma, mb)$.
In $\mathbf{R}^3$, $m(a, b, c) = (ma, mb, mc)$.

Proof. Again we only prove the result in $\mathbf{R}^3$. We have

$$m(a, b, c) = m(a\vec{i} + b\vec{j} + c\vec{k})$$
$$= ma\vec{i} + mb\vec{j} + mc\vec{k}$$
$$= (ma, mb, mc)$$

The Vector Joining Two Points

The vector from $P(p_1, p_2, p_3)$ to $Q(q_1, q_2, q_3)$ in $\mathbf{R}^3$ is

$$\vec{PQ} = (q_1 - p_1, q_2 - p_2, q_3 - p_3)$$

Proof. If O is the origin, then

$$\vec{PQ} = \vec{PO} + \vec{OQ}$$
$$= \vec{OQ} - \vec{OP}$$
$$= (q_1, q_2, q_3) + (-1)(p_1, p_2, p_3)$$
$$= (q_1, q_2, q_3) + (-p_1, -p_2, -p_3)$$
$$= (q_1 - p_1, q_2 - p_2, q_3 - p_3)$$

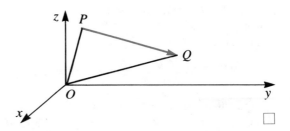

Example 1. If $\vec{u} = (2, 2, 5)$ and $\vec{v} = (0, 4, 1)$, calculate each quantity.

a. $\vec{u} + \vec{v}$ **b.** $\vec{u} - \vec{v}$ **c.** $2\vec{u}$ **d.** $-\frac{1}{2}\vec{v}$

Solution.

a.
$$\vec{u} + \vec{v} = (2, 2, 5) + (0, 4, 1)$$
$$= (2, 6, 6)$$

b.
$$\vec{u} - \vec{v} = (2, 2, 5) - (0, 4, 1)$$
$$= (2, -2, 4)$$

c.
$$2\vec{u} = 2(2, 2, 5)$$
$$= (4, 4, 10)$$

d.
$$-\frac{1}{2}\vec{v} = -\frac{1}{2}(0, 4, 1)$$
$$= (0, -2, -\tfrac{1}{2})$$

□

Example 2. If $\vec{a} = (-2, 3, 1)$ and $\vec{b} = (4, 2, -4)$, calculate

a. $\vec{u} = 2\vec{a} + 3\vec{b}$ **b.** $\vec{v} = -\vec{a} + \frac{1}{2}\vec{b}$

Solution.

a.
$$\vec{u} = 2(-2, 3, 1) + 3(4, 2, -4)$$
$$= (-4, 6, 2) + (12, 6, -12)$$
$$= (8, 12, -10)$$

b.
$$\vec{v} = -(-2, 3, 1) + \tfrac{1}{2}(4, 2, -4)$$
$$= (2, -3, -1) + (2, 1, -2)$$
$$= (4, -2, -3)$$

□

The Magnitude of a Vector

If $\vec{v} = (a, b) \in \mathbf{R}^2$, then $|\vec{v}| = \sqrt{a^2 + b^2}$.

If $\vec{v} = (a, b, c) \in \mathbf{R}^3$, then $|\vec{v}| = \sqrt{a^2 + b^2 + c^2}$.

Proof. We shall prove the result in $\mathbf{R}^3$.
Let $\vec{v} = \overrightarrow{OP}$ so that P has coordinates
(a, b, c). Let PN be the perpendicular from
P to the xy-plane and let NM be the perpendicular from N to the x-axis. Now

$$\overrightarrow{OP} = a\vec{i} + b\vec{j} + c\vec{k}$$
$$= \overrightarrow{OM} + \overrightarrow{MN} + \overrightarrow{NP}$$

Using Pythagoras' Theorem in $\triangle ONP$, we
obtain

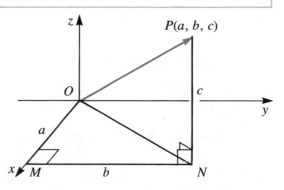

$$OP^2 = ON^2 + NP^2$$

and in $\triangle OMN$

$$ON^2 = OM^2 + MN^2$$

Hence,

$$OP^2 = ON^2 + NP^2$$
$$= OM^2 + MN^2 + NP^2$$
$$= a^2 + b^2 + c^2$$

Therefore, $|\vec{v}| = |\overrightarrow{OP}| = \sqrt{a^2 + b^2 + c^2}$. We choose the positive root because the magnitude of a vector is non-negative. □

Example 3. If $\overrightarrow{OA} = (3, -1, 4)$ and $\overrightarrow{OB} = (6, -1, 8)$ calculate

a. $|\overrightarrow{OA}|$ **b.** $|\overrightarrow{AB}|$ **c.** $|2\overrightarrow{OA} - \overrightarrow{OB}|$

Solution.

a.
$$|\overrightarrow{OA}| = \sqrt{3^2 + (-1)^2 + 4^2}$$
$$= \sqrt{26}$$

b.
$$\overrightarrow{AB} = (6, -1, 8) - (3, -1, 4)$$
$$= (6 - 3, -1 + 1, 8 - 4)$$
$$= (3, 0, 4)$$

Hence,
$$|\overrightarrow{AB}| = \sqrt{3^2 + 0^2 + 4^2}$$
$$= 5$$

c.
$$2\overrightarrow{OA} - \overrightarrow{OB} = 2(3, -1, 4) - (6, -1, 8)$$
$$= (6, -2, 8) - (6, -1, 8)$$
$$= (0, -1, 0)$$

Hence,
$$|2\overrightarrow{OA} - \overrightarrow{OB}| = \sqrt{0^2 + (-1)^2 + 0^2}$$
$$= 1$$

□

Example 4. Find the perimeter of the triangle ABC whose coordinates are $A(2, 4, 1)$, $B(-1, 2, 2)$, and $C(7, 0, -4)$.

Solution. The perimeter is

$$P = |\overrightarrow{AB}| + |\overrightarrow{BC}| + |\overrightarrow{CA}|$$
$$= |(-1, 2, 2) - (2, 4, 1)| + |(7, 0, -4) - (-1, 2, 2)| + |(2, 4, 1) - (7, 0, -4)|$$
$$= |(-3, -2, 1)| + |(8, -2, -6)| + |(-5, 4, 5)|$$
$$= \sqrt{(-3)^2 + (-2)^2 + 1^2} + \sqrt{8^2 + (-2)^2 + (-6)^2} + \sqrt{(-5)^2 + 4^2 + 5^2}$$
$$= \sqrt{14} + \sqrt{104} + \sqrt{66}$$

Hence, the perimeter is approximately 22.06 units. □

Exercises 1.6

1. Find a single vector equivalent to each expression.

a. $(2, -4) + (1, 7)$ **b.** $5(1, 4)$

c. $0(4, -5)$ **d.** $(-6, 0) + 7(1, -1)$

e. $(2, -1, 3) + (-2, 1, 3)$ **f.** $2(1, 1, -4)$

g. $(4, -1, 3) - (-2, 1, 3)$ **h.** $2(-1, 1, 3) + 3(-2, 3, -1)$

i. $2(0, 1, 0) + 5(0, 0, 1)$ **j.** $-\frac{1}{2}(4, -6, 8) + \frac{3}{2}(4, -6, 8)$

k. $5(0, -2, -4) - 4(3, 8, 0)$ **l.** $-2(-3, 2, 4) + 5(3, 2, 8)$

2. Given $\vec{a} = (2, -1, 4)$, $\vec{b} = (3, 8, -6)$, and $\vec{c} = (4, 2, 1)$, find a single vector equivalent to each expression.

a. $2\vec{a} - \vec{b}$ **b.** $\vec{a} - \vec{b}$ **c.** $3\vec{a} - \vec{b} - 2\vec{c}$

d. $\vec{a} + \vec{b} + 2\vec{c}$ **e.** $-2\vec{a} + \vec{b} - \vec{c}$ **f.** $4\vec{a} - 2\vec{b} + \vec{c}$

3. Given $\vec{x} = 2\vec{i} - \vec{j} + \vec{k}$ and $\vec{y} = 3\vec{j} + 4\vec{k}$, express each quantity in terms of $\vec{i}, \vec{j},$ and $\vec{k}$.

a. $3\vec{x} + \vec{y}$ **b.** $\vec{x} + \vec{y}$ **c.** $\vec{x} - \vec{y}$ **d.** $\vec{y} - \vec{x}$

4. If $\vec{a} = 3\vec{i} + 2\vec{j} - \vec{k}$ and $\vec{b} = -2\vec{i} + \vec{j}$, calculate each magnitude.

a. $|\vec{a} + \vec{b}|$ **b.** $|\vec{a} - \vec{b}|$ **c.** $|2\vec{a} - 3\vec{b}|$

5. If $D(3, 4, 5)$ and $E(-2, 1, 5)$ are points in $\boldsymbol{R}^3$, calculate each expression.

a. $|\overrightarrow{OD}|$ **b.** $|\overrightarrow{OE}|$ **c.** $\overrightarrow{DE}$ **d.** $|\overrightarrow{DE}|$ **e.** $\overrightarrow{ED}$ **f.** $|\overrightarrow{ED}|$

6. a. Calculate $|\vec{a}|$ when $\vec{a} = (2, 3, -2)$.

   b. Find $\dfrac{1}{|\vec{a}|}\vec{a}$ and check that it is a unit vector.

7. If $\vec{v} = (3, 4, 12)$, find a unit vector in the same direction as $\vec{v}$.

8. For each set of points $A, B, C,$ and D, determine whether $\overrightarrow{AB}$ is parallel to $\overrightarrow{CD}$ and whether $|\overrightarrow{AB}| = |\overrightarrow{CD}|$.

a. $A(2, 0), B(3, 6), C(4, 1), D(5, -5)$

b. $A(0, 1, 0), B(4, 0, 1), C(5, 1, 2), D(2, 3, 5)$

c. $A(2, 4, 6), B(3, 4, 1), C(4, 1, 3), D(5, 1, -2)$

9. If $PQRS$ is a parallelogram in the plane, where P is $(4, 2)$, Q is $(-6, 1)$, and S is $(-3, -4)$, find the coordinates of R.

10. If three vertices of a parallelogram in the plane are $(-5, 3), (5, 2),$ and $(7, -8)$, determine all the possible coordinates of the fourth vertex.

11. If $\overrightarrow{OA}$, $\overrightarrow{OB}$, and $\overrightarrow{OC}$ are three edges of a parallelepiped where O is $(0, 0, 0)$, A is $(2, 4, -2)$, B is $(3, 6, 1)$, and C is $(4, 0, -1)$, find the coordinates of the other vertices of the parallelepiped.

12. The **centroid** of the n points with position vectors $\vec{a}_1, \vec{a}_2, \ldots, \vec{a}_n$ is the point with position vector

$$\vec{g} = \frac{\vec{a}_1 + \vec{a}_2 + \cdots + \vec{a}_n}{n}$$

Find the centroid of each set of points.

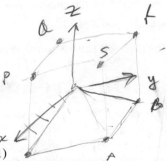

a. $A(1, 2)$, $B(4, -1)$, $C(-2, -2)$

b. $A_1(3, -1)$, $A_2(1, 1)$, $A_3(7, 0)$, $A_4(4, 4)$

c. $I(1, 0, 0)$, $J(0, 1, 0)$, $K(0, 0, 1)$

d. $O(0, 0, 0)$, $I(1, 0, 0)$, $J(0, 1, 0)$, $K(0, 0, 1)$

13. The **centre of mass** of the masses $m_1, m_2, \ldots, m_n$ at the points with position vectors $\vec{a}_1$, $\vec{a}_2, \ldots, \vec{a}_n$, respectively, is the point with position vector

$$\vec{g} = \frac{m_1\vec{a}_1 + m_2\vec{a}_2 + \cdots + m_n\vec{a}_n}{m_1 + m_2 + \cdots + m_n}$$

For the purposes of calculation, this collection of masses can sometimes be replaced by a single large mass $M = m_1 + m_2 + \ldots + m_n$ located at the centre of mass. Calculate the centre of mass in each case.

a. a mass of 2 units at $(0, 0)$, a mass of 3 units at $(4, 1)$, a mass of 5 units at $(-1, -7)$, and a mass of 1 unit at $(11, -9)$

b. a mass of 1 unit at $(1, 4, -1)$, a mass of 3 units at $(-2, 0, 1)$, and a mass of 7 units at $(1, -3, 10)$

14. A triangle has vertices $A(-1, 3, 4)$, $B(3, -1, 1)$, and $C(5, 1, 1)$.

a. Show that the triangle is right-angled.

b. Calculate the area of triangle ABC.

c. Calculate the perimeter of triangle ABC.

d. Determine the fourth vertex needed to complete a rectangle.

15. a. Find x and y if $3(x, 1) - 2(2, y) = (2, 1)$.

b. Find x, y, and z if $2(x, -1, 4) - 3(-4, y, 6) - \frac{1}{2}(4, -2, z) = (0, 0, 0)$.

16. Show that any unit vector in $\mathbf{R}^2$ can be written as $(\cos\theta, \sin\theta)$. What is the angle θ?

17. Find the point on the y-axis that is equidistant from the points $(2, -1, 1)$ and $(0, 1, 3)$.

Problems 1.6

1. Given $|\vec{x}| = 13$, $|\vec{y}| = 19$, and $|\vec{x} - \vec{y}| = 22$, find $|\vec{x} + \vec{y}|$.

2. Find the components of the unit vector in the opposite direction to that of $\overrightarrow{XY}$, where $X = (7, 4, -2)$ and $Y = (1, 2, 1)$.

3. **a.** Find the length of the median AM in the triangle ABC, for the points $A(2, \frac{3}{2}, -4)$, $B(3, -4, 2)$, and $C(1, 3, -7)$.

b. Find the distance from A to the centroid of the triangle.

1.7 The Dot Product

We have already shown how to multiply a vector by a scalar and obtain a vector as a result. We now introduce a product of two vectors, called the dot product; the result of this operation is a scalar, not a vector. It is defined as the product of the magnitudes of the two vectors and the cosine of the angle between them. The dot product will be useful for dealing with lengths, angles, and projections of vectors.

The Dot Product (or Scalar Product or Inner Product)

If $\vec{a}$ and $\vec{b}$ are two vectors and θ is the angle between them, then the dot product of $\vec{a}$ and $\vec{b}$ is

$$\vec{a} \cdot \vec{b} = |\vec{a}||\vec{b}| \cos \theta$$

Since all the quantities on the right side are scalars, the dot product of two vectors is a scalar. That is why it is also called the scalar product. A third name for the dot product is the inner product. In the next chapter we shall study the cross product of two vectors in $\mathbf{R}^3$, whose result is a vector.

Example 1. If the magnitudes of two vectors, $\vec{a}$ and $\vec{b}$, are $|\vec{a}| = 5$ and $|\vec{b}| = 3$, and the angle between them is $60°$, calculate $\vec{a} \cdot \vec{b}$ and $\vec{b} \cdot \vec{a}$.

Solution.

$$\vec{a} \cdot \vec{b} = |\vec{a}||\vec{b}| \cos 60°$$
$$= (5)(3)\tfrac{1}{2}$$
$$= 7.5$$
$$\vec{b} \cdot \vec{a} = |\vec{b}||\vec{a}| \cos 60°$$
$$= (3)(5)\tfrac{1}{2}$$
$$= 7.5$$

Example 1 illustrates that the dot product is commutative; that is, $\vec{a} \cdot \vec{b} = \vec{b} \cdot \vec{a}$ for any vectors $\vec{a}$ and $\vec{b}$.

The sign of the dot product depends on the sign of cos θ. That is, the dot product of the two vectors is positive if $0° \leq \theta < 90°$, zero if $\theta = 90°$, and negative if $90° < \theta \leq 180°$.

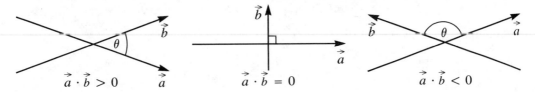

$$\vec{a} \cdot \vec{b} > 0 \qquad \vec{a} \cdot \vec{b} = 0 \qquad \vec{a} \cdot \vec{b} < 0$$

One of the most important uses of the dot product is to test whether two vectors are perpendicular.

Perpendicular Vectors

Two non-zero vectors, $\vec{a}$ and $\vec{b}$, are perpendicular if and only if

$$\vec{a} \cdot \vec{b} = 0$$

Proof. If $\vec{a}$ and $\vec{b}$ are perpendicular, then the angle between them is $90°$ and, since cos $90° = 0$, we have $\vec{a} \cdot \vec{b} = |\vec{a}||\vec{b}| \cos 90° = 0$.

Conversely, if $\vec{a} \cdot \vec{b} = 0$, then $|\vec{a}||\vec{b}| \cos \theta = 0$, where θ is the angle between the vectors. Since $\vec{a}$ and $\vec{b}$ are non-zero, we must have cos $\theta = 0$ and therefore $\theta = \pm90°$. Either of these angles means that $\vec{a}$ is perpendicular to $\vec{b}$. $\qquad\square$

Suppose that we are given the coordinates of two vectors instead of their magnitudes and the angle between them. How do we calculate the dot product? We could use trigonometry to find the angle between them, but the following is a much simpler way to calculate their dot product.

Dot Product in Component Form

In $\boldsymbol{R}^2$: If $\vec{a} = (a_1, a_2)$ and $\vec{b} = (b_1, b_2)$, then

$$\vec{a} \cdot \vec{b} = a_1b_1 + a_2b_2$$

In $\boldsymbol{R}^3$: If $\vec{a} = (a_1, a_2, a_3)$ and $\vec{b} = (b_1, b_2, b_3)$, then

$$\vec{a} \cdot \vec{b} = a_1b_1 + a_2b_2 + a_3b_3$$

Proof. We prove the result for $\vec{a}, \vec{b} \in \boldsymbol{R}^3$.
Let $\vec{a} = \overrightarrow{OA}$ and $\vec{b} = \overrightarrow{OB}$, so that

$$\overrightarrow{BA} = \vec{a} - \vec{b}$$
$$= (a_1 - b_1, a_2 - b_2, a_3 - b_3)$$

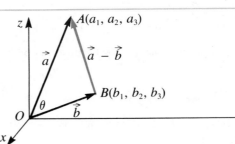

Hence,

$$|\vec{a} - \vec{b}|^2 = (a_1 - b_1)^2 + (a_2 - b_2)^2 + (a_3 - b_3)^2$$
$$= a_1^2 - 2a_1b_1 + b_1^2 + a_2^2 - 2a_2b_2 + b_2^2 + a_3^2 - 2a_3b_3 + b_3^2$$

From the cosine law in $\triangle OAB$,

$$|\vec{a} - \vec{b}|^2 = |\vec{a}|^2 + |\vec{b}|^2 - 2|\vec{a}||\vec{b}| \cos \theta$$
$$= a_1^2 + a_2^2 + a_3^2 + b_1^2 + b_2^2 + b_3^2 - 2|\vec{a}||\vec{b}| \cos\theta$$

Equating the two expressions for $|\vec{a} - \vec{b}|^2$, we obtain

$$-2|\vec{a}||\vec{b}| \cos \theta = -2a_1b_1 - 2a_2b_2 - 2a_3b_3$$
$$|\vec{a}||\vec{b}| \cos \theta = a_1b_1 + a_2b_2 + a_3b_3$$

Since $|\vec{a}||\vec{b}| \cos \theta = \vec{a} \cdot \vec{b}$, it follows that $\vec{a} \cdot \vec{b} = a_1b_1 + a_2b_2 + a_3b_3$.   □

Example 2. If $\vec{a} = (1, 2, -4)$ and $\vec{b} = (3, 4, -5)$, calculate $\vec{a} \cdot \vec{b}$.

Solution.

$$\vec{a} \cdot \vec{b} = (1, 2, -4) \cdot (3, 4, -5)$$
$$= 1(3) + 2(4) + (-4)(-5)$$
$$= 31$$ □

Example 3. For what value of k are the vectors $\vec{a} = (2, -2, 3)$ and $\vec{b} = (3, k, -4)$ perpendicular?

Solution. The vectors are perpendicular if their dot product is zero. Now

$$\vec{a} \cdot \vec{b} = (2, -2, 3) \cdot (3, k, -4)$$
$$= 6 - 2k - 12$$
$$= -6 - 2k$$

Thus, $\vec{a} \cdot \vec{b} = 0$ if $k = -3$.

Check. $(2, -2, 3) \cdot (3, -3, -4) = 6 + 6 - 12 = 0$ □

The dot product can also be used to find the angle between two vectors.

Example 4. Find the angle between the vectors $\vec{a} = (\sqrt{2} - 1, \sqrt{2} + 1, \sqrt{2})$ and $\vec{b} = (1, 1, 1)$.

Solution. If θ is the angle between the vectors, then $\vec{a} \cdot \vec{b} = |\vec{a}||\vec{b}| \cos \theta$. Hence,

$$\cos \theta = \frac{\vec{a} \cdot \vec{b}}{|\vec{a}||\vec{b}|}$$

Now,

$$\vec{a} \cdot \vec{b} = 1(\sqrt{2} - 1) + 1(\sqrt{2} + 1) + 1(\sqrt{2})$$
$$= 3\sqrt{2}$$
$$|\vec{a}| = \sqrt{(\sqrt{2} - 1)^2 + (\sqrt{2} + 1)^2 + (\sqrt{2})^2}$$
$$= \sqrt{2 - 2\sqrt{2} + 1 + 2 + 2\sqrt{2} + 1 + 2}$$
$$= \sqrt{8}$$
$$= 2\sqrt{2}$$
$$|\vec{b}| = \sqrt{1^2 + 1^2 + 1^2}$$
$$= \sqrt{3}$$

Therefore, $\cos \theta = \dfrac{3\sqrt{2}}{(2\sqrt{2})(\sqrt{3})} = \dfrac{\sqrt{3}}{2}$ and so $\theta = 30°$. Hence, the angle between $\vec{a}$ and $\vec{b}$ is $30°$. $\square$

Example 5. The parallelogram $OACB$ has one vertex, O, at the origin and two non-parallel sides determined by $\overrightarrow{OA} = (3, -1)$ and $\overrightarrow{OB} = (2, 2)$. Calculate the angle between the diagonals.

Solution. The diagonals of the parallelogram are $\overrightarrow{OC}$ and $\overrightarrow{AB}$. Now

$$\overrightarrow{OC} = \overrightarrow{OA} + \overrightarrow{OB}$$
$$= (3, -1) + (2, 2)$$
$$= (5, 1)$$

$$\overrightarrow{AB} = \overrightarrow{OB} - \overrightarrow{OA}$$
$$= (2, 2) - (3, -1)$$
$$= (-1, 3)$$

$$|\overrightarrow{OC}| = \sqrt{5^2 + 1^2}$$
$$= \sqrt{26}$$

$$|\overrightarrow{AB}| = \sqrt{(-1)^2 + 3^2}$$
$$= \sqrt{10}$$

$$\cos \theta = \frac{\overrightarrow{OC} \cdot \overrightarrow{AB}}{|\overrightarrow{OC}||\overrightarrow{AB}|}$$

$$= \frac{(5, 1) \cdot (-1, 3)}{\sqrt{26}\sqrt{10}}$$

$$= \frac{-2}{\sqrt{260}}$$

$$= \frac{-1}{\sqrt{65}}$$

Therefore, $\theta = \cos^{-1}\left(\frac{-1}{\sqrt{65}}\right)$ which is approximately 97°.

If we had chosen $\overrightarrow{OC}$ and $\overrightarrow{BA}$ as the diagonals, we would have obtained an acute angle of approximately 83°. Both answers are correct because the diagonal vectors can be taken in either direction.

The angle between the diagonals is therefore approximately 97° or 83°.

Check. A scale drawing shows that one of the angles is a little more than 90°; the other is a little less. □

Exercises 1.7

1. Calculate the dot product, $\vec{a} \cdot \vec{b}$, given the magnitudes of $\vec{a}$ and $\vec{b}$ and the angle θ between them.

   a. $|\vec{a}| = 3$, $|\vec{b}| = 4$, $\theta = 45°$ b. $|\vec{a}| = 5$, $|\vec{b}| = 6$, $\theta = 60°$

   c. $|\vec{a}| = 6$, $|\vec{b}| = 3$, $\theta = 135°$ d. $|\vec{a}| = 8$, $|\vec{b}| = 7$, $\theta = 90°$

2. Sketch the pair of vectors, find their dot product, and state whether or not the vectors are perpendicular.

   a. $\vec{a} = (4, 1)$, $\vec{b} = (-1, 4)$ b. $\vec{u} = (5, 2)$, $\vec{v} = (-5, -2)$

   c. $\vec{x} = (1, 0)$, $\vec{y} = (0, -1)$ d. $\vec{c} = (7, 8)$, $\vec{d} = (4, -7)$

3. If two vectors, $\vec{a}$ and $\vec{b}$, have an angle of 180° between them, what is their dot product?

4. If the dot product of two vectors is negative, what conclusions can be drawn about the vectors?

5. Calculate the dot product for each pair of vectors in $\mathbf{R}^3$ and determine which pairs are perpendicular.

   a. $\vec{a} = (-1, 3, 4)$, $\vec{b} = (1, 3, -2)$ b. $\vec{x} = (-2, 2, 4)$, $\vec{y} = (4, 1, -2)$

   c. $\vec{i} = (1, 0, 0)$, $\vec{j} = (0, 1, 0)$ d. $\vec{i} = (1, 0, 0)$, $\vec{i} = (1, 0, 0)$

   e. $\vec{u} = (0, 5, 6)$, $\vec{v} = (7, 0, 1)$ f. $\vec{c} = (-13, 11, -9)$, $\vec{d} = (9, 11, 13)$

6. a. Find three vectors perpendicular to $(2, -3)$.

   b. Find three vectors perpendicular to $(2, -3, 1)$.

   c. How many unit vectors are perpendicular to a given vector in $\textbf{R}^2$?

   d. How many unit vectors are perpendicular to a given vector in $\textbf{R}^3$?

7. Given $\vec{a} = (2, 3, 7)$ and $\vec{b} = (-4, y, -14)$,

   a. for what value of y are the vectors collinear?

   b. for what value of y are the vectors perpendicular?

8. Calculate, to two decimal places, the cosine of the angle between each pair of vectors.

   a. $\vec{a} = (8, 9)$, $\vec{b} = (9, 8)$ **b.** $\vec{c} = (1, -2, 3)$, $\vec{d} = (4, 2, 0)$

   c. $\vec{i} = (1, 0, 0)$, $\vec{m} = (1, 1, 1)$ **d.** $\vec{x} = (2, -4, 5)$, $\vec{y} = (0, 2, 3)$

9. Calculate the angle between $\vec{a} = (5, 6, -7)$ and $\vec{b} = (-2, 3, 1)$.

10. If $\vec{a} = (2, 3, 4)$ and $\vec{b} = (10, y, z)$, determine the algebraic condition under which $\vec{a}$ and $\vec{b}$ are perpendicular.

11. If $\vec{a} = (1, 2, 4)$ and $\vec{b} = (0, 3, -2)$, find a vector that is perpendicular to both $\vec{a}$ and $\vec{b}$. Interpret this result geometrically.

12. The angle between $\vec{a}$ and $\vec{b}$ is $\cos^{-1}\left(\frac{4}{21}\right)$. Find p if $\vec{a} = 6\vec{i} + 3\vec{j} - 2\vec{k}$ and $\vec{b} = -2\vec{i} + p\vec{j} - 4\vec{k}$.

13. Find λ so that the vectors $\vec{i} + \vec{j} + \vec{k}$ and $\lambda^2\vec{i} - 2\lambda\vec{j} + \vec{k}$ are perpendicular.

14. A contractor needs 100 m³ of concrete A and 40 m³ of concrete B. The following table gives the composition of the two types of concrete in kg/m³.

	Cement	Sand	Stone	Water
Mix A	200	600	600	120
Mix B	400	500	600	90

If the prices per kilogram of the cement, sand, and stone are 3 cents, 2 cents, and 1 cent, respectively, and the water is free, calculate the total cost.

15. a. If $\vec{a}$ and $\vec{b}$ are perpendicular, show that $|\vec{a}|^2 + |\vec{b}|^2 = |\vec{a} + \vec{b}|^2$.

   b. What is the usual name of this result?

16. The diagonals of a parallelogram are given by $\vec{a} = 3\vec{i} - 4\vec{j} - \vec{k}$ and $\vec{b} = 2\vec{i} + 3\vec{j} - 6\vec{k}$. Show that this parallelogram is a rhombus and determine the lengths of its sides and the angles between the sides.

17. Two non-zero vectors $\vec{u}$ and $\vec{v}$ are such that $|\vec{u} + \vec{v}| = |\vec{u} - \vec{v}|$. Use the dot product to show that $\vec{u}$ and $\vec{v}$ are perpendicular.

Problems 1.7

1. A body diagonal of a cube is a line joining opposite vertices. Find the angles between the body diagonals of a cube.

2. Show that $\vec{a} \cdot \vec{b} = \frac{1}{4}|\vec{a} + \vec{b}|^2 - \frac{1}{4}|\vec{a} - \vec{b}|^2$.

3. Find a unit vector that is parallel to the xy-plane and perpendicular to the vector $4\vec{i} - 3\vec{j} + \vec{k}$.

4. Prove that $|\vec{a} \cdot \vec{b}| \le |\vec{a}||\vec{b}|$. When does the equality hold? Express this inequality in terms of components when $\vec{a}, \vec{b} \in \mathbf{R}^2$, and when $\vec{a}, \vec{b} \in \mathbf{R}^3$. (This is called the Cauchy-Schwarz Inequality.)

5. Either prove the statement or give a counter-example:
   "If $\vec{a} \cdot \vec{b} = \vec{a} \cdot \vec{c}$ and $\vec{a} \ne \vec{0}$, then $\vec{b} = \vec{c}$."

6. A regular tetrahedron has one vertex at the origin, one vertex at $(0, 1, 0)$, and one vertex, with a positive x-coordinate, on the xy-plane.

   a. Find the coordinates of the four vertices.

   b. Find the coordinates of the centroid of the tetrahedron.

   c. How far is the centroid along the perpendicular from a vertex to the opposite face?

1.8 Properties of the Dot Product

The dot product, and its relationship with addition and scalar multiplication, has many useful algebraic properties. They make it easy to manipulate expressions involving the dot product.

Properties of the Dot Product

- $\vec{a} \cdot \vec{b} = \vec{b} \cdot \vec{a}$ (Commutative Law)
- $\vec{a} \cdot (\vec{b} + \vec{c}) = \vec{a} \cdot \vec{b} + \vec{a} \cdot \vec{c}$ (Distributive Law)
- $\vec{a} \cdot \vec{a} = |\vec{a}|^2$
- $(k\vec{a}) \cdot \vec{b} = \vec{a} \cdot (k\vec{b}) = k(\vec{a} \cdot \vec{b})$ for any scalar k

---

Proof of the Commutative Law. If the angle between $\vec{a}$ and $\vec{b}$ is θ, then the angle between $\vec{b}$ and $\vec{a}$ is $-\theta$. Note that $\cos \theta = \cos(-\theta)$. Hence,

$$\begin{aligned}
\vec{a} \cdot \vec{b} &= |\vec{a}||\vec{b}|\cos \theta \\
&= |\vec{b}||\vec{a}|\cos(-\theta) \\
&= \vec{b} \cdot \vec{a}
\end{aligned}$$

Alternative Proof. If $\vec{a}$ and $\vec{b}$ are in $\mathbf{R}^3$, by using the component form, we obtain

$$\vec{a} \cdot \vec{b} = a_1b_1 + a_2b_2 + a_3b_3$$
$$= b_1a_1 + b_2a_2 + b_3a_3$$
$$= \vec{b} \cdot \vec{a}$$

$\square$

Proof of the Distributive Law. We shall prove this property for vectors in $\mathbf{R}^3$. Let $\vec{a} = (a_1, a_2, a_3)$, $\vec{b} = (b_1, b_2, b_3)$, and $\vec{c} = (c_1, c_2, c_3)$. Then

$$\vec{a} \cdot (\vec{b} + \vec{c}) = (a_1, a_2, a_3) \cdot (b_1 + c_1, b_2 + c_2, b_3 + c_3)$$
$$= a_1(b_1 + c_1) + a_2(b_2 + c_2) + a_3(b_3 + c_3)$$
$$= (a_1b_1 + a_2b_2 + a_3b_3) + (a_1c_1 + a_2c_2 + a_3c_3)$$
$$= \vec{a} \cdot \vec{b} + \vec{a} \cdot \vec{c}$$

$\square$

The proofs of the last two properties follow Example 1.

Example 1. If $\vec{a} = (1, 2, 5)$, $\vec{b} = (1, -4, 6)$, and $\vec{c} = (-1, -2, 3)$, verify that $\vec{a} \cdot \vec{b} = \vec{b} \cdot \vec{a}$ and that $\vec{a} \cdot (\vec{b} + \vec{c}) = \vec{a} \cdot \vec{b} + \vec{a} \cdot \vec{c}$.

Solution. We have

$$\vec{a} \cdot \vec{b} = (1, 2, 5) \cdot (1, -4, 6)$$
$$= 1(1) + 2(-4) + 5(6)$$
$$= 23$$

and

$$\vec{b} \cdot \vec{a} = (1, -4, 6) \cdot (1, 2, 5)$$
$$= 1(1) - 4(2) + 6(5)$$
$$= 23$$

Hence, $\vec{a} \cdot \vec{b} = \vec{b} \cdot \vec{a}$.

Now, $\vec{b} + \vec{c} = (0, -6, 9)$, so that

$$\vec{a} \cdot (\vec{b} + \vec{c}) = (1, 2, 5) \cdot (0, -6, 9)$$
$$= 1(0) + 2(-6) + 5(9)$$
$$= 33$$

and

$$\vec{a} \cdot \vec{b} + \vec{a} \cdot \vec{c} = 23 + (1, 2, 5) \cdot (-1, -2, 3)$$
$$= 23 + 1(-1) + 2(-2) + 5(3)$$
$$= 33$$

Hence, $\vec{a} \cdot (\vec{b} + \vec{c}) = \vec{a} \cdot \vec{b} + \vec{a} \cdot \vec{c}$.

$\square$

Proof of $\vec{a} \cdot \vec{a} = |\vec{a}|^2$.
The angle between $\vec{a}$ and itself is $0°$ and $\cos 0° = 1$, so that

$$\vec{a} \cdot \vec{a} = |\vec{a}|^2 \cos 0° = |\vec{a}|^2$$

Alternative Proof. If $\vec{a} = (a_1, a_2, a_3) \in \mathbf{R}^3$, then

$$\vec{a} \cdot \vec{a} = (a_1, a_2, a_3) \cdot (a_1, a_2, a_3)$$
$$= a_1^2 + a_2^2 + a_3^2$$
$$= |\vec{a}|^2$$

$\square$

Proof of $(k\vec{a}) \cdot \vec{b} = \vec{a} \cdot (k\vec{b}) = k(\vec{a} \cdot \vec{b})$.

If $\vec{a} = (a_1, a_2, a_3)$ and $\vec{b} = (b_1, b_2, b_3)$ are vectors in $\mathbf{R}^3$ and k is a scalar, then

$$(k\vec{a}) \cdot \vec{b} = (ka_1, ka_2, ka_3) \cdot (b_1, b_2, b_3)$$
$$= ka_1b_1 + ka_2b_2 + ka_3b_3$$
$$= k(\vec{a} \cdot \vec{b})$$

Similarly, $\vec{a} \cdot (k\vec{b}) = k(\vec{a} \cdot \vec{b})$.   □

Example 2. If $\vec{a}$ and $\vec{b}$ are unit vectors and the angle between them is $60°$, calculate $(7\vec{a} - \vec{b}) \cdot (3\vec{a} + \vec{b})$.

Solution. Since $|\vec{a}| = |\vec{b}| = 1$, by the definition of the dot product

$$\vec{a} \cdot \vec{b} = |\vec{a}||\vec{b}| \cos 60°$$
$$= (1)(1)\left(\tfrac{1}{2}\right)$$
$$= \tfrac{1}{2}$$

Hence,

$$(7\vec{a} - \vec{b}) \cdot (3\vec{a} + \vec{b}) = 21\vec{a} \cdot \vec{a} + 7\vec{a} \cdot \vec{b} - 3\vec{b} \cdot \vec{a} - \vec{b} \cdot \vec{b}$$
$$= 21|\vec{a}|^2 + 4\vec{a} \cdot \vec{b} - |\vec{b}|^2$$
$$= 21(1) + 4\left(\tfrac{1}{2}\right) - 1$$
$$= 22$$ □

Exercises 1.8

1. For $\vec{a} = (1, 5, 8)$ and $\vec{b} = (-1, 3, -2)$ verify that

    a. $\vec{a} \cdot \vec{b} = \vec{b} \cdot \vec{a}$

    b. $\vec{a} \cdot \vec{a} = |\vec{a}|^2$ and $\vec{b} \cdot \vec{b} = |\vec{b}|^2$

    c. $(2\vec{a}) \cdot \vec{b} = \vec{a} \cdot (2\vec{b}) = 2(\vec{a} \cdot \vec{b})$

2. If $\vec{a} = (2, 2, -1)$, $\vec{b} = (3, -1, 0)$, and $\vec{c} = (1, 7, 8)$, verify that $\vec{a} \cdot (\vec{b} + \vec{c}) = \vec{a} \cdot \vec{b} + \vec{a} \cdot \vec{c}$.

3. Expand $(\vec{a} + \vec{b}) \cdot (\vec{a} - \vec{b})$ and write your answer in simplest form.

4. Expand $(\vec{a} + \vec{b}) \cdot (\vec{c} + \vec{d})$.

5. Expand and simplify.

    a. $(2\vec{a} + 3\vec{b}) \cdot (4\vec{a} + 5\vec{b})$ **b.** $(2\vec{a} - \vec{b}) \cdot (2\vec{a} + \vec{b})$

    c. $(\vec{a} + \vec{b}) \cdot (\vec{a} + \vec{b}) + (\vec{a} + \vec{b}) \cdot (\vec{a} - \vec{b})$

6. Expand and simplify $(4\vec{i} - \vec{j}) \cdot \vec{j} + \vec{k} \cdot (\vec{j} - 3\vec{k}) + (\vec{i} - 4\vec{k}) \cdot (\vec{i} - 4\vec{k})$, where $\vec{i}, \vec{j}$, and $\vec{k}$ are the standard basis vectors in 3-space.

7. The two vectors $2\vec{a} + \vec{b}$ and $\vec{a} - 3\vec{b}$ are perpendicular. Find the angle between $\vec{a}$ and $\vec{b}$ if $|\vec{a}| = 2|\vec{b}|$.

8. If $\vec{a}$ and $\vec{b}$ are unit vectors and the angle between them is $60°$, calculate $(6\vec{a} + \vec{b}) \cdot (\vec{a} - 2\vec{b})$.

9. If $\vec{a}$ and $\vec{b}$ are unit vectors and $|\vec{a} + \vec{b}| = \sqrt{3}$, determine $(2\vec{a} - 5\vec{b}) \cdot (\vec{b} + 3\vec{a})$.

10. Calculate the dot product of $4\vec{x} - \vec{y}$ and $2\vec{x} + 3\vec{y}$ if $|\vec{x}| = 3$, $|\vec{y}| = 4$, and the angle between x and y is $60°$.

Problems 1.8

1. Three vectors $\vec{x}$, $\vec{y}$, and $\vec{z}$ satisfy $\vec{x} + \vec{y} + \vec{z} = \vec{0}$. Calculate the value of $\vec{x} \cdot \vec{y} + \vec{x} \cdot \vec{z} + \vec{y} \cdot \vec{z}$, if $|\vec{x}| = 2$, $|\vec{y}| = 3$, and $|\vec{z}| = 4$.

2. **a.** Show that the following identity is true for any $\vec{x}, \vec{y} \in \mathbf{R}^3$.

$$\vec{x} \cdot \vec{y} = \tfrac{1}{2}(|\vec{x} + \vec{y}|^2 - |\vec{x}|^2 - |\vec{y}|^2)$$

   b. Interpret the result in part a.

1.9 Projections

The dot product is very useful for computing the projection of one vector on another vector. This has wide-ranging applications to physics, which we shall study in Chapter 2, and to distances between lines and planes, which we shall study in Chapter 4.

Let $\vec{a} = \overrightarrow{OA}$ and $\vec{b} = \overrightarrow{OB}$. Let N be the point on the line OB such that AN is perpendicular to OB. The vector $\overrightarrow{ON}$ is called the **vector projection** of $\vec{a}$ on $\vec{b}$. The scalar distance ON is called the **scalar projection** of $\vec{a}$ on $\vec{b}$ and is positive if $0° \le \theta < 90°$ and negative if $90° < \theta \le 180°$.

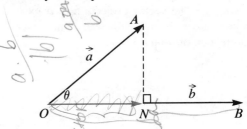

A scalar projection on an axis is often called a **component**.

Projections

If $\vec{b} \ne \vec{0}$, then the vector projection of $\vec{a}$ on $\vec{b}$ is

$$\left(\frac{\vec{a} \cdot \vec{b}}{|\vec{b}|^2}\, \vec{b}\right) \quad \text{or} \quad \left(\frac{\vec{a} \cdot \vec{b}}{\vec{b} \cdot \vec{b}}\, \vec{b}\right)$$

and the scalar projection of $\vec{a}$ on $\vec{b}$ is

$$\frac{\vec{a} \cdot \vec{b}}{|\vec{b}|}$$

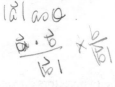

Proof. In $\triangle OAN$ of the preceding diagram, $ON = |\vec{a}| \cos \theta$. Hence, the scalar projection of $\vec{a}$ on $\vec{b}$ is

$$|\vec{a}| \cos \theta = \frac{|\vec{a}||\vec{b}| \cos \theta}{|\vec{b}|}$$

$$= \frac{\vec{a} \cdot \vec{b}}{|\vec{b}|}$$

The vector projection of $\vec{a}$ on $\vec{b}$ is the scalar projection times a unit vector in the direction of $\vec{b}$. Thus, the vector projection is

$$\left(\frac{\vec{a} \cdot \vec{b}}{|\vec{b}|} \right) \frac{\vec{b}}{|\vec{b}|} = \left(\frac{\vec{a} \cdot \vec{b}}{|\vec{b}|^2} \right) \vec{b} \qquad \square$$

Notice that if $\vec{c}$ is another vector in the same direction as $\vec{b}$, then the vector projection of $\vec{a}$ on $\vec{c}$ is the same as the vector projection of $\vec{a}$ on $\vec{b}$. The corresponding scalar projections are also the same.

The dot product can be interpreted in terms of scalar projections. The dot product, $\vec{a} \cdot \vec{b}$, is the magnitude of $\vec{b}$ times the scalar projection of $\vec{a}$ on $\vec{b}$, or equivalently, the magnitude of $\vec{a}$ times the scalar projection of $\vec{b}$ on $\vec{a}$.

Example 1. If $\vec{a} = (2, 4, -1)$ and $\vec{b} = (3, 3, 4)$, find the scalar and vector projections of $\vec{a}$ on $\vec{b}$.

Solution. The vector projection of $\vec{a}$ on $\vec{b}$ is the vector $\overrightarrow{ON}$ in the diagram. The scalar projection of $\vec{a}$ on $\vec{b}$ is

$$|\overrightarrow{ON}| = \frac{\vec{a} \cdot \vec{b}}{|\vec{b}|}$$

$$= \frac{(2, 4, -1) \cdot (3, 3, 4)}{|(3, 3, 4)|}$$

$$= \frac{6 + 12 - 4}{\sqrt{9 + 9 + 16}}$$

$$= \frac{14}{\sqrt{34}}$$

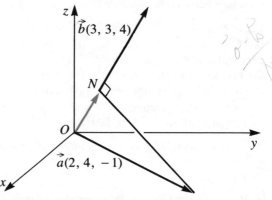

The vector projection of $\vec{a}$ on $\vec{b}$ is

$$\left(\frac{\vec{a} \cdot \vec{b}}{|\vec{b}|^2} \right) \vec{b} = \left[\frac{(2, 4, -1) \cdot (3, 3, 4)}{|(3, 3, 4)|^2} \right] (3, 3, 4)$$

$$= \tfrac{14}{34}(3, 3, 4)$$

$$= \left(\tfrac{21}{17}, \tfrac{21}{17}, \tfrac{28}{17} \right) \qquad \square$$

If $\vec{u}$ is a unit vector, then the scalar projection of $\vec{a}$ on $\vec{u}$ is just $\vec{a} \cdot \vec{u}$. For example, if $\overrightarrow{OP}$ is the position vector of the point $P(a, b, c)$, then the scalar projections of $\overrightarrow{OP} = (a, b, c)$ on the standard basis vectors $\vec{i}, \vec{j}$, and $\vec{k}$ are a, b, and c, respectively. The vector projections of $\overrightarrow{OP}$ on the axes are $a\vec{i}$, $b\vec{j}$, and $c\vec{k}$.

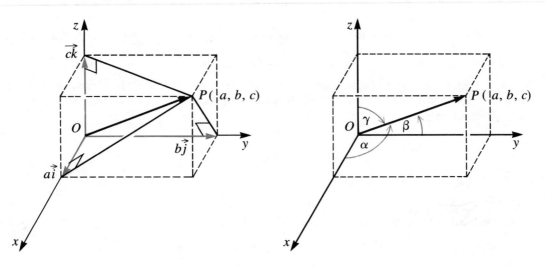

Let α, β, and γ be the angles that $\overrightarrow{OP}$ makes with the positive x-axis, positive y-axis, and positive z-axis, respectively. Then

$$\cos \alpha = \frac{\vec{i} \cdot \overrightarrow{OP}}{|\overrightarrow{OP}|}$$

$$= \frac{(1, 0, 0) \cdot (a, b, c)}{|(a, b, c)|}$$

$$= \frac{a}{\sqrt{a^2 + b^2 + c^2}}$$

Hence, the angles can be found by using the relations

$$\cos \alpha = \frac{a}{\sqrt{a^2 + b^2 + c^2}}, \quad \cos \beta = \frac{b}{\sqrt{a^2 + b^2 + c^2}}, \quad \cos \gamma = \frac{c}{\sqrt{a^2 + b^2 + c^2}}$$

Note that $\cos^2 \alpha + \cos^2 \beta + \cos^2 \gamma = 1$ and that $(\cos \alpha, \cos \beta, \cos \gamma)$ is a unit vector in the direction of $\overrightarrow{OP}$. The angles α, β, and γ are called the **direction angles** of $\overrightarrow{OP}$, and the numbers $\cos \alpha$, $\cos \beta$, and $\cos \gamma$ are called the **direction cosines** of $\overrightarrow{OP}$. Before the widespread use of vectors, the direction cosines were the standard method of describing the direction of a line in $\mathbf{R}^3$. Now it is usually more convenient to describe the direction of a line by giving any vector along the line.

Example 2. Find the angle that the vector $(2, 1, -4)$ makes with each of the coordinate axes.

Solution. The length of the vector is

$$|(2, 1, -4)| = \sqrt{2^2 + 1^2 + (-4)^2}$$
$$= \sqrt{21}$$

Hence, the direction cosines are $\cos \alpha = \frac{2}{\sqrt{21}}$, $\cos \beta = \frac{1}{\sqrt{21}}$, and $\cos \gamma = \frac{-4}{\sqrt{21}}$. The angles are $\alpha = \cos^{-1}\left(\frac{2}{\sqrt{21}}\right) \approx 64°$, $\beta = \cos^{-1}\left(\frac{1}{\sqrt{21}}\right) \approx 77°$, and $\gamma = \cos^{-1}\left(\frac{-4}{\sqrt{21}}\right) \approx 151°$. Hence, $(2, 1, -4)$ makes an angle of approximately $64°$ with the x-axis, $77°$ with the y-axis, and $151°$ with the z-axis. Note that since the z-coordinate is negative, the vector makes an obtuse angle with the positive z-axis. $\square$

Exercises 1.9

1. Find the scalar and vector projections of $\vec{a}$ on $\vec{b}$.

    a. $\vec{a} = (2, 5)$, $\vec{b} = (6, 4)$ **b.** $\vec{a} = (-2, 4)$, $\vec{b} = (-3, 2)$

    c. $\vec{a} = (3, 6, -2)$, $\vec{b} = (-4, 3, 8)$ **d.** $\vec{a} = (27, 11, -4)$, $\vec{b} = (0, 0, 8)$

2. **a.** If $\vec{a}$ and $\vec{b}$ are non-zero vectors such that the vector projection of $\vec{a}$ on $\vec{b}$ is the zero vector, what conclusion can be drawn?

    b. In the above situation, does it follow that the vector projection of $\vec{b}$ on $\vec{a}$ is the zero vector? Justify your answer.

3. Find the scalar and vector projections of $\vec{a} = (2, 3, -4)$ on each of the coordinate axes.

4. Find the angle that $(2, 3, -2)$ makes with each of the coordinate axes.

5. Find the direction cosines of $\vec{u} = (a, b, c)$, where $\vec{u}$ is a unit vector.

6. The vector $\vec{v} = (1, \sqrt{2}, c)$ makes an angle of $60°$ with the positive z-axis. Determine the angles that $\vec{v}$ makes with the positive x-axis and the positive y-axis. Explain how many answers there are.

7. Determine the angle that $\vec{j} = (0, 1, 0)$ makes with each of the coordinate axes.

8. If $|\vec{a}| = 2$, $|\vec{b}| = 3$, and the angle between the vectors is $60°$, draw a diagram and calculate the scalar projection of $\vec{a}$ on $\vec{b}$.

9. Find the components and vector projections of $\vec{PQ}$ along the axes, where the point P is $(2, 3, 5)$ and the point Q is $(-1, 2, 5)$.

10. **a.** Find the scalar projection of an edge of a unit cube on one of its body diagonals.

    b. Find the scalar projection of a body diagonal of the unit cube on one of its edges.

Problems 1.9

1. A vector in 3-space makes equal angles with the coordinate axes. Determine these angles if they are all

   a. acute.   **b.** obtuse. *greater than 90°*

2. Find the coordinates of a unit vector that is perpendicular to both of the vectors $(1, 1, 1)$ and $(1, 3, -1)$ and makes an obtuse angle with the z-axis.

3. Find a vector that is perpendicular to $(-1, 2, 2)$ and makes equal angles with $\vec{i}$ and $\vec{j}$. Explain how many answers there are.

4. Let $\vec{p}$ be the vector projection of $\vec{a} = (1, 1)$ on $\vec{b} = (4, 2)$. Verify that

$$|\vec{a} - \vec{p}| \leq |\vec{a} - k\vec{b}|, \quad \text{for all } k \in \mathbf{R}$$

   Interpret this result.

Review Exercises

1. Let $\vec{x} = (4, -1, 3)$ and $\vec{y} = (-2, 3, 0)$ be vectors in 3-space.

   a. Find $\vec{x} + \vec{y}, \vec{x} - \vec{y}, \vec{y} - \vec{x}, 2\vec{x} + \vec{y}$.

   b. Calculate $|\vec{x} + \vec{y}|, |\vec{x} - \vec{y}|, |\vec{y} - \vec{x}|, |2\vec{x} + \vec{y}|$.

2. Write each vector $\vec{AB}$ in the form $x\vec{i} + y\vec{j} + z\vec{k}$.

   a. $A = (2, 3, -8), B = (2, -3, 8)$ **b.** $A = (0, 1, 0), B = (-1, 0, -1)$

   c. $A = (5, 2, -1), B = (4, -1, -1)$ **d.** $A = (7, 8, -2), B = (7, -2, -2)$

3. Find a vector of unit length that has the same direction as the given vector.

   a. $\vec{u} = (-1, 2)$ **b.** $\vec{v} = (1, 4, 2)$ **c.** $\vec{w} = (-1, 3, 4)$

4. Two forces, $\vec{F}_1$ and $\vec{F}_2$, at right angles to each other, are applied at P to move a rock. Find the magnitude of the resultant of these forces in terms of the magnitudes of $\vec{F}_1$ and $\vec{F}_2$.

5. Find two unit vectors in $\mathbf{R}^2$ that are perpendicular to $(-3, 4)$.

6. If $\vec{a} = 2\vec{i} + 5\vec{j}$ and $\vec{b} = -\vec{i} + t\vec{j}$, determine t when

   a. $\vec{a}$ and $\vec{b}$ are perpendicular.   **b.** $\vec{a}$ and $\vec{b}$ are parallel.

   c. the angle between $\vec{a}$ and $\vec{b}$ is 45°. *DO THIS ONE! (DON'T GET*

7. If $\vec{a} = (2, 1, 0)$ and $\vec{b} = (-1, 6, 1)$, find a vector perpendicular to both $\vec{a}$ and $\vec{b}$. *IT!)*

8. Calculate the scalar and vector projections of $\vec{a}$ on $\vec{b}$.

    a. $\vec{a} = (2, 3)$, $\vec{b} = (-1, 1)$ **b.** $\vec{a} = (0, 2, 1)$, $\vec{b} = (4, 6, -1)$

9. Calculate the angle between the vectors $(2, 3, -4)$ and $(-2, 5, 0)$.

10. Calculate the angles that $(3, 4, 1)$ makes with the coordinate axes.

11. If $\vec{a} = (1, 2, -1)$ and $\vec{b} = (3, 1, 0)$, find the vector projection, $\vec{p}$, of $\vec{a}$ on $\vec{b}$ and verify that

    a. $|\vec{a} - 3\vec{b}| > |\vec{a} - \vec{p}|$.   **b.** $|\vec{a} - 0.4\vec{b}| > |\vec{a} - \vec{p}|$.

12. If $\vec{a}$ and $\vec{b}$ are vectors in 3-space, where $\vec{a} = t\vec{b}$, show that $\left(\dfrac{\vec{a} \cdot \vec{b}}{\vec{b} \cdot \vec{b}}\right) \vec{b} = \vec{a}$.

    Thus, if $\vec{a}$ and $\vec{b}$ are parallel, the projection of $\vec{a}$ on $\vec{b}$ is just $\vec{a}$.

13. If the vector projection of $\vec{b}$ on $\vec{a}$ is $\vec{p}$, express the following vector projections in terms of $\vec{p}$.

    a. $\vec{b}$ on $-\vec{a}$ **b.** $\vec{b}$ on $2\vec{a}$ **c.** $2\vec{b}$ on $\vec{a}$

14. Which of the following vectors are unit vectors and which pairs are perpendicular?

$$\vec{a} = \left(\tfrac{2}{3}, \tfrac{1}{3}, \tfrac{2}{3}\right), \qquad \vec{b} = \left(\tfrac{1}{\sqrt{26}}, \tfrac{4}{\sqrt{26}}, \tfrac{-3}{\sqrt{26}}\right), \qquad \vec{c} = \left(\tfrac{3}{4}, \tfrac{-\sqrt{3}}{4}, \tfrac{1}{2}\right), \qquad \vec{d} = \left(\tfrac{-11}{2}, 4, \tfrac{7}{2}\right)$$

15. Use vectors to calculate the angles of $\triangle ABC$.

    a. $A(3, -1)$, $B(-1, 1)$, $C(2, 4)$ **b.** $A(2, 2, 5)$, $B(4, -2, 3)$, $C(4, 1, 2)$

16. In $\triangle ABC$, E is the midpoint of AC and BE is extended to D so that $ED = BE$. Prove that $\overrightarrow{AB} = \overrightarrow{DC}$.

17. In the quadrilateral $ABCD$, the midpoints of the sides AB, BC, CD, and DA are P, Q, R, and S, respectively. Prove that PR and QS bisect each other. Do the points A, B, C, D have to lie in a plane for this result to hold?

18. If G is the centroid of $\triangle ABC$ and X is any point, prove that

$$|\overrightarrow{XA}|^2 + |\overrightarrow{XB}|^2 + |\overrightarrow{XC}|^2 = 3|\overrightarrow{XG}|^2 + |\overrightarrow{GA}|^2 + |\overrightarrow{GB}|^2 + |\overrightarrow{GC}|^2$$

19. Calculate the angles between the three body diagonals of a rectangular solid measuring $2 \times 3 \times 4$ units.

Force is an example of a vector.

Vector Applications

CHAPTER 2

In this chapter we first apply vectors to solve physical problems involving forces, velocities, and work. We then solve geometric problems, in the plane and in 3-space, using vectors. Finally we introduce another product of vectors, called the cross product, that is defined only in 3-space.

2.1 Forces

Let us describe an experiment that will demonstrate that forces are vectors and that the combined effect of forces obeys the parallelogram law of vector addition.

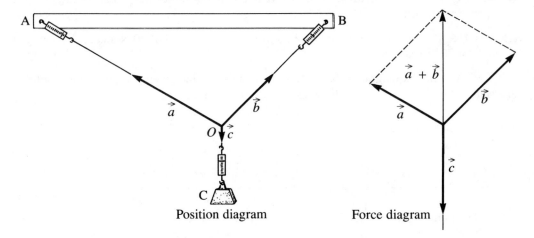

Position diagram   Force diagram

The experiment uses three spring balances to measure the tension in three pieces of string. Two of the spring balances are fixed at the points A and B. Three pieces of string of arbitrary length are tied together at O and then attached to the hooks of the spring balances. A weight is attached to the third spring balance at C. The only force in each string is its tension. The direction of this force is along the string, and its magnitude is measured by the spring balance.

Let $\vec{a}$, $\vec{b}$, and $\vec{c}$ be the forces along the strings OA, OB, and OC, respectively. By choosing a scale of measurement for these tensions, we can represent the forces $\vec{a}$, $\vec{b}$, and $\vec{c}$ by a force diagram. It will be found that, whatever weight is applied at C and whatever the length of the strings, the force $\vec{c}$ will be equal and opposite to the combined effect, or resultant, of $\vec{a}$ and $\vec{b}$. This resultant, $\vec{a} + \vec{b}$, is represented by the diagonal of the parallelogram. The force $\vec{c}$, which keeps the system in equilibrium, is called the **equilibrant** of $\vec{a}$ and $\vec{b}$. Since O does not move, the three forces must be in equilibrium and their sum must be zero. Hence, $\vec{a} + \vec{b} + \vec{c} = \vec{0}$, and so

$$\vec{c} = -(\vec{a} + \vec{b})$$

Equilibrium of Forces

If two forces are represented by vectors along the sides of a parallelogram, then their **resultant** is represented by a diagonal of the parallelogram and their **equilibrant** is equal in magnitude, but opposite in direction, to the resultant.

In the above experiment, we drew two separate diagrams — a position diagram and a force diagram. The position diagram represents the actual position of the forces in the problem, whereas the force diagram translates the vectors from the position diagram so that the Triangle or Parallelogram Law of Addition can be used. The position diagram allows us to visualize the problem, whereas the force diagram is used for calculation.

The complete description of a force requires a magnitude and a direction, though the direction is sometimes not given explicitly. Force is measured in newtons, which is abbreviated to N. Owing to the Earth's gravitational field, a 1 kg mass on the surface of the Earth exerts a force of approximately 9.8 N.

Example 1. Find the resultant and equilibrant of two forces of 20 N and 30 N, acting at an angle of $30°$ to each other.

Solution. We draw a diagram representing the position of the given vectors and also a force diagram in which AD is 30 units long and AB is 20 units long.

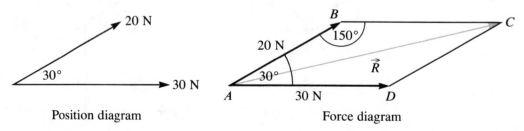

Position diagram   Force diagram

Let $\vec{R}$ represent the resultant of the two forces. Since $\angle DAB = 30°$ and $AD \parallel BC$, $\angle ABC = 150°$. Therefore, by the Cosine Law in $\triangle ABC$,

$$|\vec{R}|^2 = 30^2 + 20^2 - 2(30)(20) \cos 150°$$
$$= 900 + 400 + 2(30)(20)\frac{\sqrt{3}}{2}$$
$$= 1300 + 600\sqrt{3}$$
$$\approx 2339.23$$

Hence, $|\vec{R}|$ is approximately 48.4 N.

We can calculate $\angle BAC$, the angle between $\vec{R}$ and the 20 N force, by applying the Sine Law to $\triangle ABC$. We have

$$\frac{|\vec{R}|}{\sin(\angle ABC)} = \frac{|\overrightarrow{BC}|}{\sin(\angle BAC)}$$

$$\frac{|\vec{R}|}{\sin 30°} = \frac{30}{\sin(\angle BAC)}$$

$$\sin(\angle BAC) \approx \frac{30 \sin 30°}{48.4}$$

Hence, $\sin(\angle BAC) \approx 0.31$ and $\angle BAC \approx 18°$.

Therefore, the resultant of the two forces is approximately the force with magnitude 48.4 N acting at 18° to the 20 N force and 12° to the 30 N force. The equilibrant has the same magnitude as the resultant and acts at an angle of approximately 162° to the 20 N force and 168° to the 30 N force. □

Example 2. A girl pulls a rope, attached to a sleigh, with a force of approximately 5 N. If the rope she is pulling makes an angle of 30° with the ground, calculate

a. the force that is pulling the sleigh forward.

b. the force that tends to lift the sleigh.

Solution.

a. The magnitude of the force that tends to move the sleigh forward is the scalar projection of the 5 N force in the horizontal direction; this is called the horizontal component of the force. It is

$$|\overrightarrow{OA}| = 5 \cos 30°$$
$$= \frac{5\sqrt{3}}{2}$$

which is approximately 4.3 N.

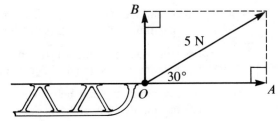

b. The magnitude of the force that tends to lift the sleigh is the scalar projection of the 5 N force in the vertical direction; this is called the vertical component. It is

$$|\overrightarrow{OB}| = 5 \sin 30°$$
$$= 2.5$$

Hence, the magnitude of this force is 2.5 N.   □

We have shown how to calculate the resultant and equilibrant of two forces by using the Parallelogram Law. We can also use the Triangle Law. If $\overrightarrow{F_1}$ and $\overrightarrow{F_2}$ are two forces acting at a point O, then their resultant, $\overrightarrow{R} = \overrightarrow{F_1} + \overrightarrow{F_2}$, can be calculated from the Triangle Law of Addition.

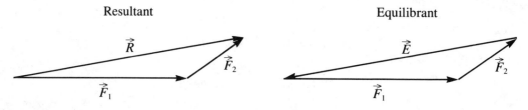

The equilibrant $\overrightarrow{E}$ is the opposite of the resultant. Hence, the sum of $\overrightarrow{F_1}$, $\overrightarrow{F_2}$, and $\overrightarrow{E}$ is the zero vector. That is, a system consisting of the vectors $\overrightarrow{F_1}$, $\overrightarrow{F_2}$, and $\overrightarrow{E}$ is in a state of equilibrium if and only if

$$\overrightarrow{F_1} + \overrightarrow{F_2} + \overrightarrow{E} = \overrightarrow{0}$$

These three vectors must form a closed triangle if the system is to be in equilibrium. This gives a relatively simple way of deciding whether or not a system is in a state of equilibrium.

Example 3. Can forces of 10 N, 20 N, and 40 N keep an object at rest?

Solution. The triangle of forces necessary to keep the system in equilibrium would have to have sides proportional to 10, 20, and 40 units. This is impossible because the Triangle Inequality states that the sum of any two sides of a triangle must be greater than the third, and in our case we have 10 + 20 < 40. Therefore, the three given forces cannot keep the system in equilibrium.   □

Exercises 2.1

1. Find the resultant and equilibrant of each pair of horizontal forces acting on an object.

   a. $\overrightarrow{F_1}$ has magnitude 10 N and acts due north.
       $\overrightarrow{F_2}$ has magnitude 10 N and acts due west.

   b. $\overrightarrow{F_1}$ has magnitude 5 N and acts due north.
       $\overrightarrow{F_2}$ has magnitude 7 N and acts due south.

   c. $\overrightarrow{F_1}$ has magnitude 9 N and acts due east.
       $\overrightarrow{F_2}$ has magnitude 12 N and acts due south.

2. A sleigh is being pulled with a 2 N force at an angle of 15° to the horizontal.

   a. What force tends to move the sleigh forwards?

   b. What force tends to lift the sleigh?

3. Which of the following sets of forces acting on an object could produce equilibrium?

   a. 5 N, 2 N, 13 N

   b. 7 N, 5 N, 5 N

   c. √3 N, 2 N, 1.5 N

   d. 14 N, 12 N, 28 N

4. Is it easier to pull oneself up when doing chin-ups if one's hands are 30 cm apart or 80 cm apart. Explain your answer.

5. A 5 kg block lies on a smooth plane inclined at 30°. What force, parallel to the incline, would prevent the block from slipping? (Assume that a 1 kg mass exerts a force of 9.8 N.)

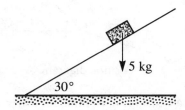

6. If two forces of F_1 and F_2 newtons act at right angles to each other, what will be the magnitude of their resultant? How can we easily calculate the direction of the resultant?

7. Find the magnitude of the resultant of the four forces shown in the diagram.

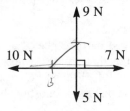

8. Three forces of 5 N, 8 N, and 10 N act from the corner of a cube along its edges. Find the magnitude of the equilibrant of these forces.

9. If two forces of equal magnitude act at 60° to each other and their resultant has a magnitude of 30 N, find the magnitude of the equal forces.

10. Three forces of 5 N, 7 N, and 8 N are applied to an object so that it is in a state of equilibrium.

   a. Show how the forces would be arranged to produce equilibrium.

   b. Calculate the angle between the lines of action of the 5 N and 7 N forces.

11. If a mass of 10 kg is suspended from a ceiling by two cords that make angles of 30° and 45° to the ceiling, find the tension in each of the cords. (Assume that a 1 kg mass exerts a force of 9.8 N.)

12. An object is suspended from two points on the ceiling 25 cm apart by two pieces of cord of lengths 7 cm and 24 cm. If the object exerts a downward force of 200 N, calculate the tension in each rope.

13. An object is in equilibrium when acted upon by the three forces $\vec{F}_1$, $\vec{F}_2$, and $\vec{F}_3$. The angle between $\vec{F}_2$ and $\vec{F}_3$ is α, the angle between $\vec{F}_3$ and $\vec{F}_1$ is β, and the angle between $\vec{F}_1$ and $\vec{F}_2$ is γ. Prove each relation.

a. $\dfrac{|\vec{F}_1|}{\sin \alpha} = \dfrac{|\vec{F}_2|}{\sin \beta} = \dfrac{|\vec{F}_3|}{\sin \gamma}$

b. $|\vec{F}_3|^2 = |\vec{F}_1|^2 + |\vec{F}_2|^2 + 2|\vec{F}_1||\vec{F}_2| \cos \gamma$

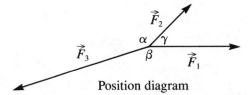

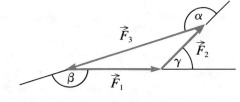

Position diagram   Force diagram

14. If a system is in equilibrium under the action of the forces $\vec{F}_1$, $\vec{F}_2$, . . . , $\vec{F}_n$, show that
$$\vec{F}_1 + \vec{F}_2 + \ldots + \vec{F}_n = \vec{0}$$

15. Show how to find the equilibrant of the forces $\vec{F}_1$, $\vec{F}_2$, . . . , $\vec{F}_k$ graphically.

Problems 2.1

1. A charged particle placed at $P(1, 1)$ is repelled from the points $A(0, 0)$, $B(2, 0)$, and $C(0, 3)$ by three forces, whose magnitudes are inversely proportional to the square of the distances PA, PB, and PC, respectively. In what direction will the particle move initially? (Assume that the proportionality constant is the same for all three forces.)

2. Three masses of 3 kg, 4 kg, and 5 kg are attached to strings as shown in the diagram. Assume that for each of the three strings the tension at each point of the string is the same. The weights are released and the system reaches equilibrium. Describe the final position of the weights.

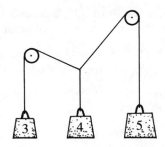

2.2 Work

A force acting on an object does work when it moves the object. In physics the **work done by a force** is a scalar quantity equal to the product of the distance the object is displaced and the component of the force in the direction of the displacement. For example, when you lift a heavy object, the work you do is equal to the weight times the height lifted.

Suppose that a force $\vec{F}$ moves a particle from O to A, so that the displacement vector is $\vec{s} = \overrightarrow{OA}$. The scalar projection of $\vec{F}$ on $\vec{s}$ is $|\overrightarrow{ON}| = |\vec{F}| \cos \theta$. The work done by $\vec{F}$ is this scalar projection times the displaced distance, $|\vec{s}|$; that is, $|\vec{F}||\vec{s}| \cos \theta$ or $\vec{F} \cdot \vec{s}$.

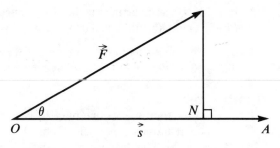

The **work done** by the force $\vec{F}$ in displacing an object through $\vec{s}$ is

$$W = \vec{F} \cdot \vec{s}$$

If force is measured in newtons and distance in metres, work will be measured in newton-metres or joules (J).

Example. Calculate the work done by a 10 N force, $\vec{F}$, in moving a particle from $A(2, 1)$ to $B(8, 5)$, when the force acts at an angle of $45°$ to $\overrightarrow{AB}$ and the distance is measured in metres.

Solution. The displacement vector is

$$\vec{s} = \overrightarrow{AB}$$
$$= (8, 5) - (2, 1)$$
$$= (6, 4)$$

The work done by the force is

$$W = \vec{F} \cdot \vec{s}$$
$$= |\vec{F}||\vec{s}| \cos 45°$$
$$= 10\sqrt{6^2 + 4^2}\left(\frac{1}{\sqrt{2}}\right)$$
$$= 10\sqrt{26}$$

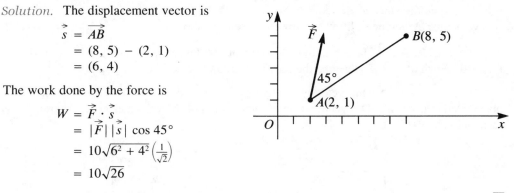

Hence, the work done by the force is approximately 51 J. □

Exercises 2.2

1. Calculate the amount of work done by a force of 10 N, acting at an angle of $60°$ to the displacement vector, when it moves an object 20 m.

2. Find the amount of work done by a 5 N force in moving an object from A to B. The angle between the force and the displacement vector is θ, and the distance is in metres.

   a. $\theta = 60°$, A is $(2, 5)$, and B is $(2, 6)$.

   b. $\theta = 30°$, A is $(-2, 1)$, and B is $(7, 8)$.

   c. $\theta = 90°$, A is $(5, -8)$, and B is $(7, 11)$.

   d. $\theta = 0°$, A is $(4, 1)$, and B is $(10, 13)$.

3. If a 10 N force, acting in the direction of the vector (1, 1), moves an object from $P(-2, 1)$ to $Q(5, 6)$, calculate the work done. The distance is measured in metres.

4. If a 30 N force acts in the direction of the vector $(-2, 1, 5)$ and moves an object from $A(2, 1, 5)$ to $B(3, -1, 2)$, calculate the work done. The distances are measured in metres.

Problems 2.2

a. Find the total work done by a 15 N force, $\vec{F}$, in the direction of the vector (1, 2, 2) when it moves a particle from $O(0, 0, 0)$ to $P(1, -3, 4)$ and then from P to $A(7, 2, 5)$. The distance is measured in metres.

b. Find the total work done by the same force $\vec{F}$ when it moves a particle from O to $R(-2, 4, 0)$, then from R to $S(11, 1, -1)$, and then from S to $A(7, 2, 5)$.

c. Is it true that the work done by a constant force $\vec{F}$ in moving an object from O to A, along a polygonal path, does not depend on the polygonal path chosen? Give reasons.

2.3 Velocity

Velocity is a vector quantity that has both magnitude and direction. Speed, on the other hand, is a scalar quantity since its direction is not specified. In this section we show how to combine two velocities by vector addition to form the resultant velocity.

Example 1. An airplane heading due north at 500 km/h encounters a wind of 150 km/h from 30° north of east. Determine the resultant ground velocity of the plane.

Solution. Let $\vec{u}$ be the wind velocity relative to the ground, and let $\vec{v}$ be the velocity of the plane relative to the air. Draw a diagram of the position of the velocities and a diagram of the resultant velocity.

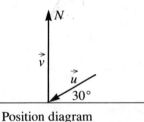

Position diagram

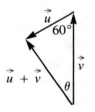

Velocity diagram

The resultant velocity of the plane relative to the ground is $\vec{u} + \vec{v}$. Let the direction of this resultant be θ west of north. To find the magnitude of the resultant, apply the Cosine Law to obtain

$$|\vec{u} + \vec{v}|^2 = 150^2 + 500^2 - 2(150)(500) \cos 60°$$
$$= 272\,500 - 150\,000 \left(\tfrac{1}{2}\right)$$
$$= 197\,500$$

Hence, $|\vec{u} + \vec{v}| \approx 444$ km/h.

To calculate the angle θ, use the Sine Law to obtain

$$\frac{\sin \theta}{|\vec{u}|} = \frac{\sin 60°}{|\vec{u} + \vec{v}|}$$

$$\frac{\sin \theta}{150} = \frac{\sqrt{3}}{2\sqrt{197\,500}}$$

Hence, $\sin \theta \approx 0.29$ and $\theta \approx 17°$. The resultant velocity of the plane is approximately 444 km/h in the direction 17° west of north. □

Example 2. A canoeist wishes to cross a river 1 km in width. If the current flows at 5 km/h and the canoeist can paddle at 13 km/h in still water, determine

a. the direction the canoeist must head to travel straight across the river;

b. the time it will take to cross the river.

Solution.

a. In order to travel directly across the river, the canoe must head slightly upstream. Let θ be the angle the canoe is heading in the upstream direction. Let $\vec{u}$ be the velocity of the current, and let $\vec{v}$ be the velocity of the canoe in still water.

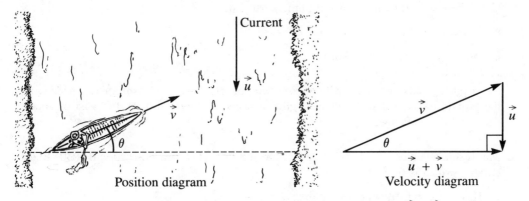

Position diagram   Velocity diagram

The velocity of the canoe relative to the bank is its resultant velocity, $\vec{u} + \vec{v}$. For the canoe to go directly across the river, $\vec{u} + \vec{v}$ must be perpendicular to the flow of the river. Therefore, the velocity diagram must give a right-angled triangle and $\sin \theta = \frac{5}{13}$. Hence, $\theta \approx 23°$ and the canoeist must head at an angle of 23° upstream.

b. To find the speed of the canoe, use Pythagoras' Theorem to obtain

$$|\vec{u} + \vec{v}|^2 = |\vec{v}|^2 - |\vec{u}|^2$$
$$= 13^2 - 5^2$$
$$= 144$$

Hence, $|\vec{u} + \vec{v}| = 12$ and the speed of the canoe relative to the bank is 12 km/h. Since the river is 1 km wide, the time taken, in minutes, is $\frac{1}{12}$ (60), or 5 min. □

Exercises 2.3

1. A woman runs around a circular track of radius 60 m at a constant rate of 3 m/s for 2 min. Why is it not correct to say that she ran with constant velocity?

2. A river is 2 km wide and flows at 6 km/h. A motor boat, which has a speed of 20 km/h in still water, heads out from one bank perpendicular to the current. A marina lies directly across the river on the opposite bank.

   a. How far downstream from the marina will it touch the other bank?

   b. How long will it take?

3. An airplane is headed north with a constant velocity of 450 km/h. The plane encounters a west wind blowing at 100 km/h.

   a. How far will the plane travel in 3 h?

   b. What is the direction of the plane?

4. The pilot of an airplane, which flies at 1000 km/h, wishes to travel to a city 100 km due east. There is a 100 km/h wind from the northeast.

   a. What should the plane's heading be?

   b. How long will the trip take?

5. An airplane heads due south with an air speed of 1000 km/h. Measurements made from the ground indicate that the plane's ground speed is 1100 km/h at 15° east of south. Calculate the wind speed.

6. Mr. Teshima leaves a dock paddling a canoe at 3 m/s. He heads downstream at 30° to the current, which is flowing at 4 m/s.

   a. How far downstream does the man travel in 10 s?

   b. What is the length of time required to cross the river if its width is 150 m?

7. A boat heads 15° west of north with a water speed of 3 m/s. Determine its velocity relative to the ground when there is a 2 m/s current from 40° east of north.

8. A monkey climbs a mast at 4 m/s on a ship travelling north at 12 m/s, while the current flows east at 3 m/s. What is the speed of the monkey relative to the ocean floor?

9. A man can swim 2 km/h in still water. Find at what angle to the bank he must head if he wishes to swim directly across a river flowing at a speed of

   a. 1 km/h.   b. 4 km/h.

Problems 2.3

1. An airplane flies from Toronto to Vancouver and back. Determine which time is shorter.

   a. The time for the round trip when there is a constant wind blowing from Vancouver to Toronto.

   b. The time for the round trip when there is no wind.

2. Write a computer program to calculate the ground speed and true heading of an airplane when the air speed, the apparent heading of the plane, and the wind velocity are known.

2.4 Linear Dependence of Vectors

The concepts of linear dependence and independence are fundamental in vector algebra. Their importance is both theoretical and practical. Two vectors are linearly dependent if they are collinear or parallel. Three vectors are linearly dependent if they are coplanar.

Let us first consider just two vectors. For example, suppose $\vec{u}$ and $\vec{v}$ are two vectors such that $\vec{u} = 2\vec{v}$. This statement can be rewritten as $\vec{u} - 2\vec{v} = \vec{0}$. Geometrically this means that multiplying $\vec{v}$ by the scalar -2 and adding it to $\vec{u}$ brings us back to the zero vector $\vec{0}$.

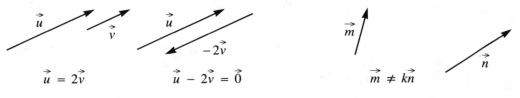

$$\vec{u} = 2\vec{v} \qquad\qquad \vec{u} - 2\vec{v} = \vec{0} \qquad\qquad \vec{m} \neq k\vec{n}$$

Parallel vectors   Non-parallel vectors

In general, we can see that whenever two vectors, u and v, are parallel, there is a relationship $a\vec{u} + b\vec{v} = \vec{0}$, where a and b are not both zero. We then say that u and v are linearly dependent vectors.

On the other hand, consider two vectors, $\vec{m}$ and $\vec{n}$, that are not parallel. There is no possible way to combine multiples of these vectors so that $a\vec{m} + b\vec{n} = \vec{0}$, unless $a = b = 0$. These vectors are called linearly independent vectors.

Linear Dependence of Two Vectors

Two vectors $\vec{u}$ and $\vec{v}$ are called **linearly dependent** if and only if there are scalars a and b, not both zero, such that

$$a\vec{u} + b\vec{v} = \vec{0}$$

Two vectors are **linearly independent** if they are not linearly dependent.

Notice that whenever one of two vectors is the zero vector, then the two vectors are linearly dependent. If $\vec{u} = \vec{0}$, we can write $a\vec{u} + b\vec{v} = \vec{0}$ with $a = 1$ and $b = 0$; hence, a and b are not **both** zero and the vectors are linearly dependent.

Example 1. Classify the following pairs of vectors as being either linearly dependent or linearly independent.

a. $\vec{u} = (2, -6), \vec{v} = (3, -9)$ **b.** $\vec{u} = (3, 1), \vec{v} = (6, 5)$

Solution.

a. It is clear that $\vec{v} = \frac{3}{2}\vec{u}$ so that $3\vec{u} - 2\vec{v} = \vec{0}$. Hence, $\vec{u}$ and $\vec{v}$ are collinear and so are linearly dependent.

b. In general, we can determine whether two vectors are linearly dependent or not by solving the equation $a\vec{u} + b\vec{v} = \vec{0}$ for the scalars a and b. If there is a solution for which a and b are not both zero, then the vectors are linearly dependent. If the only solution is $a = b = 0$, then the vectors are linearly independent.

Suppose that

$$a(3, 1) + b(6, 5) = (0, 0)$$
$$(3a + 6b, a + 5b) = (0, 0)$$

Hence, $3a + 6b = 0$ and $a + 5b = 0$; that is, $a + 2b = 0$ and $a + 5b = 0$. If we subtract these equations, we obtain $b = 0$, and hence $a = 0$. Therefore, the only solution is $a = b = 0$ and so $\vec{u}$ and $\vec{v}$ are linearly independent. $\square$

In practice, if you suspect that two vectors are linearly dependent, you can verify this simply by showing that one is a scalar multiple of the other.

An important theoretical application of linear independence is in the determination of a plane. If $\vec{u}$ and $\vec{v}$ are two linearly dependent vectors through the origin, then they lie in the same line and any combination of them, $a\vec{u} + b\vec{v}$, will still lie in this line. However, if $\vec{u}$ and $\vec{v}$ are two linearly independent vectors through the origin, then there is a unique plane containing both of them. In Theorem 1, we show that any other vector in this plane can be written in terms of $\vec{u}$ and $\vec{v}$ in the form $a\vec{u} + b\vec{v}$.

Theorem 1. Let $\vec{u}$ and $\vec{v}$ be linearly independent vectors. The vector $\vec{w}$ is coplanar with $\vec{u}$ and $\vec{v}$ if and only if $\vec{w}$ can be expressed as a linear combination of $\vec{u}$ and $\vec{v}$; that is,

$$\vec{w} = a\vec{u} + b\vec{v}$$

where a and b are scalars.

Proof. Since the statement of the theorem contains the phrase "if and only if," the result and its converse have to be proved separately.

First suppose that $\vec{w}$ lies in the plane determined by $\vec{u}$ and $\vec{v}$. Represent the vectors $\vec{u}$ and $\vec{w}$ so that the line segments both start at a point O; that is $\vec{u} = \overrightarrow{OP}$ and $\vec{w} = \overrightarrow{OR}$. Draw a line through R parallel to $\vec{v}$. Since $\vec{u}$ and $\vec{v}$ are not parallel, this line will meet the line OP (extended if necessary) at a point K. In $\triangle OKR$, $\overrightarrow{OK}$ is collinear with $\vec{u}$, so $\overrightarrow{OK} = a\vec{u}$, for some scalar a; and $\overrightarrow{KR}$ is parallel to $\vec{v}$, so $\overrightarrow{KR} = b\vec{v}$, for some scalar b. By the Triangle Law of Addition

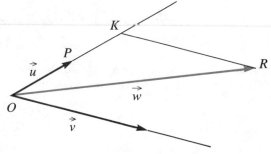

$$\begin{aligned} \vec{w} &= \overrightarrow{OR} \\ &= \overrightarrow{OK} + \overrightarrow{KR} \\ &= a\vec{u} + b\vec{v} \end{aligned}$$

Thus, $\vec{w}$ is a linear combination of $\vec{u}$ and $\vec{v}$.

Conversely, suppose that $\vec{w} = a\vec{u} + b\vec{v}$. The vectors $a\vec{u}$, $b\vec{v}$, and $\vec{w}$ can be represented by the sides of a triangle, and are therefore coplanar. Hence, $\vec{u}$, $\vec{v}$, and $\vec{w}$ are coplanar. □

The standard basis vectors in $\boldsymbol{R}^2$ are $\vec{i} = (1, 0)$ and $\vec{j} = (0, 1)$; they are linearly independent and any other vector (x, y), in the plane, can be written as a linear combination of these two basis vectors as $(x, y) = x\vec{i} + y\vec{j}$.

Theorem 1 shows that we could use any two linearly independent vectors as a basis for expressing all the vectors in the plane. These basis vectors do not have to be unit vectors, nor do they have to be perpendicular.

The definition of linear dependence can be extended to three vectors and, in fact, to any number of vectors.

Linear Dependence of Three Vectors

Three vectors $\vec{u}$, $\vec{v}$, and $\vec{w}$ are **linearly dependent** if and only if there are scalars a, b, and c, not all zero, such that

$$a\vec{u} + b\vec{v} + c\vec{w} = \vec{0}$$

Three vectors are **linearly independent** if they are not linearly dependent.

> **Theorem 2.** Three vectors are linearly dependent if and only if they are coplanar.

Proof. First, suppose that $\vec{u}$, $\vec{v}$, and $\vec{w}$ are linearly dependent so that

$$a\vec{u} + b\vec{v} + c\vec{w} = \vec{0}$$

for some scalars a, b, c, not all zero. Suppose that $c \neq 0$. (Alternatively, we could have chosen $a \neq 0$ or $b \neq 0$.) Then we can write

$$\vec{w} = -\frac{a}{c}\vec{u} - \frac{b}{c}\vec{v}$$

By Theorem 1, $\vec{w}$ is coplanar with $\vec{u}$ and $\vec{v}$.

Conversely, suppose that $\vec{u}$, $\vec{v}$, and $\vec{w}$ are coplanar. By Theorem 1, we can write

$$\vec{w} = a\vec{u} + b\vec{v}$$

Hence, $a\vec{u} + b\vec{v} - \vec{w} = \vec{0}$ and because the coefficients a, b, and -1 are not all zero, $\vec{u}$, $\vec{v}$, and $\vec{w}$ are linearly dependent. □

Theorem 2 implies that any three vectors in the plane R^2 must be linearly dependent.

Example 2. Are the vectors $\vec{u} = (3, -1, 0)$, $\vec{v} = (0, 2, 1)$, and $\vec{w} = (0, 0, 2)$ linearly dependent or linearly independent?

Solution. In order to answer this question we must solve the equation $a\vec{u} + b\vec{v} + c\vec{w} = \vec{0}$. We have

$$a(3, -1, 0) + b(0, 2, 1) + c(0, 0, 2) = (0, 0, 0)$$
$$(3a, -a + 2b, b + 2c) = (0, 0, 0)$$

Therefore, $3a = 0$, $-a + 2b = 0$, and $b + 2c = 0$. The first equation implies that $a = 0$. Substituting this into the second equation gives $b = 0$, and substituting $b = 0$ into the third equation gives $c = 0$. Therefore, the only solution is the trivial solution $a = b = c = 0$. This implies that $\vec{u}$, $\vec{v}$, and $\vec{w}$ are linearly independent vectors. □

In examples of this type, where we have to prove that three vectors are linearly independent, we have to solve three linear equations for the three variables a, b, and c. In Chapter 4 we shall give a general method for solving such a system of equations. If the only solution is the trivial solution, $a = b = c = 0$, then the vectors are linearly independent; otherwise the vectors are linearly dependent.

> **Theorem 3.** Let $\vec{u}$, $\vec{v}$, and $\vec{w}$ be three linearly independent vectors in R^3. Any other vector, $\vec{r}$, in R^3 can be expressed as a linear combination of $\vec{u}$, $\vec{v}$, and $\vec{w}$; that is,
>
> $$\vec{r} = a\vec{u} + b\vec{v} + c\vec{w}$$
>
> where a, b, and c are scalars.

Proof. Since the vectors $\vec{u}$, $\vec{v}$, and $\vec{w}$ are linearly independent, they are each non-zero and, by Theorem 2, they cannot all lie in a plane. If we consider any two of the three, say $\vec{u}$ and $\vec{v}$, they are linearly independent and so define a plane.

Represent the vectors $\vec{u}$, $\vec{v}$, $\vec{w}$, and $\vec{r}$ so that the line segments all start at a point O; that is $\vec{u} = \overrightarrow{OA}$, $\vec{v} = \overrightarrow{OB}$, $\vec{w} = \overrightarrow{OC}$, and $\vec{r} = \overrightarrow{OD}$. Construct a line through D parallel to $\vec{w}$. Since $\vec{u}$, $\vec{v}$, and $\vec{w}$ are not coplanar, $\vec{w}$ is not parallel to the plane containing $\vec{u}$ and $\vec{v}$. Therefore, the line through D, parallel to $\vec{w}$, intersects the plane OAB in a point P.

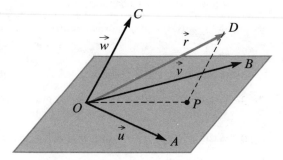

By Theorem 1 applied to this plane,

$$\overrightarrow{OP} = a\vec{u} + b\vec{v}$$

Since $\overrightarrow{PD}$ is parallel to $\vec{w}$, $\overrightarrow{PD} = c\vec{w}$, for some scalar c. Hence,

$$\begin{aligned} \vec{r} &= \overrightarrow{OD} \\ &= \overrightarrow{OP} + \overrightarrow{PD} \\ &= a\vec{u} + b\vec{v} + c\vec{w} \end{aligned} \qquad \square$$

In particular, any vector in $\mathbf{R}^3$ can be written in terms of the standard basis vectors, $\vec{i}$, $\vec{j}$, and $\vec{k}$ as

$$(x, y, z) = x\vec{i} + y\vec{j} + z\vec{k}$$

Example 3. Write the vector $(2, -3, 4)$ as a linear combination of $\vec{i}$, $\vec{j}$, and $\vec{k}$.

Solution. Since $\vec{i} = (1, 0, 0)$, $\vec{j} = (0, 1, 0)$, and $\vec{k} = (0, 0, 1)$, then

$$(2, -3, 4) = 2\vec{i} - 3\vec{j} + 4\vec{k}. \qquad \square$$

Exercises 2.4

1. Write each vector as a linear combination of $\vec{i}$ and $\vec{j}$.
   a. $(3, 4)$ **b.** $(-7, 8)$ **c.** $(5, -9)$

2. The diagram shows a three-dimensional box. Classify the following vectors as being either linearly dependent or independent.

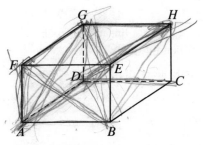

   a. $\overrightarrow{AB}$ and $\overrightarrow{DC}$ **b.** $\overrightarrow{GE}$ and $\overrightarrow{DB}$

   c. $\overrightarrow{DG}$ and $\overrightarrow{EH}$ **d.** $\overrightarrow{AE}$ and $\overrightarrow{DC}$

   e. $\overrightarrow{AF}$, $\overrightarrow{EH}$, and $\overrightarrow{DC}$

   f. $\overrightarrow{AH}$ and $\overrightarrow{BG}$ **g.** $\overrightarrow{AE}$, $\overrightarrow{BF}$, and $\overrightarrow{DH}$ **h.** $\overrightarrow{GA}$ and $\overrightarrow{BH}$

3. If $\vec{w} = a\vec{u} + b\vec{v}$, what can be said about $\vec{w}$ if

    a. $\vec{u}$ and $\vec{v}$ are linearly dependent?

    b. $\vec{u}$ and $\vec{v}$ are linearly independent?

4. If $\vec{u}$ and $\vec{v}$ are linearly independent vectors, find the numbers s and t.

    a. $s\vec{u} + t\vec{u} = \vec{0}$ **b.** $(s - 5)\vec{u} + (t - 3)\vec{v} = \vec{0}$

    c. $(s - 2)\vec{u} = (s - t - 3)\vec{v}$ **d.** $s\vec{u} + 7\vec{v} = 5\vec{u} + t\vec{v}$

5. a. Can every vector in $\boldsymbol{R}^2$ be written in terms of $\vec{u} = (1, 4)$ and $\vec{v} = (2, 5)$? Justify your answer.

    b. Write $(-298, -595)$ in terms of $\vec{u}$ and $\vec{v}$.

6. Can every vector in $\boldsymbol{R}^2$ be written in terms of $\vec{u} = (4, -6)$ and $\vec{v} = (10, 15)$? Justify your answer.

7. If $\vec{u} = (2, 1, 1)$ and $\vec{v} = (-1, 1, 3)$, which vectors can be written in the form $s\vec{u} + t\vec{v}$?

    a. $(4, 2, 2)$ **b.** $(1, 2, 4)$ **c.** $(1, 5, 11)$ **d.** $(4, 5, 8)$

8. Are the following sets of vectors coplanar?

    a. $(1, -1, 1), (0, 1, 1), (1, 0, 2)$ **b.** $(1, 0, 1), (1, 1, 1), (1, 0, -1)$

9. If $\vec{u}, \vec{v}$, and $\vec{w}$ are linearly independent, find the numbers r, s, and t.

    a. $r\vec{u} + (2s - 1)\vec{v} + (r + s + t)\vec{w} = \vec{0}$

    b. $(r - s - 5)\vec{u} + (r + s + 1)\vec{v} + (r + st)\vec{w} = \vec{0}$

10. An object is in equilibrium under the forces $\vec{F}_1$, $\vec{F}_2$, and $\vec{F}_3$. Are these vectors linearly dependent or independent? Give reasons.

Problems 2.4

1. If $\vec{u}, \vec{v}$, and $\vec{w}$ are mutually perpendicular linearly independent vectors, are the vectors $\vec{u} + \vec{w}, \vec{u} + \vec{v}$, and $\vec{v} + \vec{w}$ linearly dependent or linearly independent?

2. If $\vec{u}$ are $\vec{v}$ are linearly independent, show that each vector $\vec{w}$ coplanar with $\vec{u}$ and $\vec{v}$ can be written **uniquely** as $\vec{w} = a\vec{u} + b\vec{v}$.

Find values of a, b, and c that satisfy each equation.

    a. $a(2, 1, 0) + b(-3, 4, 5) + c(2, 0, 3) = (-4, 10, 7)$

    b. $a(3, -1, 2) + b(-1, 1, 3) + c(2, 1, 5) = (2, 5, 16)$

4. If $\vec{u}, \vec{v}$, and $\vec{w}$ are linearly dependent, show that at least one of the vectors can be written as a linear combination of the others.

5. If $\vec{u}$, $\vec{v}$, and $\vec{w}$ are linearly independent, find the values of t.

   a. $(t^2 - 1)\vec{u} + (3t^2 + t - 2)\vec{v} + (t + 1)(3t + 1)\vec{w} = \vec{0}$

   b. $(t^2 - t - 2)\vec{u} + (2t^2 - 3t - 2)\vec{v} + (3t^2 - 5t - 2)\vec{w} = \vec{0}$

6. The vectors $\vec{u}$ and $\vec{v}$ are linearly independent. Find s if the vectors $(1 - s)\vec{u} - \frac{2}{3}\vec{v}$ and $3\vec{u} + s\vec{v}$ are parallel.

2.5 The Division of a Line Segment

How can you find the midpoint of a line segment? We shall show that it is very easy to calculate the coordinates of the midpoint from the coordinates of the end points. More generally, we shall show how to find the point that divides a line segment into any given ratio.

The Midpoint of a Line Segment

Let $A(a_1, a_2, a_3)$ and $B(b_1, b_2, b_3)$ be points in 3-space with position vectors $\vec{a}$ and $\vec{b}$, respectively. The midpoint of the line segment AB has position vector $\dfrac{\vec{a} + \vec{b}}{2}$ and

coordinates $\left(\dfrac{a_1 + b_1}{2}, \dfrac{a_2 + b_2}{2}, \dfrac{a_3 + b_3}{2} \right)$.

Proof. Let O be the origin in $\mathbf{R}^3$ so that

$$\vec{a} = \overrightarrow{OA} = (a_1, a_2, a_3) \qquad \text{and}$$
$$\vec{b} = \overrightarrow{OB} = (b_1, b_2, b_3).$$

If P is the midpoint of AB with position vector $\vec{p} = \overrightarrow{OP}$, then $\overrightarrow{AP} = \overrightarrow{PB}$. Hence,

$$\overrightarrow{OP} - \overrightarrow{OA} = \overrightarrow{OB} - \overrightarrow{OP}$$
$$\vec{p} - \vec{a} = \vec{b} - \vec{p}$$
$$2\vec{p} = \vec{a} + \vec{b}$$
$$\vec{p} = \frac{\vec{a} + \vec{b}}{2}$$

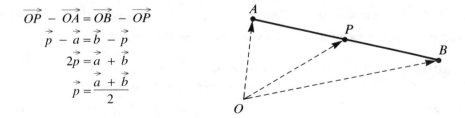

Hence, the midpoint of AB has position vector $\dfrac{\vec{a} + \vec{b}}{2}$ and coordinates

$\left(\dfrac{a_1 + b_1}{2}, \dfrac{a_2 + b_2}{2}, \dfrac{a_3 + b_3}{2} \right)$.

The coordinates of the midpoint can be thought of as the average of the coordinates of the end points.

For example, if the coordinates of A are $(2, -1, 3)$ and the coordinates of B are $(4, 2, 5)$, then the midpoint of AB has coordinates

$$\left(\frac{2+4}{2}, \frac{-1+2}{2}, \frac{3+5}{2}\right) = \left(3, \frac{1}{2}, 4\right)$$

The midpoint P of AB can be considered as the point that divides the segment AB in the ratio $AP{:}PB = 1{:}1$. More generally, if m and n are positive numbers, we say that the point P divides the segment AB in the ratio $AP{:}PB = m{:}n$ if P is the point on the segment AB such that

$$\frac{|\overrightarrow{AP}|}{|\overrightarrow{PB}|} = \frac{m}{n}$$

Since P lies between A and B, the line segment is divided **internally** in the ratio $m{:}n$.

We can also consider points anywhere on the entire line containing AB. We say that P **divides the segment** AB **in the ratio** $AP{:}PB = m{:}n$ if there is a vector $\vec{v}$, along the line AB, such that $\overrightarrow{AP} = m\vec{v}$ and $\overrightarrow{PB} = n\vec{v}$.

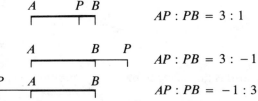

Since we are dealing with ratios, we can multiply each part by any number without changing the ratio. Hence, the ratio $m{:}n$ is the same as $km{:}kn$, for any non-zero number k (positive or negative).

If P lies on AB extended, the line segment is divided **externally** in the ratio $m{:}n$. In this case the vectors $\overrightarrow{AP}$ and $\overrightarrow{PB}$ point in opposite directions and so the numbers m and n have opposite signs.

$AP : PB = 3 : 1$

$AP : PB = 3 : -1$

$AP : PB = -1 : 3$

In general, if $\frac{m}{n}$ is positive the division is internal, and if $\frac{m}{n}$ is negative the division is external. In the external division of AB, the division point is on an extension of AB.

Example 1. The points P and Q lie on the line segment AB, which is 14 units long, $AP = 2$ units, $PQ = 4$ units, and $QB = 8$ units. In what ratio does

a. P divide AB? **b.** P divide BA?

c. P divide QB? **d.** A divide QP?

A	P	Q		B
2 units	4 units		8 units	

Solution.

a. This division is internal in the ratio $AP:PB$, which is 2:12, or equivalently, 1:6.

b. The division is internal in the ratio $BP:PA$, which is 12:2, or equivalently, 6:1.

c. The division is external in the ratio $QP:PB$, which is −4:12, or equivalently, −1:3, or 1:−3.

d. The division is external in the ratio $QA:AP$, which is −6:2, or equivalently, −3:1, or 3:−1. ☐

Example 2. Express $\overrightarrow{OP}$ as a linear combination of $\overrightarrow{OA}$ and $\overrightarrow{OB}$ when P divides AB in the ratio 4:1.

Solution. Since $AP:PB = 4:1$, we have $\overrightarrow{AP} = 4\overrightarrow{PB}$. By the Triangle Law, $\overrightarrow{OP} = \overrightarrow{OA} + \overrightarrow{AP}$, and so $\overrightarrow{AP} = \overrightarrow{OP} - \overrightarrow{OA}$. Also, by the Triangle Law, $\overrightarrow{OB} = \overrightarrow{OP} + \overrightarrow{PB}$, so that $\overrightarrow{PB} = \overrightarrow{OB} - \overrightarrow{OP}$. Therefore,

$$\overrightarrow{AP} = 4\overrightarrow{PB}$$
$$\overrightarrow{OP} - \overrightarrow{OA} = 4(\overrightarrow{OB} - \overrightarrow{OP})$$
$$5\overrightarrow{OP} = \overrightarrow{OA} + 4\overrightarrow{OB}$$
$$\overrightarrow{OP} = \tfrac{1}{5}\overrightarrow{OA} + \tfrac{4}{5}\overrightarrow{OB}$$

☐

The Division of a Line Segment

Let P be the point that divides the line segment AB in the ratio $AP:PB = m:n$. If O is any point, then

$$\overrightarrow{OP} = \frac{n}{m+n}\overrightarrow{OA} + \frac{m}{m+n}\overrightarrow{OB}$$

Proof. Since $\overrightarrow{AP} = m\vec{v}$ and $\overrightarrow{PB} = n\vec{v}$ for some vector $\vec{v}$, it follows that $n\overrightarrow{AP} = m\overrightarrow{PB}$. By the Triangle Law, $\overrightarrow{OP} = \overrightarrow{OA} + \overrightarrow{AP}$, so $\overrightarrow{AP} = \overrightarrow{OP} - \overrightarrow{OA}$. Also $\overrightarrow{OB} = \overrightarrow{OP} + \overrightarrow{PB}$, so $\overrightarrow{PB} = \overrightarrow{OB} - \overrightarrow{OP}$. Hence,

$$n\overrightarrow{AP} = m\overrightarrow{PB}$$
$$n(\overrightarrow{OP} - \overrightarrow{OA}) = m(\overrightarrow{OB} - \overrightarrow{OP})$$
$$(m+n)\overrightarrow{OP} = n\overrightarrow{OA} + m\overrightarrow{OB}$$
$$\overrightarrow{OP} = \frac{n}{m+n}\overrightarrow{OA} + \frac{m}{m+n}\overrightarrow{OB}$$

☐

Note that in Example 2, the coefficients of $\overrightarrow{OA}$ and $\overrightarrow{OB}$ add up to one; $\tfrac{1}{5} + \tfrac{4}{5} = 1$. In the general case, when P divides AB in the ratio $m:n$, the coefficients of $\overrightarrow{OA}$ and $\overrightarrow{OB}$ add up to one since $\frac{n}{m+n} + \frac{m}{m+n} = 1$. In fact, the ratio $m:n$ can always be written as $\frac{m}{m+n}:\frac{n}{m+n}$, where the numbers $\frac{m}{m+n}$ and $\frac{n}{m+n}$ sum to one. We can use this fact to obtain a condition for three points to be collinear.

Theorem 4. The three points A, B, and P are collinear if and only if it is possible to express $\overrightarrow{OP}$ in the form

$$\overrightarrow{OP} = t\overrightarrow{OA} + (1 - t)\overrightarrow{OB} \quad \text{for some } t \in \mathbf{R},$$

where O is any point. If this equation holds, then P divides AB in the ratio $(1 - t):t$.

Proof. First suppose that A, B, and P are collinear. Then P divides AB in some ratio $m:n$. By the previous result,

$$\overrightarrow{OP} = \frac{n}{m+n}\overrightarrow{OA} + \frac{m}{m+n}\overrightarrow{OB}$$

If we let $t = \frac{n}{m+n}$, then $1 - t = \frac{m}{m+n}$ and we obtain the required result

$$\overrightarrow{OP} = t\overrightarrow{OA} + (1 - t)\overrightarrow{OB}$$

Conversely, suppose that $\overrightarrow{OP} = t\overrightarrow{OA} + (1 - t)\overrightarrow{OB}$. Then

$$t(\overrightarrow{OB} - \overrightarrow{OA}) = \overrightarrow{OB} - \overrightarrow{OP}$$
$$t\overrightarrow{AB} = \overrightarrow{PB}$$

This means that the vectors $\overrightarrow{AB}$ and $\overrightarrow{PB}$ are parallel and so A, B, and P are collinear. Moreover, $\overrightarrow{AP} = \overrightarrow{AB} - \overrightarrow{PB} = (1 - t)\overrightarrow{AB}$ and so $AP:PB = (1 - t):t$. □

Theorem 4 can be used to calculate the coordinates of P if the coordinates of A and B are known. If we take O as the origin, then $\vec{a} = \overrightarrow{OA}$, $\vec{b} = \overrightarrow{OB}$, and $\vec{p} = \overrightarrow{OP}$ are the position vectors of A, B, and P, respectively. If P, divides AB in the ratio $m:n$, then

$$\vec{p} = \frac{n}{m+n}\vec{a} + \frac{m}{m+n}\vec{b}$$

Alternatively, if P divides AB in the ratio $(1 - t):t$ then

$$\vec{p} = t\vec{a} + (1 - t)\vec{b}$$

Example 3. Find the coordinates of the point that divides AB in the ratio 5:3 where A is $(2, -1, 4)$ and B is $(3, 1, 7)$.

Solution 1. The point dividing AB in the ratio 5:3 has coordinates

$$\frac{3}{5+3}(2, -1, 4) + \frac{5}{5+3}(3, 1, 7) = \tfrac{3}{8}(2, -1, 4) + \tfrac{5}{8}(3, 1, 7)$$
$$= \left(\tfrac{21}{8}, \tfrac{2}{8}, \tfrac{47}{8}\right)$$

Solution 2. The ratio 5:3 is equivalent to $\frac{5}{8} : \frac{3}{8}$, where $\frac{5}{8} + \frac{3}{8} = 1$. Hence, the required point has coordinates

$$\tfrac{3}{8}(2, -1, 4) + \tfrac{5}{8}(3, 1, 7) = \left(\tfrac{21}{8}, \tfrac{2}{8}, \tfrac{47}{8}\right) \qquad \square$$

Example 4. Find the coordinates of the point that divides AB in the ratio $7: -5$, where A is $(4, 9)$ and B is $(-3, 11)$.

Solution. The point dividing AB in the ratio $7: -5$ has coordinates

$$\tfrac{-5}{7-5}(4, 9) + \tfrac{7}{7-5}(-3, 11) = -\tfrac{5}{2}(4, 9) + \tfrac{7}{2}(-3, 11)$$
$$= \left(-\tfrac{41}{2}, 16\right) \qquad \square$$

Example 5. If $\overrightarrow{OP} = \tfrac{11}{7}\overrightarrow{OQ} - \tfrac{4}{7}\overrightarrow{OR}$, are the points P, Q, and R collinear?

Solution. Since $\tfrac{11}{7} - \tfrac{4}{7} = 1$, the points P, Q, and R are collinear. $\qquad \square$

Exercises 2.5

1. Points A, B, C, and D are located on a line as shown in the diagram.

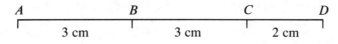

Determine

a. the ratio in which C divides AD.

b. the ratio in which B divides AD.

c. the ratio in which D divides AC.

d. the ratio in which A divides DC.

e. the ratio in which C divides BA.

2. Draw a sketch of each situation, showing the line segment and the point of division.

a. Point A divides BC in the ratio 2:1.

b. Point U divides ST in the ratio -3:1.

c. Point Q divides PR in the ratio -1:2.

d. Point K divides MN in the ratio 5:8.

e. Point D divides EF in the ratio 2:-3.

3. The point P divides AB in the ratio 1:2, and the point Q divides AB in the ratio $-1:2$.

   a. In what ratio does A divide QB?

   b. In what ratio does B divide QP?

   c. In what ratio does Q divide AP?

   d. In what ratio does P divide QA?

   e. In what ratio does B divide PA?

4. If T divides AB in the ratio $2:-1$, prove from first principles that $\overrightarrow{OT} = 2\overrightarrow{OB} - \overrightarrow{OA}$.

5. If $\overrightarrow{OB} = \frac{2}{3}\overrightarrow{OC} + \frac{1}{3}\overrightarrow{OD}$, prove from first principles that B, C, and D are collinear points.

6. Which statements indicate that A, B, and C are collinear points?

   a. $\overrightarrow{OA} = \frac{3}{4}\overrightarrow{OB} + \frac{1}{4}\overrightarrow{OC}$ **b.** $\overrightarrow{OC} = \frac{3}{5}\overrightarrow{OA} + \frac{3}{5}\overrightarrow{OB}$

   c. $\overrightarrow{OA} = 5\overrightarrow{OB} - 4\overrightarrow{OC}$ **d.** $\overrightarrow{OA} + \overrightarrow{OB} + \overrightarrow{OC} = \vec{0}$

7. Find the vector $\overrightarrow{OA}$ such that A divides BC in the given ratio.

   a. 1:2   **b.** 2:1   **c.** $1:-2$ **d.** $2:-1$

8. Find the midpoint of the line segment joining $A(3, 4, 6)$ to $B(7, 8, -3)$.

9. Find the points that trisect the line segment from $A(3, 6, 8)$ to $B(6, 0, -1)$.

10. If A is $(2, 10)$ and B is $(1, -5)$, find the point which divides AB in the given ratio.

    a. 1:5   **b.** $2:-1$ **c.** $4:-7$ **d.** 3:12

Problems 2.5

1. Can a line segment be divided in the ratio $-1:1$? Explain.

2. Prove that the diagonals of a parallelogram bisect each other.

2.6 Applications to Geometry (Optional)

Many geometric problems can be solved most efficiently by using vectors. In particular, problems involving parallel lines, midpoints, and division of line segments into given ratios are often amenable to the vector method. Problems involving perpendicular lines can be tackled by using the dot product.

Example 1. Show that if the midpoints of adjacent sides of any quadrilateral are joined, then the resulting figure is a parallelogram.

Solution. Let *ABCD* be any quadrilateral, and let *K*, *L*, *M*, and *N* be the midpoints of the sides *AB*, *BC*, *CD*, and *DA*, respectively. Hence, $\overrightarrow{KB} = \frac{1}{2}\overrightarrow{AB}$, $\overrightarrow{BL} = \frac{1}{2}\overrightarrow{BC}$, $\overrightarrow{DM} = \frac{1}{2}\overrightarrow{DC}$, and $\overrightarrow{ND} = \frac{1}{2}\overrightarrow{AD}$. Now

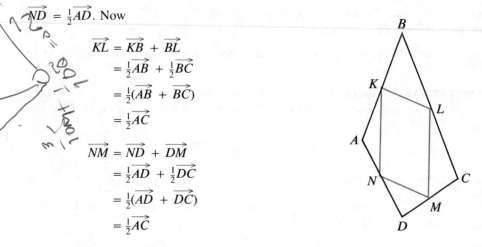

$$\begin{aligned}\overrightarrow{KL} &= \overrightarrow{KB} + \overrightarrow{BL} \\ &= \tfrac{1}{2}\overrightarrow{AB} + \tfrac{1}{2}\overrightarrow{BC} \\ &= \tfrac{1}{2}(\overrightarrow{AB} + \overrightarrow{BC}) \\ &= \tfrac{1}{2}\overrightarrow{AC}\end{aligned}$$

$$\begin{aligned}\overrightarrow{NM} &= \overrightarrow{ND} + \overrightarrow{DM} \\ &= \tfrac{1}{2}\overrightarrow{AD} + \tfrac{1}{2}\overrightarrow{DC} \\ &= \tfrac{1}{2}(\overrightarrow{AD} + \overrightarrow{DC}) \\ &= \tfrac{1}{2}\overrightarrow{AC}\end{aligned}$$

Hence, $\overrightarrow{KL} = \overrightarrow{NM}$ and the line segments *KL* and *NM* are parallel and of equal length. Therefore, *KLMN* is a parallelogram. $\square$

Example 2.

Prove that the three medians of a triangle meet in a point that divides each median in the ratio of 2:1. (This point is called the **centroid** of the triangle.)

Solution. Take any triangle *ABC* and let *D* be the midpoint of the side *BC*. The median from *A* is the line segment *AD*. Let *G* be the point that divides *AD* in the ratio *AG*:*GD* = 2:1. We shall show that *G* lies on all three medians.

Let *O* be any point. Since *D* is the midpoint of *BC*,

$$\overrightarrow{OD} = \frac{\overrightarrow{OB} + \overrightarrow{OC}}{2}$$

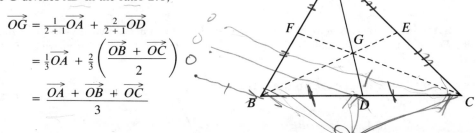

Since *G* divides *AD* in the ratio 2:1,

$$\begin{aligned}\overrightarrow{OG} &= \tfrac{1}{2+1}\overrightarrow{OA} + \tfrac{2}{2+1}\overrightarrow{OD} \\ &= \tfrac{1}{3}\overrightarrow{OA} + \tfrac{2}{3}\left(\frac{\overrightarrow{OB} + \overrightarrow{OC}}{2}\right) \\ &= \frac{\overrightarrow{OA} + \overrightarrow{OB} + \overrightarrow{OC}}{3}\end{aligned}$$

Notice that this expression is symmetrical in *A*, *B*, and *C*; that is, any permutation of *A*, *B*, and *C* will leave the expression unchanged. Therefore, if we performed the same procedure with the median *BE* by selecting a point *G'* so that *BG'*:*G'E* = 2:1, we would find that

$$\overrightarrow{OG'} = \frac{\overrightarrow{OA} + \overrightarrow{OB} + \overrightarrow{OC}}{3}$$

Hence, $\overrightarrow{OG} = \overrightarrow{OG'}$, and G must be the same point as G'. Similarly, it is also the point that divides the third median CF in the ratio 2:1.

Hence, the medians of the triangle intersect in a point that divides each median in the ratio 2:1. □

Note that the coordinates of the centroid, G, are the averages of the coordinates of the vertices. If the vertices are $A(a_1, a_2)$, $B(b_1, b_2)$, and $C(c_1, c_2)$, then the coordinates of the centroid are

$$\left(\frac{a_1 + b_1 + c_1}{3}, \frac{a_2 + b_2 + c_2}{3} \right)$$

Example 3. Prove that the diagonals of a rhombus intersect at right angles.

Solution. A rhombus is a parallelogram having all of its sides of equal length. Let $ABCD$ be a rhombus so that $\overrightarrow{AB} = \overrightarrow{DC}$, $\overrightarrow{AD} = \overrightarrow{BC}$, and $|\overrightarrow{AB}| = |\overrightarrow{BC}|$.

The diagonals of the rhombus are $\overrightarrow{AC}$ and $\overrightarrow{BD}$. They are perpendicular if their dot product is zero. Now

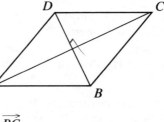

$$\overrightarrow{AC} \cdot \overrightarrow{BD} = (\overrightarrow{AB} + \overrightarrow{BC}) \cdot (\overrightarrow{BC} + \overrightarrow{CD})$$
$$= (\overrightarrow{AB} + \overrightarrow{BC}) \cdot (\overrightarrow{BC} - \overrightarrow{AB})$$
$$= \overrightarrow{AB} \cdot \overrightarrow{BC} + \overrightarrow{BC} \cdot \overrightarrow{BC} - \overrightarrow{AB} \cdot \overrightarrow{AB} - \overrightarrow{AB} \cdot \overrightarrow{BC}$$
$$= \overrightarrow{BC} \cdot \overrightarrow{BC} - \overrightarrow{AB} \cdot \overrightarrow{AB}$$
$$= |\overrightarrow{BC}|^2 - |\overrightarrow{AB}|^2$$
$$= 0$$

The last step follows since BC and AB have the same length. Therefore, $\overrightarrow{AC}$ is perpendicular to $\overrightarrow{BD}$. □

Example 4. In parallelogram $ABCD$, E is the point on BC that divides it in the ratio $BE{:}EC = 2{:}1$. The diagonal BD intersects AE at K. Calculate the ratio in which K divides AE.

Solution. Let K divide AE in the ratio $(1 - t){:}t$ so that

$$\overrightarrow{BK} = t\overrightarrow{BA} + (1 - t)\overrightarrow{BE}$$

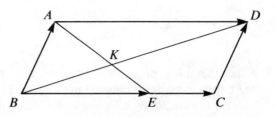

Since $BE{:}EC = 2{:}1$, $\overrightarrow{BE} = \frac{2}{3}\overrightarrow{BC} = \frac{2}{3}\overrightarrow{AD}$ and

$$\overrightarrow{BK} = t\overrightarrow{BA} + \tfrac{2}{3}(1 - t)\overrightarrow{AD}$$

Let K divide BD in the ratio $s:(1 - s)$ so that

$$\begin{aligned}
\overrightarrow{BK} &= s\overrightarrow{BD} \\
&= s(\overrightarrow{BA} + \overrightarrow{AD}) \\
&= s\overrightarrow{BA} + s\overrightarrow{AD}
\end{aligned}$$

Equating these two expressions for $\overrightarrow{BK}$, we obtain

$$t\overrightarrow{BA} + \tfrac{2}{3}(1 - t)\overrightarrow{AD} = s\overrightarrow{BA} + s\overrightarrow{AD}$$

$$(t - s)\overrightarrow{BA} + \left(\tfrac{2}{3} - \tfrac{2}{3}t - s\right)\overrightarrow{AD} = \vec{0}$$

Since $\overrightarrow{BA}$ and $\overrightarrow{AD}$ are not parallel, they are linearly independent and

$$t - s = 0 \qquad \text{and} \qquad \tfrac{2}{3} - \tfrac{2}{3}t - s = 0$$

by the definition of linear independence. That is, $s = t$ and $2 - 5t = 0$; hence $t = \tfrac{2}{5}$.

Therefore, K divides AE in the ratio $(1 - t):t = \tfrac{3}{5} : \tfrac{2}{5} = 3:2$. $\qquad\square$

Exercises 2.6

1. For each triangle ABC, determine the midpoints of the sides and the coordinates of the centroid.

   a. $A(0, 0)$, $B(5, -6)$, $C(2, 0)$

   b. $A(4, 7, 2)$, $B(6, 1, -1)$, $C(0, -1, 4)$

2. If the diagonals of a quadrilateral bisect each other, prove that the quadrilateral is a parallelogram.

3. In the trapezoid $ABCD$, $\overrightarrow{AB} = n\overrightarrow{DC}$. If the diagonals BD and AC meet at K, show that

$$\overrightarrow{AK} = \frac{n}{n + 1}\overrightarrow{AD} + \frac{1}{n + 1}\overrightarrow{AB}$$

4. If G is the centroid of the triangle ABC, prove that
$$\overrightarrow{AG} + \overrightarrow{BG} + \overrightarrow{CG} = \vec{0}$$

5. If D, E, and F are the midpoints of the sides of the triangle ABC, and O is any point, prove that
$$\overrightarrow{OA} + \overrightarrow{OB} + \overrightarrow{OC} = \overrightarrow{OD} + \overrightarrow{OE} + \overrightarrow{OF}$$

6. In any parallelogram, show that the sum of the squares of the diagonals equals the sum of the squares of the four sides.

7. Let AB be the diameter of a circle with center D. If C is any point on this circle, prove that $\angle ACB = 90°$.

8. In the triangle ABC, the altitudes from B and C meet at the point D.

    a. Prove that $\overrightarrow{AC} \cdot (\overrightarrow{DA} + \overrightarrow{AB}) = 0$.

    b. Prove that $\overrightarrow{AB} \cdot (\overrightarrow{DA} + \overrightarrow{AC}) = 0$.

    c. Use parts a and b to prove that $\overrightarrow{DA} \cdot \overrightarrow{BC} = 0$.
       (This shows that the three altitudes of a triangle are concurrent.)

9. The points D, E, and F are the midpoints of the sides BC, CA, and AB of the triangle ABC. The perpendicular at E to AC meets the perpendicular at F to AB at the point Q.

    a. Prove that $\overrightarrow{AB} \cdot (\overrightarrow{QD} - \frac{1}{2}\overrightarrow{AC}) = 0$.

    b. Prove that $\overrightarrow{AC} \cdot (\overrightarrow{QD} - \frac{1}{2}\overrightarrow{AB}) = 0$.

    c. Use parts a and b to prove that $\overrightarrow{CB} \cdot \overrightarrow{QD} = 0$.
       (This shows that the perpendicular bisectors of the sides of a triangle meet in a point, called the circumcentre of the triangle.)

10. Let $ABCD$ be a rectangle. If P is any point, let $\vec{a} = \overrightarrow{PA}$, $\vec{b} = \overrightarrow{PB}$, $\vec{c} = \overrightarrow{PC}$, and $\vec{d} = \overrightarrow{PD}$. Prove that

    a. $\vec{a} \cdot \vec{c} = \vec{b} \cdot \vec{d}$ **b.** $|\vec{a}|^2 + |\vec{c}|^2 = |\vec{b}|^2 + |\vec{d}|^2$

11. In the parallelogram $ABCD$, DC is extended to E so that $DE:EC = 3:-2$. The line AE meets BC at F.

    a. Determine, using similar triangles, the ratios in which F divides BC, and F divides AE.

    b. Determine, using vector methods, the ratios in which F divides BC, and F divides AE.

12. The point P divides the side AC of the triangle ABC in the ratio $3:4$ and Q divides AB in the ratio $1:6$. Let R be the point of intersection of CQ and BP. Determine the ratios in which R divides CQ and BP.

Problems 2.6

1. A regular hexagon $ABCDEF$ has two of its diagonals, AC and BE, meeting in the point K. Determine the ratios in which K divides AC and BE.

2. In triangle ABC, the point E is selected on BC so that $BE:EC = 1:2$. The point F divides AC in the ratio $2:3$. The two line segments BF and AE intersect at D.

    a. Find the ratios in which D divides AE and BF.

    b. Determine the ratio of the area of the quadrilateral $CEDF$ to the area of the triangle ABC.

3. Prove that in any tetrahedron, the lines joining its vertices to the centroids of the opposite faces are concurrent and are divided in the ratio $3:1$ by the point of concurrency.

2.7 The Cross Product

We have already defined one product of vectors, namely the dot product of two vectors, whose result is a scalar quantity. In this section we introduce another product called the cross product or vector product. The cross product of two vectors $\vec{a}$ and $\vec{b}$ will be a **vector** that is perpendicular to both $\vec{a}$ and $\vec{b}$. Hence, this cross product will be **defined only in 3-space**. The cross product is useful in many geometric and physical problems in 3-space; it is used to help define torque and angular velocity in statics and dynamics, and it is also used in electromagnetic theory. We shall use it in the next two chapters to find vectors perpendicular to two given vectors.

Let $\vec{a} = (a_1, a_2, a_3)$ and $\vec{b} = (b_1, b_2, b_3)$ be two vectors in $\mathbf{R}^3$. Let us find all the vectors, $\vec{v} = (x, y, z)$, that are perpendicular to both $\vec{a}$ and $\vec{b}$. These vectors satisfy both $\vec{a} \cdot \vec{v} = 0$ and $\vec{b} \cdot \vec{v} = 0$. Hence,

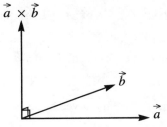

$$a_1x + a_2y + a_3z = 0 \qquad (1)$$
$$b_1x + b_2y + b_3z = 0 \qquad (2)$$

We shall solve these two equations for x, y, and z. Multiply equation (1) by b_3 and equation (2) by a_3 to obtain

$$a_1b_3x + a_2b_3y + a_3b_3z = 0 \qquad (3)$$
$$a_3b_1x + a_3b_2y + a_3b_3z = 0 \qquad (4)$$

Now eliminate z by subtracting equation (3) from equation (4) to obtain

$$(a_3b_1 - a_1b_3)x + (a_3b_2 - a_2b_3)y = 0$$

This is equivalent to

$$\frac{x}{a_2b_3 - a_3b_2} = \frac{y}{a_3b_1 - a_1b_3}$$

Using a similar procedure, we could eliminate x from the original equations to obtain

$$\frac{y}{a_3b_1 - a_1b_3} = \frac{z}{a_1b_2 - a_2b_1}$$

Let $y = k(a_3b_1 - a_1b_3)$, for some constant k, so that $x = k(a_2b_3 - a_3b_2)$ and $z = k(a_1b_2 - a_2b_1)$. Then the vector $\vec{v}$, perpendicular to both $\vec{a}$ and $\vec{b}$, is of the form

$$\vec{v} = (x, y, z) = k(a_2b_3 - a_3b_2, a_3b_1 - a_1b_3, a_1b_2 - a_2b_1)$$

The cross product of $\vec{a}$ and $\vec{b}$ is chosen to be the vector of this form that has $k = 1$.

> The **Cross Product** or **Vector Product** of $\vec{a} = (a_1, a_2, a_3)$ and $\vec{b} = (b_1, b_2, b_3)$ is the vector
>
> $$\vec{a} \times \vec{b} = (a_2b_3 - a_3b_2, a_3b_1 - a_1b_3, a_1b_2 - a_2b_1)$$

This is a rather complicated expression to remember. It can be expressed in terms of determinants (as shown in section 5.6) as follows:

$$\vec{a} \times \vec{b} = \left(\begin{vmatrix} a_2 & a_3 \\ b_2 & b_3 \end{vmatrix}, -\begin{vmatrix} a_1 & a_3 \\ b_1 & b_3 \end{vmatrix}, \begin{vmatrix} a_1 & a_2 \\ b_1 & b_2 \end{vmatrix} \right)$$

where $\begin{vmatrix} a & b \\ c & d \end{vmatrix} = ad - bc$.

We showed above that any vector perpendicular to both the vectors $\vec{a}$ and $\vec{b}$ could be written as $k(\vec{a} \times \vec{b})$. This is one of the most useful properties of the cross product.

Finding a Vector Perpendicular to Two Vectors

If $\vec{a}$ and $\vec{b}$ are linearly independent vectors in 3-space, then every vector perpendicular to both $\vec{a}$ and $\vec{b}$ is of the form $k(\vec{a} \times \vec{b})$, for $k \in \mathbf{R}$.

Example 1. Find a vector perpendicular to both $(1, 3, 2)$ and $(4, -6, 7)$.

Solution. The cross product will be one such vector. From the definition of the cross product,

$$(1, 3, 2) \times (4, -6, 7) = (3(7) - 2(-6), 2(4) - 1(7), 1(-6) - 3(4))$$
$$= (33, 1, -18)$$

Hence, one vector perpendicular to $(1, 3, 2)$ and $(4, -6, 7)$ is $(33, 1, -18)$.

Check. It is very easy to make errors in calculating or remembering a cross product. However, there is an excellent check that should always be done after calculating any cross product. If $\vec{v} = \vec{a} \times \vec{b}$, you should always check that $\vec{a} \cdot \vec{v} = 0$ and $\vec{b} \cdot \vec{v} = 0$.

In our example,

$$(1, 3, 2) \cdot (33, 1, -18) = 1(33) + 3(1) + 2(-18)$$
$$= 0$$
$$(4, -6, 7) \cdot (33, 1, -18) = 4(33) - 6(1) + 7(-18)$$
$$= 0$$

Hence, $(33, 1, -18)$ is perpendicular to both $(1, 3, 2)$ and $(4, -6, 7)$. □

We now describe some other properties of the cross product.

The Magnitude of the Cross Product

If $\vec{a}$ and $\vec{b}$ are vectors in 3-space and θ is the angle between them, where $0 \leq \theta \leq 180°$, then

$$|\vec{a} \times \vec{b}| = |\vec{a}| |\vec{b}| \sin \theta.$$

This is the area of the parallelogram with sides along $\vec{a}$ and $\vec{b}$.

Proof. Let $\vec{a} = (a_1, a_2, a_3)$ and $\vec{b} = (b_1, b_2, b_3)$, so that

$$\vec{a} \times \vec{b} = (a_2b_3 - a_3b_2, a_3b_1 - a_1b_3, a_1b_2 - a_2b_1)$$

Then

$$|\vec{a} \times \vec{b}|^2 = (a_2b_3 - a_3b_2)^2 + (a_3b_1 - a_1b_3)^2 + (a_1b_2 - a_2b_1)^2$$

Expand the right side and refactor to obtain

$$\begin{aligned}
|\vec{a} \times \vec{b}|^2 &= (a_1^2 + a_2^2 + a_3^2)(b_1^2 + b_2^2 + b_3^2) - (a_1b_1 + a_2b_2 + a_3b_3)^2 \\
&= |\vec{a}|^2|\vec{b}|^2 - (\vec{a} \cdot \vec{b})^2 \\
&= |\vec{a}|^2|\vec{b}|^2 - (|\vec{a}||\vec{b}| \cos \theta)^2 \\
&= |\vec{a}|^2|\vec{b}|^2(1 - \cos^2 \theta) \\
&= |\vec{a}|^2|\vec{b}|^2 \sin^2 \theta
\end{aligned}$$

Since $0 \leq \theta \leq 180°$, $\sin \theta \geq 0$ and so $|\vec{a} \times \vec{b}| = |\vec{a}||\vec{b}| \sin \theta$.

In a parallelogram, with sides represented by the vectors $\vec{a}$ and $\vec{b}$, let $\vec{a}$ be the base and h the perpendicular height. Then the area of the parallelogram is

$$\begin{aligned}
\text{base} \times \text{height} &= |\vec{a}|h \\
&= |\vec{a}|(|\vec{b}| \sin \theta) \\
&= |\vec{a} \times \vec{b}|
\end{aligned}$$

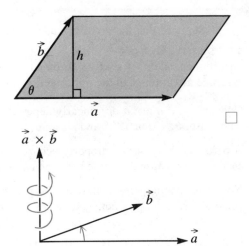

There are two vectors perpendicular to $\vec{a}$ and $\vec{b}$ with the same magnitude, but opposite in direction. The choice of direction of the cross product is such that $\vec{a}$, $\vec{b}$, and $\vec{a} \times \vec{b}$ form a right-handed system (see section 1.5, though $\vec{a}$ and $\vec{b}$ are not usually perpendicular). Hence, we have the following geometric description of the cross product.

The **Cross Product** of the vectors $\vec{a}$ and $\vec{b}$ in 3-space is the vector whose magnitude is $|\vec{a}||\vec{b}| \sin \theta$ and whose direction is perpendicular to $\vec{a}$ and $\vec{b}$, and such that $\vec{a}$, $\vec{b}$, and $\vec{a} \times \vec{b}$ form a right-handed system.

This description shows why the cross product only applies to dimension three. In the plane there is no direction perpendicular to two distinct vectors, whereas in dimensions higher than three, there will be an infinite number of directions perpendicular to two distinct vectors.

Example 2. Calculate the area of the parallelogram with sides represented by the vectors $\vec{a} = (4, 2, -1)$ and $\vec{b} = (-1, -3, -1)$.

Solution. First calculate and check the cross product.

$$\vec{a} \times \vec{b} = (2(-1) - (-1)(-3), (-1)(-1) - 4(-1), 4(-3) - 2(-1))$$
$$= (-5, 5, -10)$$

As a check we have $(4, 2, -1) \cdot (-5, 5, -10) = 4(-5) + 2(5) + (-1)(-10) = 0$ and $(-1, -3, -1) \cdot (-5, 5, -10) = (-1)(-5) + (-3)(5) + (-1)(-10) = 0$. Hence,

$$|\vec{a} \times \vec{b}| = \sqrt{(-5)^2 + 5^2 + (-10)^2}$$
$$= \sqrt{150}$$
$$= 5\sqrt{6}$$

Thus, the area of the parallelogram is $5\sqrt{6}$ square units.   □

Cross Product of Parallel Vectors in 3-space

The vectors $\vec{a}$ and $\vec{b}$ are linearly dependent if and only if $\vec{a} \times \vec{b} = \vec{0}$.

Proof. Suppose that the cross product is the zero vector. Then its magnitude, $|\vec{a}||\vec{b}| \sin \theta$, must be zero. Hence, $\vec{a} = \vec{0}$, $\vec{b} = \vec{0}$, or $\sin \theta = 0$. If $\vec{a}$ or $\vec{b}$ is the zero vector, $\vec{a}$ and $\vec{b}$ are linearly dependent. If $\sin \theta = 0$, then $\theta = 0$ or $180°$; that is, $\vec{a}$ and $\vec{b}$ are parallel, either in the same direction or in the opposite direction. Parallel vectors are linearly dependent.

Conversely, if $\vec{a}$ and $\vec{b}$ are linearly dependent, $\vec{a} = \vec{0}$, $\vec{b} = \vec{0}$, or $\vec{a}$ and $\vec{b}$ are parallel. In the latter case, $\theta = 0$ or $180°$ and so $\sin \theta = 0$. Thus $\vec{a} \times \vec{b}$ has zero magnitude.   □

A particular case of this property occurs when $\vec{b} = \vec{a}$. We always have $\vec{a} \times \vec{a} = \vec{0}$. This is easy to see because the angle between two equal vectors is zero.

Notice that parallel vectors have a cross product equal to the zero vector, whereas perpendicular vectors have a dot product equal to the scalar zero.

Properties of the Cross Product

Let $\vec{a}$, $\vec{b}$, and $\vec{c}$ be vectors in 3-space and let $t \in \mathbf{R}$.

- $\qquad \vec{a} \times \vec{b} = -(\vec{b} \times \vec{a})$ (Anti-commutative Law)
- $\vec{a} \times (\vec{b} + \vec{c}) = (\vec{a} \times \vec{b}) + (\vec{a} \times \vec{c})$ (Distributive Law)
- $\qquad k(\vec{a} \times \vec{b}) = (k\vec{a}) \times \vec{b} = \vec{a} \times (k\vec{b})$

These properties can be checked by using the definition of the cross product. Notice that the first property means that the cross product is not commutative. For example, $\vec{i} \times \vec{j} = \vec{k}$ but $\vec{j} \times \vec{i} = -\vec{k}$.

The cross product can be used to calculate the torque of a force about a point.

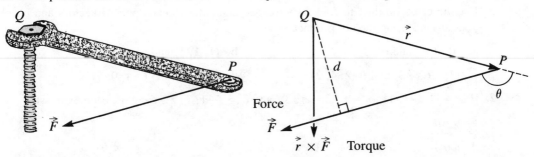

Consider the act of using a wrench to tighten a bolt with a right-hand thread. Apply a force $\vec{F}$ to the wrench at the point P. Let Q be the point about which the bolt will turn, and let $\vec{r} = \overrightarrow{QP}$ be the position vector of P with respect to Q. Then the **moment** or **torque** of the force $\vec{F}$ about the point Q is the vector

$$\vec{r} \times \vec{F}$$

Its magnitude measures the twisting effect of the force while its direction gives the direction of the axis through Q about which the force tends to twist. If the force is measured in newtons and the distance is measured in metres, then the magnitude of the torque is measured in newton-metres.

If $\vec{r}$ makes an angle θ with $\vec{F}$ and if d is the perpendicular distance from Q to the line of action of $\vec{F}$, then the magnitude of the torque of $\vec{F}$ about Q is

$$|\vec{r} \times \vec{F}| = |\vec{r}||\vec{F}| \sin \theta$$
$$= d|\vec{F}|$$

Notice that if you were applying a force of a given magnitude at the point P to turn the wrench, it would be most efficient to apply $\vec{F}$ at right angles to $\vec{r}$, so that the torque would be the greatest. For example, when we push a door open, we instinctively maximize $|\vec{r} \times \vec{F}|$ by making $|\vec{r}|$ and $\sin \theta$ as large as possible. ($|\vec{F}|$ is fixed, depending on our strength.) That is, we push as far away from the hinges as possible and at right angles to the door.

Example 3. Suppose a 10 N force is applied at the end of a 30 cm wrench with which it makes a 60° angle. Calculate the magnitude of the torque about the other end of the wrench.

Solution. If we measure distance in metres, the magnitude of the torque of the force $\vec{F}$ about the end of the wrench is

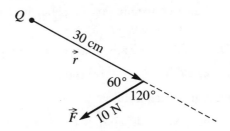

$$|\vec{r} \times \vec{F}| = |\vec{r}||\vec{F}| \sin 120°$$
$$= (0.3)(10)\frac{\sqrt{3}}{2}$$
$$= \frac{3\sqrt{3}}{2}$$

Hence, the magnitude of the torque is about 2.6 N-m. □

Exercises 2.7

1. Use the cross product to find a vector perpendicular to each pair of vectors and check your answer using the dot product.

    a. $(0, 0, 1)$ and $(0, 1, 0)$ **b.** $(1, 1, 1)$ and $(2, -7, 3)$

    c. $(3, -6, -3)$ and $(-2, 4, 2)$ **d.** $(2, 5, 0)$ and $(-4, 0, 9)$

2. If $\vec{a} = (1, -1, 1)$, $\vec{b} = (-2, -1, 3)$, and $\vec{c} = (-1, 2, 2)$, compute each expression.

    a. $\vec{a} \cdot \vec{b}$ **b.** $\vec{a} \times \vec{b}$ **c.** $\vec{a} \cdot \vec{c}$

    d. $\vec{a} \times \vec{c}$ **e.** $\vec{c} \times \vec{a}$ **f.** $(\vec{a} \times \vec{b}) \cdot \vec{c}$

    g. $\vec{c} \cdot (\vec{a} \times \vec{b})$ **h.** $\vec{c} \cdot (\vec{b} \times \vec{a})$ **i.** $(\vec{b} \times \vec{c}) \cdot \vec{a}$

3. If $\vec{p}$, $\vec{q}$, and $\vec{r}$ are vectors in 3-space, state whether the following expressions are vectors or scalars or are meaningless.

    a. $\vec{p} \cdot \vec{q} + \vec{r}$ **b.** $\vec{p} \cdot (\vec{q} + \vec{r})$ **c.** $(\vec{p} \times \vec{q}) + \vec{r}$

    d. $(|\vec{p} \times \vec{q}|)\vec{r}$ **e.** $(\vec{p} \times \vec{q}) \times \vec{r}$ **f.** $(\vec{p} \cdot \vec{q})(\vec{p} \times \vec{q})$

4. Find a unit vector perpendicular to both $(2, 3, 0)$ and $(0, 3, 4)$.

5. A 10 N force is applied to the end of a 20 cm wrench and makes an angle of $30°$ with the wrench. Calculate the magnitude of the torque of this force about the other end of the wrench.

6. A girl steps on a bicycle pedal with a vertical force of f newtons. Find the torque of this force about the crankshaft when the arm is of length ℓ metres and makes an angle of θ with the vertical. For which angle is this torque greatest, and for which angle is it least? Why does this make sense intuitively?

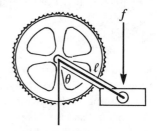

7. If $\vec{a} = (2, 3, -1)$, $\vec{b} = (0, 3, 4)$, and $\vec{c} = (1, 0, 5)$, verify that
$$\vec{a} \times (\vec{b} + \vec{c}) = \vec{a} \times \vec{b} + \vec{a} \times \vec{c}$$

8. Calculate the area of the parallelogram with sides represented by $\vec{a} = (1, 2, -2)$ and $\vec{b} = (-1, 3, 0)$.

9. Find the area of the triangle with the given vertices.

    a. $(7, 3, 4)$, $(1, 0, 6)$, and $(4, 5, -2)$ **b.** $(1, 0, 0)$, $(0, 1, 0)$, and $(0, 0, 1)$

10. Verify each identity.

    a. $\vec{i} \times \vec{j} = \vec{k} = -\vec{j} \times \vec{i}$ **b.** $\vec{j} \times \vec{k} = \vec{i} = -\vec{k} \times \vec{j}$

    c. $\vec{k} \times \vec{i} = \vec{j} = -\vec{i} \times \vec{k}$

11. Show that the cross product is not associative by finding vectors $\vec{a}$, $\vec{b}$, and $\vec{c}$ such that

$$(\vec{a} \times \vec{b}) \times \vec{c} \neq \vec{a} \times (\vec{b} \times \vec{c})$$

Problems 2.7

1. Prove that $(\vec{a} - \vec{b}) \times (\vec{a} + \vec{b}) = 2\vec{a} \times \vec{b}$.

2. For any vectors $\vec{a}$, $\vec{b}$, and $\vec{c}$, show that $(\vec{a} \times \vec{b}) \times \vec{c}$ lies in the plane of $\vec{a}$ and $\vec{b}$ and that

$$(\vec{a} \times \vec{b}) \times \vec{c} = (\vec{a} \cdot \vec{c})\vec{b} - (\vec{b} \cdot \vec{c})\vec{a}$$

3. Write a computer program to calculate the cross product of two vectors in $\mathbf{R}^3$.

Review Exercises

1. A man weighing 70 kg lies in a hammock whose ropes make angles of 30° and 45° with the horizontal. What is the tension in each rope? (Assume that a 1 kg mass exerts a force of 9.8 N.)

2. A 10 kg weight is supported by two strings of length 5 m and 7 m attached to two points in the ceiling 10 m apart. Find the tension in each string. (Assume that a 1 kg mass exerts a force of 9.8 N.)

3. Two tugs are towing a ship. The smaller tug is 10° off the port bow and the larger tug is 20° off the starboard bow. The larger tug pulls twice as hard as the smaller tug. In what direction will the ship move?

4. Find the work done by the force $\vec{F}$ exerted on an object moving along the vector $\vec{s}$. Assume that the force is measured in newtons and that the distance is in metres.

   a. $\vec{F} = (3, 2)$, $\vec{s} = (4, 1)$ **b.** $\vec{F} = (2, 1, 0)$, $\vec{s} = (-3, 1, 4)$

5. Find the values of t if $\vec{a}$ and $\vec{b}$ are linearly independent.

   a. $(t - 1)\vec{a} + (t^2 - 1)\vec{b} = \vec{0}$

   b. $(t^2 + t - 6)\vec{a} + (3t^2 - 7t + 2)\vec{b} = \vec{0}$

   c. $(t^2 - t - 30)\vec{a} = (t^2 + t - 20)\vec{b}$

6. Classify the following sets of vectors as being either linearly dependent or linearly independent. Give reasons for your answer.

   a. $(3, 5, 6)$, $(6, 10, 12)$, $(-3, -5, 6)$

   b. $(5, 1, -1)$, $(6, -5, -2)$, $(3, 8, -2)$, $(-40, 39, 29)$

   c. $(7, 8, 9)$, $(0, 0, 0)$, $(3, 8, 6)$

   d. $(7, -8)$, $(14, 19)$

   e. $(0, 1, 0)$, $(0, 0, -7)$, $(7, 0, 0)$

7. The vectors $\vec{a}$ and $\vec{b}$ are linearly independent. For what values of t are $\vec{c} = t^2\vec{a} + \vec{b}$ and $\vec{d} = (2t - 3)(\vec{a} - \vec{b})$ linearly dependent?

8. If the vectors $\vec{a}$, $\vec{b}$, and $\vec{c}$ are linearly independent, show that $\vec{a} - 2\vec{b} - \vec{c}$, $2\vec{a} + \vec{b}$, and $\vec{a} + \vec{b} + \vec{c}$ are also linearly independent.

9. Let $\overrightarrow{OM} = \frac{3}{5}\overrightarrow{ON} + \frac{2}{5}\overrightarrow{OP}$ and $\overrightarrow{OM} = \frac{4}{5}\overrightarrow{ON} + \frac{1}{5}\overrightarrow{OQ}$.

  a. In what ratio does P divide NQ?

  b. In what ratio does Q divide NM?

10. Prove from first principles that the points M, N, and Q are collinear if

$$\overrightarrow{ON} = \frac{2}{7}\overrightarrow{OM} + \frac{5}{7}\overrightarrow{OQ}.$$

11. In the parallelogram $ABCD$, E divides AB in the ratio 1:4 and F divides BC in the ratio 3:1. The line segments DE and AF meet at K. In what ratio does K divide AF and in what ratio does K divide DE?

12. If M divides AB in a ratio of 1:7 and O is any point, show that $\overrightarrow{OM} = \frac{7}{8}\overrightarrow{OA} + \frac{1}{8}\overrightarrow{OB}$.

13. The triangle ABC has vertices $A(-2, 1, 3)$, $B(4, -1, 6)$, and $C(1, 3, 0)$.

  a. Determine the coordinates of its centroid G.

  b. Calculate the area of the triangle using the cross product.

14. Find a vector perpendicular to both $\vec{u}$ and $\vec{v}$.

  a. $\vec{u} = (-2, 3, 1)$, $\vec{v} = (-1, 4, 0)$ **b.** $\vec{u} = (4, 5, -2)$, $\vec{v} = (2, 0, 3)$

15. If $\vec{a}$ and $\vec{b}$ are perpendicular unit vectors, what is the length of $\vec{a} \times \vec{b}$?

16. a. Find $\vec{a} \times \vec{b}$ if $\vec{a} = (2, -1, 5)$ and $\vec{b} = (0, 3, 7)$.

  b. Find $\vec{b} \times \vec{a}$.

  c. What property of the cross product does this illustrate?

17. If $\vec{a} = (3, 1, 1)$, $\vec{b} = (1, -1, 2)$, and $\vec{c} = (2, 1, 5)$, compute each expression.

  a. $\vec{a} \cdot \vec{b} + \vec{b} \cdot \vec{c}$ **b.** $\vec{a} \times \vec{b}$

  c. $2(\vec{a} \times \vec{b}) - (\vec{b} \times \vec{c})$ **d.** $\vec{a} \times (\vec{b} \times \vec{c})$

18. Find two unit vectors perpendicular to both $(2, 0, -1)$ and $(1, 1, 1)$.

The lines and planes of the Canadian Pavilion at Expo '70 in Osaka, Japan.
(Architects: Erickson-Massey)

Lines and Planes

In this chapter, the results of the previous two chapters on geometric and Cartesian vectors will be used to develop various forms of equations of lines in 2-space and 3-space and equations of planes in 3-space. The methods developed can be generalized to describe lines and "hyperplanes" in R^n for $n > 3$.

3.1 Vector and Parametric Equations of a Line in 2-space

Two points in the plane determine a line. Equivalently, a line can be determined by one point on the line and a vector parallel to the line, because once two points are specified, the vector joining these points is determined. We shall use this description of a line to find the vector equation of a line in 2-space. A **direction vector** is a non-zero vector that is parallel to the line. The components of a direction vector are called the **direction numbers** of the line. A direction vector is all that is required to describe the direction of a line.

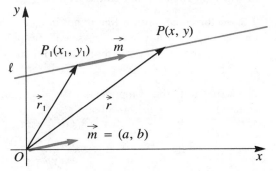

Let ℓ be a line passing through a particular point $P_1(x_1, y_1)$, with position vector $\overrightarrow{OP_1} = \underset{\sim}{r_1}$, and having a non-zero direction vector $\underset{\sim}{m} = (a, b)$. Let $P(x, y)$ be a general point on ℓ having position vector $\overrightarrow{OP} = \underset{\sim}{r}$.

By the Triangle Law for Addition of Vectors,

$$\overrightarrow{OP} = \overrightarrow{OP_1} + \overrightarrow{P_1P}$$

Since $\overrightarrow{P_1P}$ is parallel to $\overrightarrow{m}$, $\overrightarrow{P_1P}$ is a scalar multiple of $\overrightarrow{m}$; that is, $\overrightarrow{P_1P} = t\overrightarrow{m}$, for some scalar $t \in \mathbf{R}$. Hence, the position vector of any point on ℓ can be expressed in terms of the vectors $\overrightarrow{r_1}$ and $\overrightarrow{m}$.

The **Vector Equation of the Line** through the point with position vector $\overrightarrow{r_1}$, in the direction $\overrightarrow{m}$, is of the form

$$\overrightarrow{r} = \overrightarrow{r_1} + t\overrightarrow{m}, \quad \text{where } t \in \mathbf{R}$$

Example 1. Find a vector equation of the line that passes through the point $P_1(-1, 1)$ and has direction vector $\overrightarrow{m} = (3, 2)$. Find four points on the line and graph the line.

Solution. A vector equation is

$$\overrightarrow{r} = (-1, 1) + t(3, 2), \quad t \in \mathbf{R}$$

By substituting any real number for t, a point on the line is obtained. Setting $t = 0$ gives the point $(-1, 1)$, that is, P_1. Setting $t = 1$ gives the point $(-1, 1) + (3, 2) = (2, 3)$, and setting $t = 2$ gives the point $(-1, 1) + 2(3, 2) = (5, 5)$. Finally, set $t = -1$ to obtain a fourth point $(-4, -1)$.

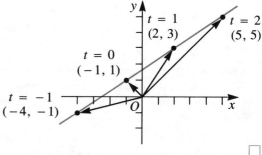

Each real number t specifies one point on the line, and to each point on the line there corresponds one value of t; t is called a **parameter**.

When a line is described by the equation $y = mx + b$, we specify any x-coordinate and the equation tells us how to find the y-coordinate, which gives us a point (x, y) on the line. As x ranges over $\mathbf{R}$, we get all the points on the line. When a line is described by the vector equation $\overrightarrow{r} = \overrightarrow{r_1} + t\overrightarrow{m}$, we specify any value of the parameter t and the equation tells us how to find $\overrightarrow{r}$, which gives us a point on the line. As t ranges over $\mathbf{R}$, we get all the points on the line.

The vector equation of a line is not unique. The particular point chosen could be anywhere on the line, and any non-zero scalar multiple of the direction vector could be used. For example, the line in Example 1 could also be written as $\overrightarrow{r} = (-1, 1) + t(6, 4)$ or $\overrightarrow{r} = (2, 3) + s(-3, -2)$.

If we substitute the components of $\overrightarrow{r} = (x, y)$, $\overrightarrow{r_1} = (x_1, y_1)$, and $\overrightarrow{m} = (a, b)$ in the vector equation $\overrightarrow{r} = \overrightarrow{r_1} + t\overrightarrow{m}$, we obtain

$$(x, y) = (x_1, y_1) + t(a, b)$$
$$(x, y) = (x_1, y_1) + (ta, tb)$$
$$(x, y) = (x_1 + ta, y_1 + tb)$$

Hence, by equating components, the line can be described in terms of coordinates as follows.

The **Parametric Equations of the Line** passing through (x_1, y_1) in the direction (a, b) are of the form

$$x = x_1 + ta$$
$$y = y_1 + tb, \quad \text{where } t \in \mathbf{R}$$

When a line is described by these parametric equations, we specify a parameter t and the equations give us a point (x, y) on the line.

Example 2. What are the parametric equations of the line passing through the points $P(1, 4)$ and $Q(-2, -6)$?

Solution. A direction vector of the line is

$$\overrightarrow{PQ} = \overrightarrow{OQ} - \overrightarrow{OP}$$
$$= (-2, -6) - (1, 4)$$
$$= (-3, -10)$$

The line through $P(1, 4)$ with direction vector $(-3, -10)$ has parametric equations

$$x = 1 - 3t$$
$$y = 4 - 10t, \quad t \in \mathbf{R}$$

Check. $Q(-2, -6)$ lies on the line since $-2 = 1 - 3t$ and $-6 = 4 - 10t$ when $t = 1$. □

Example 3. Consider the line with equation $\vec{r} = (5, 2) + t(-3, 1), t \in \mathbf{R}$.

a. Find the value of t that corresponds to the point K at which the line meets the x-axis.

b. Find the coordinates of K.

Solution.

a. The coordinates of the point K on the x-axis must be of the form $(k, 0)$. Therefore, if $(k, 0) = (5, 2) + t(-3, 1)$, it follows that $k = 5 - 3t$ and $0 = 2 + t$. The second equation gives the parameter $t = -2$.

b. Substitute $t = -2$ into $k = 5 - 3t$ to obtain $k = 5 - 3(-2) = 11$. Hence, the coordinates of K are $(11, 0)$. □

Exercises 3.1

1. Find vector and parametric equations of the line that passes through the point P_1 with direction vector $\vec{m}$. In each case, find two points on the line different from P_1. $t \neq 0$

a. $P_1(-2, 7), \vec{m} = (3, -4)$　　　　　　**b.** $P_1(0, 7), \vec{m} = (-5, 2)$

c. $P_1(\sqrt{2}, -1), \vec{m} = (0, 6)$　　　　　**d.** $P_1(0, 0), \vec{m} = (2, 7)$

2. Find vector and parametric equations of the line P_1P_2.

    a. $P_1(0, 5)$, $P_2(-6, 5)$ **b.** $P_1(\sqrt{3}, -1)$, $P_2(2\sqrt{3}, -2)$

    c. $P_1(0, k)$, $P_2(k, 0)$ **d.** $P_1\left(2, \frac{1}{3}\right)$, $P_2\left(-\frac{1}{4}, 0\right)$

3. Determine the coordinates of the three points corresponding to the parameters, 0, 1, and 2 on each line.

    a. $\vec{r} = (2, 3) + t(-4, 1)$, $t \in \mathbf{R}$

    b. $x = 5t$, $y = 3 - 4t$, $t \in \mathbf{R}$

    c. $x = 3 - t$, $y = 7$, $t \in \mathbf{R}$

4. Find vector and parametric equations of the line that passes through the point $\left(5, -\frac{1}{2}\right)$ and is parallel to

    a. the vector $(9, 2)$.

    b. the x-axis. $\vec{m} = (1, 0)$

    c. the line $\vec{r} = (4, 7) + t(-3, 7)$, $t \in \mathbf{R}$.

5. a. Show that these vector equations represent the same line.

$$\vec{r} = (3, 2) + t(1, 3), \quad t \in \mathbf{R}$$
$$\vec{r} = (3, 2) + k(2, 6), \quad k \in \mathbf{R}$$
$$\vec{r} = (4, 5) + s(1, 3), \quad s \in \mathbf{R}$$

    b. If the point $(2, b)$ lies on this line, find the value of b.

6. Determine which points lie on the line $x = 3 + t$, $y = 2 - 2t$, $t \in \mathbf{R}$.

    a. $(2, 4)$ **b.** $\left(\frac{7}{2}, 1\right)$ **c.** $(0, 7)$

7. For each line, name a direction vector with integer components and, if possible, name a point on the line with integer coordinates.

    a. $\vec{r} = \left(\frac{1}{2}, 3\right) + t\left(-\frac{1}{2}, 5\right)$, $t \in \mathbf{R}$

    b. $\vec{r} = \left(\frac{1}{3}, -\frac{1}{2}\right) + t\left(\frac{1}{3}, \frac{1}{4}\right)$, $t \in \mathbf{R}$

    c. $x = \frac{1}{3} + 2t$, $y = 3 - \frac{2}{3}t$, $t \in \mathbf{R}$

8. Which pairs of lines are parallel, and which are perpendicular?

    a. $\vec{r} = (1, 7) + t(-3, 4)$, $t \in \mathbf{R}$; and $\vec{r} = (2, 0) + t(4, -3)$, $t \in \mathbf{R}$

    b. $\vec{r} = (1, 7) + t(-3, 4)$, $t \in \mathbf{R}$; and $\vec{r} = (2, 0) + t(3, -4)$, $t \in \mathbf{R}$

    c. $x = 1 - 3t$, $y = 7 + 4t$, $t \in \mathbf{R}$; and $x = 2 - 4t$, $y = -3t$, $t \in \mathbf{R}$

9. Find a vector equation of the line that passes through the point $(4, 5)$ and is perpendicular to the line $\vec{r} = (1, 8) + t(3, 7)$, $t \in \textbf{\textit{R}}$.

10. Find the points where the line intersects the axes, and graph the line.

   a. $\vec{r} = (2, 3) + t(3, -1)$, $t \in \textbf{\textit{R}}$

   b. $\vec{r} = (-5, 10) + t(1, 5)$, $t \in \textbf{\textit{R}}$

   c. $\vec{r} = (6, 1) + t(0, 7)$, $t \in \textbf{\textit{R}}$ $\dfrac{7}{0}$ $\dfrac{\downarrow}{4}$

11. Find parametric equations of the line that passes through the point $P_1(x_1, y_1)$ and is

   a. parallel to the x-axis. $\vec{m} = (1, 0)$ **b.** parallel to the y-axis. $\vec{m} = (0, 1)$

12. Show that both lines $\vec{r} = (3, 9) + t(2, 5)$ and $\vec{r} = (-5, 6) + s(3, -1)$ contain the point $(1, 4)$. Find the acute angle of intersection of these lines, to the nearest degree.

13. The line ℓ_1 passes through the points $(2, -1)$ and $(3, -4)$, and the line ℓ_2 passes through $(4, 3)$ and $(-1, 6)$. Find the acute angle between ℓ_1 and ℓ_2, to the nearest degree.

Problems 3.1

1. **a.** Show that $(5, 8)$ and $(17, -22)$ are points on the line that passes through $A(7, 3)$ with direction vector $(2, -5)$.

   b. Use parametric equations with suitable restrictions on the parameter to describe the line segment from $(5, 8)$ to $(17, -22)$.

2. **a.** If $\vec{p}$ and $\vec{q}$ are the position vectors of the points P and Q in the plane, show that the line that passes through P and Q has the vector equation $\vec{r} = (1 - t)\vec{p} + t\vec{q}$, $t \in \textbf{\textit{R}}$.

   b. For what values of t does the point with position vector $\vec{r}$ lie on the segment PQ?

3. Find vector equations of the two lines that bisect the angles between the lines $\vec{r} = (6, 1) + t(1, 1)$, $t \in \textbf{\textit{R}}$, and $\vec{r} = (1, 0) + s(-1, 3)$, $s \in \textbf{\textit{R}}$.

3.2 The Cartesian Equation of a Line in 2-space

In this section we shall discuss the relationship between the vector and parametric equations of a line in 2-space and the familiar Cartesian equation $Ax + By + C = 0$.

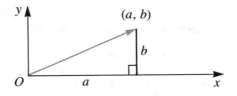

The direction of a line in the plane can be described by a direction vector $\vec{m} = (a, b)$, or it can be described by its slope. The slope of the line that passes through the origin and the point (a, b) is

$$\text{slope} = \frac{\text{rise}}{\text{run}} = \frac{b}{a}$$

> The **slope** of the line with direction vector (a, b) in 2-space is $\dfrac{b}{a}$, provided that $a \neq 0$.

If $a = 0$, the slope is undefined and the line is vertical.

Example 1. Find a vector equation of the line in the plane that has the Cartesian equation $y = \frac{3}{2}x - 1$.

Solution. We have to find any point on the given line and a direction vector. The line meets the y-axis where $x = 0$ and $y = -1$; hence, $(0, -1)$ is one point on the line. The slope of the line is $\frac{3}{2}$ and, therefore, a direction vector is $(2, 3)$. A vector equation of the line is

$$\vec{r} = (0, -1) + t(2, 3),\, t \in \mathbf{R}.$$ □

The vector or parametric equations of a line in 2-space can be converted into Cartesian form by eliminating the parameter. Consider the parametric equations

$$x = x_1 + ta$$
$$y = y_1 + tb \quad t \in \mathbf{R}$$

Solving each equation for the parameter gives $t = \dfrac{x - x_1}{a}$ and $t = \dfrac{y - y_1}{b}$, provided that neither a nor b is zero. Hence,

$$\frac{x - x_1}{a} = \frac{y - y_1}{b}$$

and

$$y - y_1 = \frac{b}{a}(x - x_1)$$

This represents the line that passes through the point (x_1, y_1) and has slope $\frac{b}{a}$. If $a = 0$, the line is vertical and it follows from the first of the parametric equations that its equation is $x = x_1$. If $b = 0$, the line is horizontal and its equation is $y = y_1$.

Another way of developing the Cartesian equation of a line is in terms of a vector that is at right angles to the line. A vector that is perpendicular to a given line in the plane is called a **normal vector**, or simply a **normal** to the line.

Let ℓ be a line passing through the point $P_1(x_1, y_1)$, and let $\vec{n} = (A, B)$ be a normal vector to the line. Let $P(x, y)$ be any point on the line. Since $\vec{n}$ is perpendicular to $\vec{P_1P}$, it follows that

$$\vec{n} \cdot \vec{P_1P} = 0$$

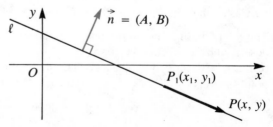

If $\vec{r}$ is the position vector of P, and if $\vec{r}_1$ is the position vector of P_1, then $\overrightarrow{P_1P} = \vec{r} - \vec{r}_1$, and

$$\vec{n} \cdot (\vec{r} - \vec{r}_1) = 0$$

Hence,

$$(A, B) \cdot (x - x_1, y - y_1) = 0$$
$$A(x - x_1) + B(y - y_1) = 0$$
$$Ax + By + (-Ax_1 - By_1) = 0$$

If we denote the constant term $(-Ax_1 - By_1)$ by C, we obtain the following equation of the line.

The **Cartesian or Scalar Equation of the Line** in 2-space with normal (A, B) is of the form

$$Ax + By + C = 0$$

Example 2. Find the Cartesian equation of the line that passes through $P_1(8, 2)$ and has normal vector $\vec{n} = (3, -5)$.

Solution 1. If $P(x, y)$ is any point on the line, then it satisfies $\vec{n} \cdot \overrightarrow{P_1P} = 0$. Hence,

$$(3, -5) \cdot (x - 8, y - 2) = 0$$
$$3x - 24 - 5y + 10 = 0$$

Therefore, the Cartesian equation of the line is $3x - 5y - 14 = 0$.

Solution 2. The Cartesian equation must be of the form $Ax + By + C = 0$. Since $(3, -5)$ is a normal vector, the equation is of the form $3x - 5y + C = 0$. Since $P_1(8, 2)$ lies on the line, its coordinates will satisfy the equation. Therefore, $3(8) - 5(2) + C = 0$; that is, $C = -14$. Hence, the Cartesian equation is $3x - 5y - 14 = 0$. $\square$

Two lines in the plane are parallel if their normal vectors are parallel, and the two lines are perpendicular if their normal vectors are perpendicular.

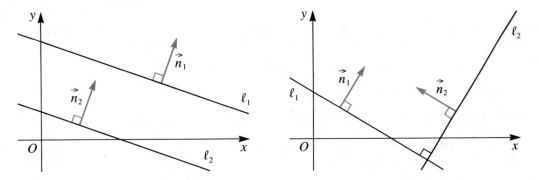

Example 3. For what values of d, if any, are the lines $\ell_1: 3x - 4y + 7 = 0$ and $\ell_2: 5x + dy - 9 = 0$

a. parallel?

b. perpendicular?

Solution.

a. A normal vector to ℓ_1 is $\vec{n}_1 = (3, -4)$, and a normal vector to ℓ_2 is $\vec{n}_2 = (5, d)$. For the lines to be parallel, their normals must be parallel; that is, $\vec{n}_1 = k\vec{n}_2$, for some non-zero $k \in \mathbf{R}$. Hence,

$$(3, -4) = k(5, d)$$
$$= (5k, dk)$$

Therefore, $3 = 5k$ and $-4 = dk$. Solving gives $k = \frac{3}{5}$ and $d = -\frac{20}{3}$. Hence, the lines are parallel if $d = -\frac{20}{3}$.

b. For the lines to be perpendicular, their normals must be perpendicular; that is, $\vec{n}_1 \cdot \vec{n}_2 = 0$. Hence, $(3, -4) \cdot (5, d) = 0$ and $15 - 4d = 0$. Therefore, the lines are perpendicular if $d = \frac{15}{4}$. □

Dot Product + Vectors.

Exercises 3.2

1. Find a Cartesian equation of the line that passes through the point P_1 and has normal vector $\vec{n}$.

   a. $P_1(4, -2)$, $\vec{n} = (2, 5)$ **b.** $P_1\left(\frac{1}{2}, 2\right)$, $\vec{n} = (-4, 0)$

   c. $P_1(0, 0)$, $\vec{n} = (1, 1)$ **d.** $P_1(\sqrt{2}, \sqrt{3})$, $\vec{n} = (0, 1)$

2. Find a normal vector, a direction vector, and a point on each line.

   a. $3x + 4y - 12 = 0$ **b.** $2x - y = 18$

   c. $x = 3$ **d.** $y = 5x - 10$

3. Find a Cartesian equation of the line that passes through $(-6, -3)$ and

   a. is parallel to the line $2x - 3y + 5 = 0$.

   b. is parallel to the line $y - 7 = 0$.

   c. is parallel to the line $x = 5 + 2t$, $y = 6 - 5t$, $t \in \mathbf{R}$.

   d. has slope $\frac{1}{3}$.

   e. passes through $(3, 6)$.

4. Find a Cartesian equation of the line that passes through $(1, -5)$ and is

a. perpendicular to the vector $(6, -4)$.

b. perpendicular to the line $\vec{r} = (1, 8) + t(-4, 0)$, $t \in \mathbf{R}$.

c. perpendicular to the line $x + y + 5 = 0$.

d. perpendicular to the y-axis.

5. For what values of k will the lines ℓ_1 and ℓ_2 be perpendicular?   *use vectors !*

a. $\ell_1: 3x + 6y - 11 = 0$ $\ell_2: 6x - ky - 7 = 0$

b. $\ell_1: kx + 2y + 9 = 0$ $\ell_2: 4x + 3y = 0$

c. $\ell_1: x + ky - 5 = 0$ $\ell_2: 9x - ky = 0$

6. Find a Cartesian equation of each line.

a. $\vec{r} = (3, -4) + t(2, 5)$ **b.** $\vec{r} = (1, 0) + t(-1, 0)$

c. $x = 3, y = 7 + 5t$ **d.** $\vec{r} = s(-2, 7)$

7. Find a vector equation of each line.

a. $y = 2x + 1$ **b.** $y - 4 = 0$ **c.** $2x - 3y - 6 = 0$

Problems 3.2

1. Prove that the angle between two intersecting lines is equal to the angle between their normal vectors. Find the angle, to the nearest degree, between the lines $x - 2y - 9 = 0$ and $5x + y - 5 = 0$.

2. Show that if $P_1(x_1, y_1)$ and $P_2(x_2, y_2)$ are distinct points on the line $Ax + By + C = 0$, then $(y_1 - y_2, x_2 - x_1)$ is a normal vector to the line.

3. a. Show that the Cartesian equation of a line that does not pass through the origin can be written in the form

$$x \cos \theta + y \sin \theta = c$$

where c is the distance from the origin to the line and θ is the angle indicated in the diagram.

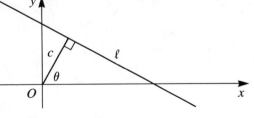

b. If the line passes through the origin, show that the Cartesian equation can be written in the form

$$x \cos \theta + y \sin \theta = 0$$

Describe the angle θ.

3.3 Equations of a Line in 3-space

The vector and parametric equations of a line can be generalized from 2-space to 3-space. The Cartesian equation of a line in 2-space does not generalize to 3-space because a line in 3-space has an infinite number of different normals.

As in two dimensions, the most convenient description of a line in three dimensions is by means of one point on the line and a direction vector. Let $P_1(x_1, y_1, z_1)$ be a point on a line ℓ, and let $\vec{m} = (a, b, c)$ be a direction vector for the line. Let $P(x, y, z)$ be any point on the line. By the Triangle Law of Addition in triangle OP_1P,

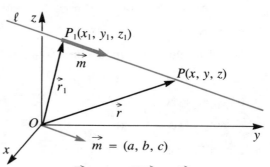

$$\overrightarrow{OP} = \overrightarrow{OP_1} + \overrightarrow{P_1P}$$

Since $\overrightarrow{P_1P}$ is parallel to $\vec{m}$, it must be a scalar multiple of $\vec{m}$; hence, $\overrightarrow{P_1P} = t\vec{m}$, where $t \in \mathbf{R}$. Therefore,

$$\overrightarrow{OP} = \overrightarrow{OP_1} + t\vec{m}$$

If $\vec{r}$ and $\vec{r_1}$ are the position vectors of P and P_1, respectively, we obtain the following vector equation in terms of the parameter t.

The **Vector Equation of the Line** through the point with position vector $\vec{r_1}$, in the direction $\vec{m}$, is of the form

$$\vec{r} = \vec{r_1} + t\vec{m}, \quad \text{where } t \in \mathbf{R}$$

Example 1. Find a vector equation of the line that passes through $(1, 0, -1)$ and has direction vector $(1, 2, 3)$. Does the point $Q(3, 4, 2)$ lie on this line?

Solution. A vector equation of the line is

$$\vec{r} = (1, 0, -1) + t(1, 2, 3), \quad t \in \mathbf{R}$$

If $Q(3, 4, 2)$ lies on this line, then

$$(3, 4, 2) = (1, 0, -1) + t(1, 2, 3), \quad \text{for some } t \in \mathbf{R}$$

That is,

$$3 = 1 + t \tag{1}$$
$$4 = 0 + 2t \tag{2}$$
$$2 = -1 + 3t \tag{3}$$

From equation (1), $t = 2$, from equation (2), $t = 2$, and from equation (3), $t = 1$. Since there is no single value of the parameter t for which the vector equation is satisfied, Q does not lie on the line. □

As in two dimensions, the vector equation of a line is not unique. For example, the line in Example 1 could also be written as

$$\vec{r} = (2, 2, 2) + t(2, 4, 6), \quad t \in R$$

or in an infinite number of other ways.

If we express each vector in the vector equation $\vec{r} = \vec{r_1} + t\vec{m}$ in component form, using $\vec{r} = (x, y, z)$, $\vec{r_1} = (x_1, y_1, z_1)$, and $\vec{m} = (a, b, c)$, we obtain

$$(x, y, z) = (x_1, y_1, z_1) + t(a, b, c)$$

Hence, $(x, y, z) = (x_1 + ta, y_1 + tb, z_1 + tc)$, and, equating components, we obtain the following description of a line.

The **Parametric Equations of the Line** through (x_1, y_1, z_1) in the direction (a, b, c) are of the form

$$x = x_1 + ta$$
$$y = y_1 + tb$$
$$z = z_1 + tc, \quad t \in R$$

The parametric equations of the line in Example 1 are

$$x = 1 + t$$
$$y = 2t$$
$$z = -1 + 3t, \quad t \in R$$

The direction vector, (a, b, c), of a line cannot be the zero vector, and so at least one of the direction numbers a, b, and c, must be non-zero. If all of these components are non-zero, we can solve each of the parametric equations of the line for the parameter t to obtain

$$t = \frac{x - x_1}{a}, \quad t = \frac{y - y_1}{b}, \quad t = \frac{z - z_1}{c}$$

Hence, all of these ratios are equal, and we obtain a set of equations for a line that does not contain a parameter.

The **Symmetric Equations of the Line** passing through (x_1, y_1, z_1) with non-zero direction numbers, a, b, and c are of the form

$$\frac{x - x_1}{a} = \frac{y - y_1}{b} = \frac{z - z_1}{c}$$

For example, the symmetric equations of the line in Example 1 are

$$\frac{x - 1}{1} = \frac{y}{2} = \frac{z + 1}{3}$$

Note that these symmetric equations actually consist of the two equations $\dfrac{x-1}{1} = \dfrac{y}{2}$ and $\dfrac{y}{2} = \dfrac{z+1}{3}$, from which a third equation $\dfrac{x-1}{1} = \dfrac{z+1}{3}$ can be derived. Any two of these three equations suffice to define the line.

Example 2. Find vector, parametric, and symmetric equations of the line that passes through $P_1(2, 4, 0)$ and $P_2(5, 0, 7)$. Does the point $Q(-4, 12, -14)$ lie on this line?

Solution. A direction vector of the line is

$$\begin{aligned} \overrightarrow{P_1P_2} &= (5, 0, 7) - (2, 4, 0) \\ &= (3, -4, 7) \end{aligned}$$

Hence, a vector equation of this line is

$$\vec{r} = (2, 4, 0) + t(3, -4, 7), \quad t \in \mathbf{R}$$

The corresponding set of parametric equations for the line is

$$\begin{aligned} x &= 2 + 3t \\ y &= 4 - 4t \\ z &= 7t, \quad t \in \mathbf{R} \end{aligned}$$

The corresponding set of symmetric equations for the line is

$$\frac{x-2}{3} = \frac{y-4}{-4} = \frac{z}{7}$$

The point $Q(-4, 12, -14)$ will lie on the line if and only if there is one value of the parameter t such that

$$(-4, 12, -14) = (2, 4, 0) + t(3, -4, 7)$$

That is, $(-6, 8, -14) = t(3, -4, 7)$. This vector equation is satisfied by $t = -2$. Hence, $Q(-4, 12, -14)$ does lie on the line. $\square$

Example 3.

a. Find symmetric equations of the line through $A(1, 2, 3)$ and $B(2, -1, 3)$.

b. Find the direction cosines of this line and the direction angles to the nearest degree.

Solution.

a. A direction vector is $\vec{AB} = (2, -1, 3) - (1, 2, 3) = (1, -3, 0)$. Since one of the direction numbers, c, is zero, the line does not have symmetric equations. However, the parametric equations of the line are

$$x = 1 + t$$
$$y = 2 - 3t$$
$$z = 3, \quad t \in \mathbf{R}$$

We can eliminate the parameter, t, from the first two equations and leave the third equation alone, so that the equations of the line become

$$\frac{x - 1}{1} = \frac{y - 2}{-3}, \quad z = 3$$

Check. The points $A(1, 2, 3)$ and $B(2, -1, 3)$ lie on this line since $\frac{1-1}{1} = \frac{2-2}{-3}$, $3 = 3$, and $\frac{2-1}{1} = \frac{-1-2}{-3}$, $3 = 3$.

b. The direction cosines of the line are the direction cosines of the direction vector $\vec{AB} = (1, -3, 0)$. This vector has length $\sqrt{1^2 + (-3)^2} = \sqrt{10}$. Hence, a unit vector in the direction of the line is $\left(\frac{1}{\sqrt{10}}, \frac{-3}{\sqrt{10}}, 0\right)$ and its direction cosines are

$$\cos \alpha = \frac{1}{\sqrt{10}}, \quad \cos \beta = \frac{-3}{\sqrt{10}}, \quad \cos \gamma = 0$$

The direction angles are

$$\alpha = \cos^{-1}\left(\frac{1}{\sqrt{10}}\right) \approx 72°$$
$$\beta = \cos^{-1}\left(\frac{-3}{\sqrt{10}}\right) \approx 162°$$
$$\gamma = \cos^{-1}(0) = 90°$$

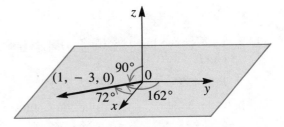

The unit vector in the opposite direction, $\left(\frac{-1}{\sqrt{10}}, \frac{3}{\sqrt{10}}, 0\right)$, could also be used to find the direction cosines and angles.

Example 4. Do the equations $\ell_1: \frac{x-5}{2} = \frac{y+4}{3} = \frac{z+1}{-5}$ and $\ell_2: \frac{x+1}{-4} = \frac{y-1}{-6} = \frac{z+3}{10}$ represent the same line?

Solution. The line ℓ_1 passes through $(5, -4, -1)$ with direction vector $(2, 3, -5)$, and ℓ_2 passes through $(-1, 1, -3)$ with direction vector $(-4, -6, 10)$. Since $(-4, -6, 10) = -2(2, 3, -5)$, the lines are parallel. They represent the same line if all points on one line also lie on the other line. The point $(5, -4, -1)$ does not lie on ℓ_2 since

$$\frac{5 + 1}{-4} \neq \frac{-4 - 1}{-6}$$

Hence, the lines are parallel and distinct.

Example 5. Find vector, parametric, and symmetric equations of the y-axis in 3-space.

Solution. Since the y-axis is the line through the origin $O(0, 0, 0)$ in the direction $\vec{j} = (0, 1, 0)$, the vector equation is $\vec{r} = t\vec{j}$, $t \in \mathbf{R}$. The parametric equations are

$$
\begin{array}{lcl}
x = 0 + 0t & & x = 0 \\
y = 0 + 1t & \text{or} & y = t \\
z = 0 + 0t, \quad t \in \mathbf{R} & & z = 0, \quad t \in \mathbf{R}
\end{array}
$$

Since two of the direction numbers are zero, the y-axis does not have symmetric equations. However, we can write its equations as

$$x = 0, \quad z = 0$$

Since the equations are in 3-space and no y term appears, the value of y can be arbitrary; that is, y is any real number. □

Exercises 3.3

1. Find vector, parametric, and, if possible, symmetric equations of the line that passes through P_1 and has direction vector $\vec{m}$. In each case find two points on the line that are different from P_1.

   a. $P_1(2, 4, 6), \vec{m} = (-1, -3, 2)$ **b.** $P_1(0, 1, 0), \vec{m} = (1, 0, 0)$

   c. $P_1\left(\frac{1}{2}, \frac{1}{3}, 0\right), \vec{m} = (2, 0, 1)$ **d.** $P_1(0, 0, 0), \vec{m} = (1, -1, 1)$

2. **a.** Let ℓ be the line $\vec{r} = (0, 3, 1) + t(2, 1, 1)$, $t \in \mathbf{R}$. Which of the following points lie on ℓ?

   $P(2, 4, 2)$ $Q(-2, 2, 1)$ $R(4, 5, 2)$ $S(6, 6, 4)$

   b. If the point $(a, -1, -3)$ lies on ℓ, find the value of a.

3. Find vector, parametric, and, if possible, symmetric equations of the line that passes

   a. through the point $(1, -1, 1)$ and is parallel to the vector $(3, 1, 7)$.

   b. through the point $\left(6, 0, -\frac{1}{2}\right)$ and is parallel to the z-axis.

   c. through the point $(5, 5, -4)$ and is parallel to the line
   $$\vec{r} = (4, 0, 1) + t(5, 2, 0), t \in \mathbf{R}$$

   d. through the points $(-3, 4, 0)$ and $(2, 1, -8)$. ✳ ask if this is the same
                                                                              see notes.

   e. through the points $(1, 1, -2)$ and $(0, 1, -2)$.

4. Find a vector equation of the line that passes through the point $(0, -1, 1)$ and the midpoint of the line segment from $(2, 3, -2)$ to $(4, -1, 5)$.

5. Let ℓ be the line that passes through the points $(4, 3, 1)$ and $(-2, -4, 3)$. Find a vector equation of the line that passes through the origin and is parallel to ℓ.

6. Show that the lines $\frac{x+5}{2} = \frac{y-3}{-4} = \frac{z}{8}$ and $\frac{x+7}{-1} = \frac{y-1}{2} = \frac{z+4}{-4}$ are parallel.

7. Describe in words the lines having these parametric equations and sketch the lines.

   a. $x = 1, y = 2, z = t, t \in R$

   b. $x = 2 + t, y = 4 + 7t, z = 5, t \in R$

   c. $x = -3 + 2t, y = 0, z = 5 + 2t, t \in R$

8. **a.** Show that the lines with equations $\vec{r} = (1, 0, 3) + t(1, -2, 1)$ and $\vec{r} = (2, -2, 5) + s(2, -4, 2)$ are parallel and distinct. *parallel, but not on top of each other?*

   b. Show that the equations $\vec{r} = (1, -1, 1) + t(6, 2, 0)$ and $\vec{r} = (-5, -3, 1) + s(-3, -1, 0)$ represent the same line.

9. Find the direction cosines and direction angles of the line $\vec{r} = t\vec{i} + (3 - \sqrt{3}t)\vec{j} + 5\vec{k}$, $t \in R$.

10. Consider the line defined by the equations $x = 2 - 3t, y = 12t, z = \frac{1}{2} + 4t$.

    a. State a vector equation of the line.

    b. State a set of direction numbers of the line.

    c. Determine the direction angles of the line to the nearest degree.

    d. Find the values of a and b if $(7, a, b)$ lies on the line.

Problems 3.3

1. Find values of k so that the lines

$$\frac{x-1}{k} = \frac{y+2}{3} = \frac{z}{2} \quad \text{and} \quad \frac{x+2}{k} = \frac{y+7}{k-2} = z - 5$$

   are perpendicular.

2. Find symmetric equations of the line that is perpendicular to the lines

$$\frac{x}{-4} = \frac{y+10}{-7} = \frac{z+2}{3} \quad \text{and} \quad \frac{x-5}{3} = \frac{y-5}{2} = \frac{z+5}{4}$$

   and passes through the point $(2, -5, 0)$.

3. **a.** Show that the points $A(-9, -3, -16)$ and $B(6, 2, 14)$ lie on the line that passes through $(0, 0, 2)$ and has direction vector $(3, 1, 6)$.

   b. Use parametric equations with suitable restrictions on the parameter to describe the line segment from A to B.

4. Let $\vec{r} = (1, 2, -3) + t(1, -1, 1)$ and $\vec{r} = (5, -2, -3) + s(2, -2, -2)$ be two lines in 3-space. Show that the lines intersect, and find values of the parameters s and t that produce the point of intersection.

5. Let $\ell_1: x = -8 + t, y = -3 - 2t, z = 8 + 3t$ and $\ell_2: \dfrac{x-1}{2} = \dfrac{y+1}{1} = \dfrac{z}{3}$

be two lines in 3-space.

a. Show that ℓ_1 and ℓ_2 are skew lines (that is, neither parallel nor intersecting).

b. Find a point P_1 on ℓ_1 and a point P_2 on ℓ_2 so that $\overrightarrow{P_1 P_2}$ is perpendicular to both ℓ_1 and ℓ_2.

3.4 Vector and Parametric Equations of a Plane in 3-space

In this section and the next, we shall develop different forms of the equation of a plane in 3-space. There are many different ways to describe a plane. For example, three non-collinear points determine a plane, or one point in the plane and two non-parallel vectors lying in the plane also determine the plane. The latter description will be used in this section to form the vector and parametric equations of a plane. However, the most compact way to describe a plane, and the one that leads to the simplest equation, is the generalization of the Cartesian equation of a line in 2-space. In the next section the Cartesian equation of a plane will be derived by using one point in the plane and a normal vector to the plane.

A plane in 3-space can be described by means of parametric equations in a way that is analogous to the parametric equations of a line; however a plane requires two parameters, and for this reason we say that a plane is "two-dimensional".

Three non-collinear points, A, B, and P_1, determine a plane π_1. Let $\vec{a} = \overrightarrow{P_1 A}$ and $\vec{b} = \overrightarrow{P_1 B}$. The plane is also determined by one point, P_1, and two non-parallel direction vectors, $\vec{a}$ and $\vec{b}$, lying in it.

A point P lies in the plane π_1 if and only if the vector $\overrightarrow{P_1 P}$ is parallel to the plane, that is, if and only if $\overrightarrow{P_1 P}$ is a linear combination of the vectors $\vec{a}$ and $\vec{b}$. (See Theorem 1 of section 2.4.) Hence,

$$\overrightarrow{P_1 P} = s\vec{a} + t\vec{b}, \quad \text{for some} \quad s, t \in \mathbf{R}$$

By the Triangle Law of Addition,

$$\overrightarrow{OP} = \overrightarrow{OP_1} + \overrightarrow{P_1 P}$$
$$= \overrightarrow{OP_1} + s\vec{a} + t\vec{b}$$

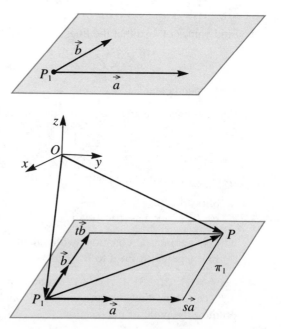

If we set $\overrightarrow{OP} = \vec{r}$ and $\overrightarrow{OP_1} = \vec{r_1}$, we obtain the following description of the plane.

The **Vector Equation of the Plane** containing the non-parallel vectors $\vec{a}$ and $\vec{b}$ and the point with position vector $\vec{r_1}$ is of the form

$$\vec{r} = \vec{r_1} + s\vec{a} + t\vec{b}, \quad \text{where } s, t \in \mathbf{R}$$

The real numbers s and t are the two parameters for this description of the plane. A pair of numbers s and t produce a unique point on the plane, and conversely each point determines a unique pair of parameters.

If we replace the vectors by their components, $\vec{r} = (x, y, z)$, $\vec{r_1} = (x_1, y_1, z_1)$, $\vec{a} = (a_1, a_2, a_3)$, and $\vec{b} = (b_1, b_2, b_3)$, we obtain

$$(x, y, z) = (x_1, y_1, z_1) + s(a_1, a_2, a_3) + t(b_1, b_2, b_3)$$
$$= (x_1 + sa_1 + tb_1, y_1 + sa_2 + tb_2, z_1 + sa_3 + tb_3)$$

Equating components, we obtain the following description of a plane.

The **Parametric Equations of the Plane** containing the non-parallel vectors (a_1, a_2, a_3) and (b_1, b_2, b_3) and the point (x_1, y_1, z_1) are of the form

$$x = x_1 + sa_1 + tb_1$$
$$y = y_1 + sa_2 + tb_2$$
$$z = z_1 + sa_3 + tb_3, \quad \text{where } s, t \in \mathbf{R}$$

Example 1. Find vector and parametric equations of the plane containing the points $A(1, 0, -3)$, $B(2, -3, 1)$, and $C(3, 5, -3)$. Does the point $Q(5, 7, 1)$ lie on the plane?

Solution. Two vectors in the plane are
$$\vec{a} = \overrightarrow{AB} = (2, -3, 1) - (1, 0, -3) = (1, -3, 4)$$
and
$$\vec{b} = \overrightarrow{AC} = (3, 5, -3) - (1, 0, -3) = (2, 5, 0)$$

If the vector $\overrightarrow{OA}$ is used for $\vec{r_1}$, a vector equation of the plane is

$$\vec{r} = (1, 0, -3) + s(1, -3, 4) + t(2, 5, 0), \quad s, t \in \mathbf{R}$$

The corresponding parametric equations of the plane are

$$x = 1 + s + 2t$$
$$y = -3s + 5t$$
$$z = -3 + 4s, \quad s, t \in \mathbf{R}$$

The point $Q(5, 7, 1)$ lies on the plane if there are values of s and t such that the following equations are simultaneously satisfied.

$$5 = 1 + s + 2t \tag{1}$$
$$7 = -3s + 5t \tag{2}$$
$$1 = -3 + 4s \tag{3}$$

From equation (3), $s = 1$. Substituting this in equation (2) gives $7 = -3 + 5t$ and so $t = 2$. Substituting $s = 1$ and $t = 2$ in the right side of equation (1) gives $1 + 1 + 2(2) = 6$, which is not equal to the left side. Therefore, there are no values of s and t satisfying all the equations and Q does not lie on the plane.   □

The vector and parametric equations of a plane are by no means unique. Any point could be chosen on the plane, and any two non-parallel vectors could be chosen in the plane. In Example 1, $\vec{a} + \vec{b} = (3, 2, 4)$ and $2\vec{a} - \vec{b} = (0, -11, 8)$ are two vectors in the plane, and $B(2, -3, 1)$ is a point in the plane. Hence, another vector equation representing the plane is

$$\vec{r} = (2, -3, 1) + u(3, 2, 4) + v(0, -11, 8), \quad u, v \in \mathbf{R}$$

Example 2. If π_1 is a plane with parametric equations

$$x = 7 + 3s + 2t$$
$$y = 1 - s - t$$
$$z = 2 + s - 3t, \quad \text{where } s, t \in \mathbf{R}$$

find a vector equation of the plane that is parallel to π_1 and contains the point $(1, 2, 3)$.

Solution. Since the required plane and the given plane π_1 are parallel, they will be parallel to the same vectors $\vec{a} = (3, -1, 1)$ and $\vec{b} = (2, -1, -3)$. Therefore, the vector equation of the required plane containing the point $(1, 2, 3)$ is

$$\vec{r} = (1, 2, 3) + s(3, -1, 1) + t(2, -1, -3), \quad \text{where } s, t \in \mathbf{R} \qquad □$$

A pair of distinct parallel lines determines a unique plane, as the next example shows.

Example 3. Consider the lines $\ell_1: \vec{r} = (2, 4, 1) + t(3, -1, 1)$ and $\ell_2: \vec{r} = (1, 4, 4) + s(-6, 2, -2)$.

a. Show that the lines are parallel and distinct.

b. Find a vector equation of the plane containing the lines.

Solution.
a. A direction vector of ℓ_1 is $\vec{u} = (3, -1, 1)$, and a direction vector of ℓ_2 is $\vec{v} = (-6, 2, -2)$. Since $\vec{v} = -2\vec{u}$, $\vec{v}$ is parallel to $\vec{u}$ and the lines are parallel. A point on ℓ_1 is $A_1(2, 4, 1)$. Substituting this in the equation for ℓ_2 gives $(2, 4, 1) = (1, 4, 4) + s(-6, 2, -2)$, which yields $(1, 0, -3) = s(-6, 2, -2)$. Equating components gives $s = -\frac{1}{6}$, $s = 0$, and $s = \frac{3}{2}$. Hence, there is no single value of s for which the vector equation is satisfied. Therefore, $A_1(2, 4, 1)$ does not lie on ℓ_2 and the lines are distinct.

b. The vector equation of the plane is $\vec{r} = \vec{r_1} + s\vec{a} + t\vec{b}$. We can choose $\vec{r_1} = (2, 4, 1)$ and $\vec{a} = (3, -1, 1)$, where $A_1(2, 4, 1)$ lies on ℓ_1 and $\vec{a}$ is the direction vector of ℓ_1. However, we cannot choose $\vec{b}$ to be the direction vector of ℓ_2 since it is parallel to $\vec{a}$. Therefore, let $\vec{b} = \overrightarrow{A_1A_2}$, where $A_1(2, 4, 1)$ lies on ℓ_1 and $A_2(1, 4, 4)$ lies on ℓ_2. Then $\vec{b} = (-1, 0, 3)$, and a vector equation of the plane is

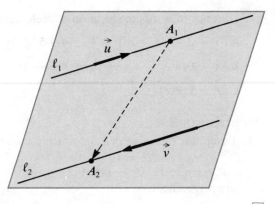

$$\vec{r} = (2, 4, 1) + s(3, -1, 1) + t(-1, 0, 3), \quad \text{where } s, t \in \mathbf{R}. \qquad \square$$

Exercises 3.4

1. Find vector and parametric equations of each plane described below. In parts a, b, and c, find three points on each plane.

   a. the plane passing through the point $(2, 1, 5)$ and parallel to the vectors $(0, 1, 7)$ and $(5, -2, 1)$

   b. the plane passing through the origin and containing the vectors $(1, 1, 1)$ and $(-1, 1, 1)$

   c. the plane passing through the points $(0, 1, -2)$ and $(-3, -4, 5)$ and containing the vector $(-3, 0, 1)$

   d. the plane passing through the points $(1, 0, 1)$, $(2, 2, 1)$ and $(2, 1, 0)$

2. Find a vector equation of the plane that contains the point $(5, 4, 3)$ and is parallel to the yz-plane. $\vec{a} = (0, 1, 0) \quad \vec{b} = (0, 0, 1)$

3. Find parametric equations of the plane that contains the point $(5, -1, 7)$ and the line $\vec{r} = (2, 1, 9) + t(1, 0, 2), t \in \mathbf{R}$.

4. Find vector and parametric equations of the plane that contains the line $x = 7 - t$, $y = -2t, z = -7 + t$ and that does not intersect the z-axis.

5. Determine which of the following points lie on the plane

   $$\vec{r} = (1, 0, 5) + s(3, -1, 0) + t(0, 4, -3), \quad s, t \in \mathbf{R}.$$

   a. $(4, -1, 5)$ **b.** $(-1, 5, 7)$ **c.** $(3, 7, -5)$

6. Determine whether the pairs of planes are parallel. $\vec{m} = k\vec{m_1}$

   a. $\vec{r} = (6, 0, 1) + s(1, 1, 2) + t(4, 2, 3)$ and
   $\vec{r} = (1, 1, -9) + u(5, 3, 5) + v(3, 1, 1)$

   b. $\vec{r} = (1, 1, 1) + s(0, 0, 1) + t(0, 1, 0)$ and
   $\vec{r} = (0, 0, 0) + u(0, 0, 1) + v(1, 0, 0)$

7. Describe in words the location of each plane. 3.6

    ➙ Don't do this.

  a. $x = 3 + 3s - t, y = 4, z = -5 + 2s - t$

  b. $x = 0, y = 2 + s + 5t, z = 3 - 2s + t$

  c. $\vec{r} = \vec{i} + s\vec{j} + t\vec{k}$

Problems 3.4

1. Determine the value of k for which the planes
$$\vec{r} = (1, 2, 7) + s(4, 2, 0) + t(k, 1, 2), \quad s, t \in \mathbf{R}$$
and $\vec{r} = (3, 0, -5) + u(1, 0, 5) + v(0, 1, -1), \quad u, v \in \mathbf{R}$
are perpendicular.

2. a. If $\vec{a}, \vec{b}$, and $\vec{c}$ are the position vectors of three non-collinear points, show that a vector equation of the plane determined by these three points is

$$\vec{r} = (1 - s - t)\vec{a} + s\vec{b} + t\vec{c}, \quad s, t \in \mathbf{R}$$

  b. What region of the plane is determined by the equation if $0 \le s \le 1$ and $0 \le t \le 1$?

3.5 The Cartesian Equation of a Plane in 3-space

In section 3.2, we developed the Cartesian equation of a line in 2-space by specifying one point and a normal vector. In a similar way the Cartesian equation of a plane in 3-space will be derived by specifying one point in the plane and a vector that is perpendicular to every vector in the plane. This non-zero perpendicular vector is called a **normal vector** to the plane.

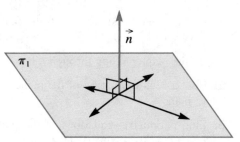

Let π_1 be a plane containing the point $P_1(x_1, y_1, z_1)$, and let $\vec{n} = (A, B, C)$ be a normal vector to π_1. The point $P(x, y, z)$ lies in the plane if and only if P_1P lies in the plane, that is, if and only if $\vec{n}$ is perpendicular to $\overrightarrow{P_1P}$. This happens when $\vec{n} \cdot \overrightarrow{P_1P} = 0$.

If P and P_1 have position vectors $\vec{r}$ and $\vec{r}_1$, respectively, then

$$\vec{n} \cdot (\vec{r} - \vec{r}_1) = 0$$

Substituting components gives

$$(A, B, C) \cdot (x - x_1, y - y_1, z - z_1) = 0$$
$$A(x - x_1) + B(y - y_1) + C(z - z_1) = 0$$
$$Ax + By + Cz + (-Ax_1 - By_1 - Cz_1) = 0$$

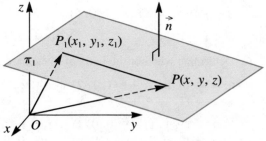

If we denote the constant $(-Ax_1 - By_1 - Cz_1)$ by D, we obtain the following equation of the plane.

The **Cartesian or Scalar Equation of the Plane** in 3-space with normal (A, B, C) is of the form

$$Ax + By + Cz + D = 0$$

Note that this is a first-degree equation and that the coefficients of x, y, and z are the components of a normal vector to the plane.

The Cartesian equation of a plane in 3-space is used most often in practice because it has a simpler form than either the vector or the parametric equations of a plane.

Example 1. Find a Cartesian equation of the plane that passes through the point $(-3, 1, -7)$ and has normal vector $(2, 4, -5)$.

Solution 1. The equation is of the form $\vec{n} \cdot (\vec{r} - \vec{r}_1) = 0$. If $\vec{n} = (2, 4, -5)$, $\vec{r} = (x, y, z)$, and $\vec{r}_1 = (-3, 1, -7)$, then

$$(2, 4, -5) \cdot (x + 3, y - 1, z + 7) = 0$$
$$2(x + 3) + 4(y - 1) - 5(z + 7) = 0$$

Hence, the Cartesian equation of the plane is

$$2x + 4y - 5z - 33 = 0$$

Solution 2. Since $(2, 4, -5)$ is a normal vector, the equation of the plane has the form $2x + 4y - 5z + D = 0$. Since $(-3, 1, -7)$ lies on the plane, it must satisfy this equation. Therefore,

$$2(-3) + 4(1) - 5(-7) + D = 0$$

Hence, $D = -33$, and the equation is $2x + 4y - 5z - 33 = 0$. ☐

Example 2. Find the Cartesian equations of the three coordinate planes.

Solution. The xy-plane contains the origin, and any vector along the z-axis, say $\vec{k} = (0, 0, 1)$, is a normal. Therefore, the equation of the xy-plane is

$$(0, 0, 1) \cdot (x - 0, y - 0, z - 0) = 0$$

or $\qquad z = 0$.

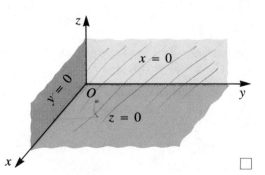

Similarly the equation of the yz-plane is $x = 0$ and the equation of the xz-plane is $y = 0$. ☐

We can find the Cartesian equation of a plane π_1 that passes through three given non-collinear points by determining a normal vector to the plane.

If A, B, and C are non-collinear points on π_1, then the vector $\overrightarrow{AB} \times \overrightarrow{AC}$ is non-zero and is perpendicular to both $\overrightarrow{AB}$ and $\overrightarrow{AC}$. Therefore, $\overrightarrow{AB} \times \overrightarrow{AC}$ is a normal vector to the plane, and it can be used with any one of the points A, B, or C to determine the equation of the plane π_1.

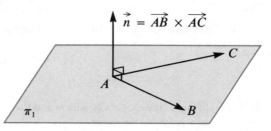

Example 3. Find a Cartesian equation of the plane containing the points $A(2, 4, -1)$, $B(3, 0, 2)$, and $C(-1, -2, 5)$.

Solution.

$$\overrightarrow{AB} = (3, 0, 2) - (2, 4, -1)$$
$$= (1, -4, 3)$$

$$\overrightarrow{AC} = (-1, -2, 5) - (2, 4, -1)$$
$$= (-3, -6, 6)$$

A normal to the plane is

$$\vec{n} = \overrightarrow{AB} \times \overrightarrow{AC}$$
$$= (1, -4, 3) \times (-3, -6, 6)$$
$$= (-4(6) - 3(-6), 3(-3) - 1(6), 1(-6) - (-4)(-3))$$
$$= (-6, -15, -18)$$

Since any scalar multiple of a normal can be used, we take $-\frac{1}{3}(-6, -15, -18) = (2, 5, 6)$ as a normal, so that an equation of the plane is

$$(2, 5, 6) \cdot (x - 2, y - 4, z + 1) = 0$$
$$2(x - 2) + 5(y - 4) + 6(z + 1) = 0$$

Hence, an equation of the plane is $2x + 5y + 6z - 18 = 0$.

Check. The points A, B, and C satisfy the equation since $2(2) + 5(4) + 6(-1) - 18 = 0$, $2(3) + 5(0) + 6(2) - 18 = 0$, and $2(-1) + 5(-2) + 6(5) - 18 = 0$. $\qquad\square$

Example 4. Find the equation of the plane containing the point $Q(2, 2, 5)$ and the line $\vec{r} = (1, 0, -3) + t(3, -4, 7)$.

Solution. Since the point $P(1, 0, -3)$ lies in the plane, $\overrightarrow{PQ}$ is a vector in the plane, where

$$\overrightarrow{PQ} = (2, 2, 5) - (1, 0, -3)$$
$$= (1, 2, 8)$$

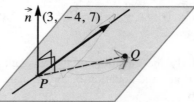

The direction vector, $(3, -4, 7)$, for the line also lies in the plane, and therefore a normal to the plane is

$$\vec{n} = (1, 2, 8) \times (3, -4, 7)$$
$$= (2(7) - 8(-4), 8(3) - 1(7), 1(-4) - 2(3))$$
$$= (46, 17, -10)$$

Hence, the plane has an equation of the form $46x + 17y - 10z + D = 0$. Since $Q(2, 2, 5)$ lies on the plane, $46(2) + 17(2) - 10(5) + D = 0$ and $D = -76$. Therefore, an equation of the plane is $46x + 17y - 10z - 76 = 0$.

Check. Any point on the line is of the form $(1 + 3t, -4t, -3 + 7t)$, and on substituting this into the equation of the plane, we obtain

$$46x + 17y - 10z - 76 = 46(1 + 3t) + 17(-4t) - 10(-3 + 7t) - 76$$
$$= 46 + 138t - 68t + 30 - 70t - 76$$
$$= 0$$

Since the equation is satisfied for all t, the line lies in the plane. □

Two planes are parallel if and only if their normal vectors are parallel, and two planes are perpendicular if and only if their normal vectors are perpendicular. Similarly, a line and a plane are parallel if and only if the direction vector of the line and the normal vector of the plane are perpendicular. A line and a plane are perpendicular if and only if the direction vector of the line and the normal vector of the plane are parallel.

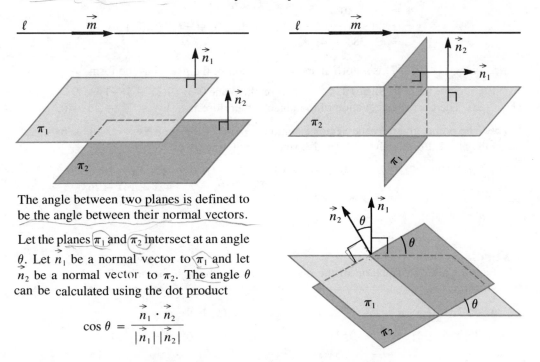

The angle between two planes is defined to be the angle between their normal vectors.

Let the planes π_1 and π_2 intersect at an angle θ. Let $\vec{n}_1$ be a normal vector to π_1 and let $\vec{n}_2$ be a normal vector to π_2. The angle θ can be calculated using the dot product

$$\cos \theta = \frac{\vec{n}_1 \cdot \vec{n}_2}{|\vec{n}_1| |\vec{n}_2|}$$

Example 5. Find the angle between the planes $x - z + 7 = 0$ and $2x + y - z + 8 = 0$.

Solution. Normal vectors to the planes are $(1, 0, -1)$ and $(2, 1, -1)$. If θ is the required angle, then

$$
\begin{aligned}
\cos \theta &= \frac{(1, 0, -1) \cdot (2, 1, -1)}{|(1, 0, -1)||(2, 1, -1)|} \\
&= \frac{2 + 1}{\sqrt{2}\sqrt{6}} \\
&= \frac{3}{\sqrt{12}} \\
&= \frac{\sqrt{3}}{2}
\end{aligned}
$$

Therefore, the angle between the planes is $30°$ (or $\frac{\pi}{6}$ radians).   □

Example 6. Find a Cartesian equation of the plane described by the vector equation

$$\vec{r} = (0, 1, -1) + s(4, 2, 6) + t(5, -1, -2), \quad \text{where } s, t \in R$$

Solution. Since $(4, 2, 6)$ and $(5, -1, -2)$ are non-parallel vectors lying in the plane, a normal to the plane is

$$
\begin{aligned}
\vec{n} &= (4, 2, 6) \times (5, -1, -2) \\
&= (2(-2) - 6(-1), 6(5) - 4(-2), 4(-1) - 2(5)) \\
&= (2, 38, -14)
\end{aligned}
$$

Hence, $\frac{1}{2}\vec{n} = (1, 19, -7)$ is a normal and the equation of the plane has the form

$x + 19y - 7z + D = 0$. Since $(0, 1, -1)$ lies on the plane $0 + 19(1) - 7(-1) + D = 0$, and $D = -26$. The Cartesian equation of the plane is therefore $x + 19y - 7z - 26 = 0$.

Check. The points given by the vector equation $\vec{r} = (4s + 5t, 1 + 2s - t, -1 + 6s - 2t)$ lie on the plane, for all values of s and t, since substituting gives

$$
\begin{aligned}
x + 19y - 7z - 26 &= (4s + 5t) + 19(1 + 2s - t) - 7(-1 + 6s - 2t) - 26 \\
&= 4s + 5t + 19 + 38s - 19t + 7 - 42s + 14t - 26 \\
&= 0
\end{aligned}
$$
                                                                                                     □

Exercises 3.5

1. Find a Cartesian equation of the plane that passes through the point P_1 and has normal vector $\vec{n}$.

    a. $P_1(2, 1, -3), \vec{n} = (7, 1, -1)$ **b.** $P_1(5, 1, 9), \vec{n} = \vec{i}$

    c. $P_1(0, 6, -2), \vec{n} = (2, 0, 3)$ **d.** $P_1(0, 0, 0), \vec{n} = (2, -1, 4)$

2. Determine a Cartesian equation of the plane that passes through $(1, 2, -3)$ such that its normal

   a. is parallel to the normal of the plane $x - y - 2z + 19 = 0$.

   b. is in the direction of the z-axis.

   c. makes equal angles with the three positive coordinate axes.

3. Determine whether the pairs of planes are parallel and distinct, coincident, perpendicular, or none of these.

   a. $x + y - z - 4 = 0$ and $2x + 2y - 2z - 8 = 0$

   b. $2x - y + z - 3 = 0$ and $x + y - z = 0$

   c. $2x - y + z - 3 = 0$ and $x + y + z = 0$

   d. $2x - 2y - 2z + 6 = 0$ and $3x - 3y - 3z - 9 = 0$

4. Find a Cartesian equation of the plane that passes through the given points.

   a. $(1, 1, -1), (1, 2, 3), (3, -1, 2)$

   b. $(2, -2, 4), (1, 1, -4), (3, 1, -6)$

   c. $(1, 1, 1), (-1, 1, 1), (2, 1, 2)$

5. Find a Cartesian equation of the plane containing the y-axis and the point $(4, 2, 1)$.

6. Find a Cartesian equation of the plane containing the intersecting lines

$$\frac{x - 2}{1} = \frac{y}{2} = \frac{z + 3}{3} \quad \text{and} \quad \frac{x - 2}{-3} = \frac{y}{4} = \frac{z + 3}{2}.$$

7. Find parametric equations for the plane $2x - y + 3z - 24 = 0$.

8. Find a Cartesian equation of the plane that has vector equation
$\vec{r} = (2, 1, 0) + s(1, -1, 3) + t(2, 0, -5), \quad s, t \in \mathbf{R}$.

9. If the positive z-axis points up, show that the line $x = 0, y = t, z = 2t, \quad t \in \mathbf{R}$

   a. is parallel to and below the plane $2x - 10y + 5z = 1$.

   b. is parallel to and above the plane $x + 4y - 2z = 7$.

10. Which line is parallel to the plane $4x + y - z = 10$? Do any of the lines lie in the plane?

   a. $\vec{r} = (3, 0, 2) + t(1, -2, 2), \quad t \in \mathbf{R}$

   b. $x = -3t, y = -5 + 2t, z = -10t, \quad t \in \mathbf{R}$

   c. $\frac{x - 1}{4} = \frac{y + 6}{-1} = \frac{z}{1}$

11. Find the angle θ ($0° \le \theta \le 90°$), to the nearest degree, between the given planes.

    a. $x + 2y - 3z - 4 = 0$, $x - 3y + 5z + 7 = 0$

    b. $2x + 3y - z + 9 = 0$, $x + 2y + 4 = 0$

    c. $x - y - z - 1 = 0$, $2x + 3y - z + 4 = 0$

12. Find a Cartesian equation of the plane that contains the line
$\vec{r} = (2, 6, -1) + t(3, 0, -1)$, $t \in R$, and is parallel to the line
$\vec{r} = (1, 7, 7) + t(2, 1, -1)$, $t \in R$.

13. Find a Cartesian equation of the plane that contains the point $(-1, 5, 6)$, has a y-intercept of 6, and is perpendicular to the plane $2x + 3y - z = 13$.

14. **a.** Find an equation for the set of points $P(x, y, z)$ that are equidistant from both $P_1(1, 2, -3)$ and $P_2(4, 0, 1)$.

    b. What does this equation represent geometrically?

15. Show that every linear equation of the form $Ax + By + Cz + D = 0$, where not all of A, B, and C are zero, represents a plane in 3-space that has normal vector (A, B, C).

Problems 3.5

1. Show that the equation of the plane that has an x-intercept of a, a y-intercept of b, and a z-intercept of c, none of which is zero, is

$$\frac{x}{a} + \frac{y}{b} + \frac{z}{c} = 1$$

2. a. Suppose that a line ℓ intersects a plane at a point A. The angle between the line and the plane is defined to be the smallest angle between ℓ and a line in the plane that passes through A. If the line ℓ has direction vector $\vec{m}$ and a normal to the plane is $\vec{n}$, show that

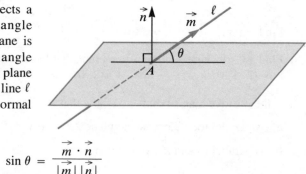

$$\sin \theta = \frac{\vec{m} \cdot \vec{n}}{|\vec{m}||\vec{n}|}$$

    b. Find the angle, to the nearest degree, between the plane $3x + y - z + 5 = 0$, and the line $\vec{r} = (-1, 0, -6) + t(3, 4, -4)$, $t \in R$.

3. Determine the Cartesian equation of a plane containing the points $P(5, 0, 0)$, $Q(0, 3, 0)$, and $R(15, -6, 0)$. Why are there infinitely many such planes?

4. The point-normal equation, $\vec{n} \cdot (\vec{r} - \vec{r}_1) = 0$, in 2-space represents a line having normal $\vec{n}$ and passing through the point with position vector $\vec{r}_1$. In 3-space, it is the equation of a plane having normal $\vec{n}$ and passing through the point with position vector $\vec{r}_1$. In higher-dimensional space, $\mathbf{R}^n$, where $n > 3$, the equation represents a "hyperplane" of dimension $n - 1$ having normal $\vec{n}$ and passing through the point with position vector $\vec{r}_1$.

   a. Find the equation of the hyperplane in $\mathbf{R}^4$ that contains the point $(2, 7, 3, 0)$ and has normal $(-1, 3, 4, 5)$.

   b. Find the equation of the hyperplane in $\mathbf{R}^4$ that passes through the point $(4, 1, 2, -3)$ and is perpendicular to the line $\vec{r} = (1, -1, -1, 1) + t(3, 1, 2, 2)$, $t \in \mathbf{R}$.

   c. Express the Cartesian equation $2x_1 + 3x_2 - 4x_3 - 2x_4 + 6x_5 - 9 = 0$ in point-normal form for a hyperplane in $\mathbf{R}^5$.

3.6 Sketching Planes in 3-space

In this section we shall show how to sketch a plane in 3-space, given its Cartesian equation.

Consider the equation $x = 3$, which has a different geometrical interpretation depending on the dimension of the space in which it is considered to lie.

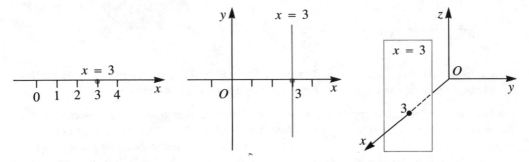

On the real-number line, $\mathbf{R}$, the equation $x = 3$ represents a point. In the plane, $\mathbf{R}^2$, the equation $x = 3$ represents a line consisting of all points of the form $(3, y)$, where y can take any real value. This is a line through $(3, 0)$ parallel to the y-axis. In 3-space, $\mathbf{R}^3$, the equation $x = 3$ is a plane parallel to, and at a distance of 3 units from, the yz-plane. All points on the plane $x = 3$ are of the form $(3, y, z)$, where y and z can take any real values. Since

$$(3, y, z) = (3, 0, 0) + y(0, 1, 0) + z(0, 0, 1)$$

the vector equation of the plane that passes through $(3, 0, 0)$ and is parallel to both the y-axis and z-axis is

$$\vec{r} = (3, 0, 0) + y(0, 1, 0) + z(0, 0, 1), \quad \text{where } y, z \in \mathbf{R}$$

Similarly, the equation $y = b$ in 3-space represents a plane through $(0, b, 0)$ parallel to the xz-plane and the equation $z = c$ in 3-space represents a plane through $(0, 0, c)$ parallel to the xy-plane.

Now consider the points common to the two planes $x = 3$ and $y = 4$ in 3-space. These points will be of the form $(3, 4, z)$, which can be written as $(3, 4, 0) + z(0, 0, 1)$. Therefore, the points form a line through $(3, 4, 0)$ in the direction of $\vec{k} = (0, 0, 1)$. Hence, the points satisfying both equations $x = 3$ and $y = 4$ lie on the intersection of the planes $x = 3$ and $y = 4$, which is the line that passes through $(3, 4, 0)$ and is parallel to the z-axis.

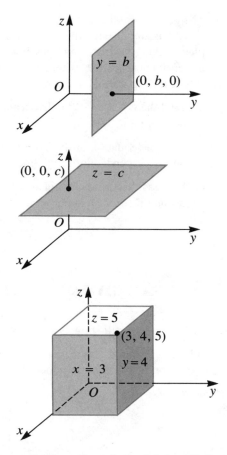

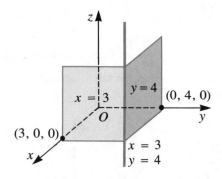

Now consider the three planes $x = 3$, $y = 4$, and $z = 5$. The only point satisfying all three equations is $(3, 4, 5)$, and this point is the intersection of the three planes.

Let us now investigate the general problem of sketching the graph of the linear equation $Ax + By + Cz + D = 0$ in 3-space, when not all of A, B, and C are zero. It is useful to examine the intersection of this plane with the coordinate axes and coordinate planes, and also to recall that (A, B, C) is a normal vector to the plane. Consider the following cases, which depend on how many of the coefficients A, B, C are zero.

Case I. Two of A, B, C are zero.

Equations of this type represent planes that are parallel to the coordinate planes and have been discussed above.

Case II. One of A, B, C is zero.

Equations of this type represent planes that are parallel to the axis corresponding to the coefficient that is zero, as Examples 1 and 2 show.

Example 1. Sketch the plane in 3-space that has equation $2y + 3z - 12 = 0$.

Solution. We can obtain the point of intersection of the plane with the y-axis
by substituting the equations of the y-axis,
$x = 0$, $z = 0$, into the equation of the
plane; hence the plane has a y-intercept of
6. Similarly, the plane has a z-intercept of
4. The x-axis has equation $y = 0$, $z = 0$,
and, substituting this into the left side of the
equation of the plane, we obtain -12,
which can never be zero. Hence, there is
no x-intercept and the plane is parallel to
the x-axis.

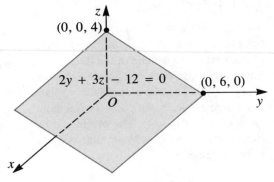

This is sufficient information to sketch the plane. Note that only a small section has been
sketched in the diagram. ☐

Example 2. Sketch the plane in 3-space that has equation $3x - y = 0$.

Solution. Since $D = 0$, the plane contains
the origin. The x-intercept is zero, and the
y-intercept is zero. All points of the form
$(0, 0, z)$ satisfy the equation $3x - y = 0$,
and therefore the plane contains the whole
z-axis. However, we need more information
to sketch the graph.

The plane intersects the xy-plane in the line $3x - y = 0$, $z = 0$. This line passes through the
origin and $(1, 3, 0)$. Using this information, we can complete the sketch. ☐

Case III. None of A, B, C, is zero.

If the plane does not pass through the origin, the three intercepts give three distinct non-
collinear points on the plane and therefore provide a convenient method of sketching the plane.

Example 3. Sketch the plane that has equation $3x - 2y + 5z - 10 = 0$.

Solution. The x-intercept is $\frac{10}{3}$, the y-inter-
cept is -5, and the z-intercept is 2. The
three points $\left(\frac{10}{3}, 0, 0\right)$, $(0, -5, 0)$, and
$(0, 0, 2)$ determine the plane. In the sketch,
the triangular region is part of the plane;
the edges of the triangle are the intersections
of the given plane with the coordinate
planes.

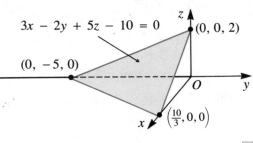

☐

Example 4. Sketch the plane determined by the equation
$16x + 4y - 3z = 0$.

Solution. Since the constant term is zero, the plane passes through the origin. The plane meets the xy-plane in the line $16x + 4y = 0$, $z = 0$; one point on this line is $(1, -4, 0)$. The plane meets the yz-plane in the line $4y - 3z = 0$, $x = 0$; one point on this line is $(0, 3, 4)$. The origin and the two points on the coordinate planes determine the plane. □

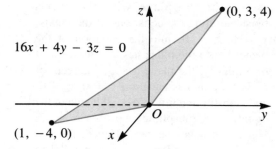

Exercises 3.6

1. Graph the points or lines in 3-space.

   a. $x = 1$, $y = 3$, $z = 4$ **b.** $x = 0$, $y = 5$, $z = -2$

   c. $x = 0$, $y = 0$, $z = 2$ **d.** $x = 1$, $y = 2$

   e. $x = 2$, $z = -3$ **f.** $y = 5$, $z = 0$

2. Sketch the planes in 3-space.

   a. $12x + 3y + 4z - 12 = 0$ **b.** $x - 2y - z - 5 = 0$

   c. $2x - y + z + 8 = 0$ **d.** $x + 3y - z = 0$

   e. $x + y - 4 = 0$ **f.** $x = 3$

   g. $2y + 1 = 0$ **h.** $3x + z - 6 = 0$

   i. $y = 2z$ **j.** $x + y = z$

3. a. Graph the plane $x + 2y + 3z - 16 = 0$, using intercepts with the coordinate axes.

   b. Plot the point $P_1(4, 3, 2)$ that lies on this plane, and graph the normal, $\vec{n} = (1, 2, 3)$, originating at P_1.

   c. Construct a vector in the plane from P_1 to the z-axis and verify algebraically that it is perpendicular to n.

essentially proves $\vec{m} \cdot \vec{n} = 0$

Problems 3.6

1. Graph the equations in 3-space and describe each graph in words.

   a. $x^2 - 4 = 0$ **b.** $xyz = 0$

   c. $z^2 - 3z - 4 = 0$ **d.** $(x - 3)^2 + (y + 4)^2 = 0$

   e. $xy - 3y = 0$ **f.** $x^2 - 2x - xy + 2y = 0$

Review Exercises

1. Find vector and parametric equations of the line

   a. that passes through the points $(1, 7)$ and $(-9, 3)$.

   b. that passes through the point $(-2, 0)$ and is parallel to the line
   $\vec{r} = (2, -4) + t(0, 5)$, $t \in \mathbf{R}$.

   c. that passes through the point $\left(\frac{1}{2}, 3\right)$ and is perpendicular to the line $\frac{x-2}{4} = \frac{y-3}{-1}$.

2. Find vector, parametric, and symmetric equations (if possible) of the line

   a. that passes through the point $(0, -1, 2)$ and is parallel to the line $x = 3 + 2t$, $y = 5t$, $z = -1 - t$, $t \in \mathbf{R}$.

   b. that passes through the point $(1, 2, -5)$ and is parallel to the y-axis.

   c. that passes through the points $(0, 0, 1)$ and $(1, 0, 0)$.

   d. that passes through the point $\left(\frac{3}{2}, 0, -2\right)$ and has direction vector $\left(\frac{2}{3}, -\frac{1}{3}, \frac{2}{3}\right)$.

3. Find vector and parametric equations of the plane

   a. that passes through the point $(-1, -1, 2)$ and is parallel to the plane
   $\vec{r} = (2, -1, 0) + s(5, 4, 2) + t(0, 0, 1)$, $s, t \in \mathbf{R}$.

   b. that passes through the points $(1, 1, 0)$ and $(-2, 0, 3)$ and is parallel to the y-axis.

   c. that has intercepts $x = -2$, $y = -3$, and $z = 4$.

   d. that contains the point $(1, 1, 1)$ and the line $\frac{x}{3} = \frac{y}{4} = \frac{z}{5}$.

   e. that contains the two intersecting lines $\vec{r} = (3, -1, 2) + t(4, 0, 1)$ and
   $\vec{r} = (3, -1, 2) + t(4, 0, 2)$.

4. Find a Cartesian equation for each line in the plane.

   a. the line that passes through the point $(-1, -2)$ and is parallel to the line
   $3x - 4y + 5 = 0$

   b. the line that passes through the point $(-7, 3)$ and is perpendicular to the line
   $x = 2 + t$, $y = -3 + 2t$, $t \in \mathbf{R}$

   c. the line that passes through the origin and is perpendicular to the line $x + 4y + 1 = 0$

5. Find a Cartesian equation for each plane in 3-space.

   a. the plane that passes through the point $(1, 7, 9)$ and has normal $\vec{n} = (1, 3, 5)$

   b. the plane that passes through the points $(3, 2, 3)$, $(-4, 1, 2)$, and $(-1, 3, 2)$

   c. the plane that passes through the point $(0, 0, 6)$ and is parallel to the plane $y + z = 5$

   d. the plane containing the point $(3, -3, 0)$ and the line $x = 2$, $y = 3 + t$, $z = -4 - 2t$, $t \in \mathbf{R}$

   e. the plane that contains the line $\vec{r} = (2, 1, 7) + t(0, 1, 0)$ and is parallel to the line $\vec{r} = (3, 0, 4) + t(2, -1, 0)$

   f. the plane that contains the points $(6, 1, 0)$ and $(3, 0, 2)$ and is parallel to the z-axis

6. a. Find the parametric equations of the line ℓ that passes through the point $A(6, 4, 0)$ and is parallel to the line passing through $B(-2, 0, 4)$ and $C(3, -2, 1)$.

   b. State the symmetric equations of ℓ.

   c. If $(-4, m, n)$ is a point on the line ℓ, find m and n.

7. Find a vector equation of the line that contains the point $(1, 2, 1)$ and is perpendicular to the plane determined by the points $(1, 3, -4)$, $(2, 1, 7)$, and $(0, 5, -2)$.

8. Determine if the pairs of lines are parallel and distinct, coincident, perpendicular, or none of these.

   a. $\vec{r} = (2, 3) + t(-3, 1)$ and $\vec{r} = (-1, 4) + s(6, -2)$

   b. $x = 1 + 2t$, $y = -3 - t$ and $x = s$, $y = \frac{1}{3} + 2s$

   c. $\dfrac{x - 1}{2} = \dfrac{y + 4}{1}$, $z = 1$ and $x = 4t$, $y = 1 + 2t$, $z = 6$

   d. $(x, y, z) = (1, 7, 2) + t(-1, -1, 1)$ and $(x, y, z) = (-3, 0, 1) + s(2, -2, -2)$

9. For what value of k, if any, will the planes $3x + ky + z - 6 = 0$ and $6x + (1 - k)y + 2z - 9 = 0$ be

   a. parallel?   **b.** perpendicular?

10. A line ℓ passes through the point $A(1, 4, 4)$ and is perpendicular to the plane $2x - 3z - 4 = 0$.

   a. Find a vector equation of ℓ.

   b. What point on the line has a z-coordinate of 0?

   c. Find the direction angles of ℓ, to the nearest degree.

11. Find a Cartesian equation of the plane that contains the parallel and distinct lines
$$x = 1, \frac{y - 3}{4} = \frac{z}{2} \text{ and } x = 5, \frac{y + 5}{2} = \frac{z - 3}{1}.$$

12. Where does the plane $4x + 5y - z + 20 = 0$ meet the coordinate axes?

13. Where does the line $\dfrac{x + 4}{2} = \dfrac{y - 6}{-1} = \dfrac{z + 2}{4}$ meet the coordinate planes?

14. **a.** Find a Cartesian equation in 2 space of the line $\vec{r} = (2, 3) + t(-1, 5)$, $t \in R$.

    b. Find a vector equation in 2-space of the line $5x - 2y + 10 = 0$.

    c. Find parametric equations of the plane $x - y + z - 9 = 0$ in 3-space.

    d. Find the Cartesian equation in 3-space of the plane $x = 2 + 3s + 4t$, $y = s - t$, $z = -4 - s - t$, $s, t \in R$.

15. Find the angle θ ($0° \le \theta \le 90°$), to the nearest degree, between

    a. the lines $\dfrac{x - 3}{5} = \dfrac{y + 6}{2}$ and $\dfrac{x - 3}{2} = \dfrac{y + 6}{5}$.

    b. the lines $x - 4y + 7 = 0$ and $4x + y + 9 = 0$.

    c. the planes $x - 2y - 5 = 0$ and $y + 3z = 0$.

    d. the planes $\vec{r} = (2, 1, 7) + s(1, 4, 3) + t(-1, 2, 0)$, $s, t \in R$ and $r = (-1, -1, 0) + u(3, 0, 1) + v(4, 4, 1)$, $u, v \in R$.

    e. the line $\dfrac{x}{4} = \dfrac{y - 3}{2} = \dfrac{z + 4}{1}$ and the plane $2x + 2y - 2z - 3 = 0$.

16. Find a vector equation of the plane that contains the origin and the point $(2, -3, 2)$ and is perpendicular to the plane $x + 2y - z + 3 = 0$.

17. Find a Cartesian equation of the plane that passes through the point $(1, 2, 3)$ and is parallel to the vectors $6\vec{k}$ and $\vec{i} + 2\vec{j} - 3\vec{k}$.

18. A line that passes through the origin is perpendicular to a plane π and intersects the plane at the point $(1, -3, 2)$. Find a Cartesian equation of the plane.

19. Find a Cartesian equation of the plane that contains the intersecting lines $\dfrac{x - 1}{2} = \dfrac{y - 1}{3} = \dfrac{z - 1}{-1}$ and $\dfrac{x - 1}{-1} = \dfrac{y - 1}{5} = \dfrac{z - 1}{4}$.

20. **a.** Find a Cartesian equation of the plane that contains the point $(6, -4, 3)$ and the line $\vec{r} = (-1, 2, 0) + t(-2, 4, 7)$.

    b. At what point does this plane intersect the z-axis?

21. Graph the following equations in 3-space and describe each graph in words.

    a. $x = 0$, $y = 1$, $z = 2$ **b.** $2x + y + z - 3 = 0$

    c. $y = 5$, $z = 4$ **d.** $5y + 4z = 20$

    e. $3z - 9 = 0$ **f.** $x = y$, $z = 0$

Three Intersecting Planes, by M.C. Escher.

Intersections of Lines and Planes

In Chapter 3 we studied several forms of the equations of lines in 2-space and 3-space and equations of planes in 3-space. In this chapter we consider their various intersections: line with line, line with plane, and plane with plane. Finding the intersection of planes with each other can be reduced to solving systems of linear equations. We use a method known as Gaussian elimination to solve these systems. The solution of linear systems is very important in the many disciplines that use mathematics. Such systems will be classified as being consistent (having one or more solutions) or inconsistent (having no solutions). The various types of solutions of systems of linear equations will be interpreted geometrically. The chapter concludes with a discussion about finding various distances in 2-space and 3-space.

4.1 The Intersection of a Line with a Plane and the Intersection of Two Lines

There are three possibilities for the intersection of a line and a plane in 3-space.

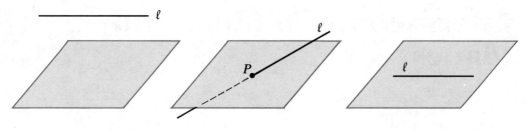

Case I.
The line is parallel to and distinct from the plane, in which case there is no intersection.

Case II.
The line intersects the plane in a single point.

Case III.
The line lies entirely in the plane, in which case the intersection consists of all the points on the line.

To find the intersection of a line with a plane in $\boldsymbol{R}^3$, we substitute the parametric equations of the line in the Cartesian equation of the plane and solve for the parameter. The coordinates of the point of intersection can then be calculated by using the value of this parameter.

Example 1. Find the intersection of the line $(x, y, z) = (1, -6, -5) + t(2, 3, 2)$ with the plane $4x - 2y + z - 19 = 0$.

Solution. The point on the line with parameter t is $(1 + 2t, -6 + 3t, -5 + 2t)$, and this point lies on the plane if

$$4(1 + 2t) - 2(-6 + 3t) + (-5 + 2t) - 19 = 0$$
$$4 + 8t + 12 - 6t - 5 + 2t - 19 = 0$$
$$4t - 8 = 0$$
$$t = 2$$

Therefore, the line intersects the plane in a single point and the coordinates of the point of intersection are $(1, -6, -5) + 2(2, 3, 2)$, or $(5, 0, -1)$.

Check. The point $(5, 0, -1)$ lies on the plane since its coordinates satisfy the equation of the plane; that is, $4(5) - 2(0) + (-1) - 19 = 0$. $\qquad\qquad\square$

Example 2. Find the intersection of the line $x = 2t, y = 1 - t, z = -4 + t$ with the plane $x + 4y + 2z - 4 = 0$.

Solution. The point $(2t, 1 - t, -4 + t)$ lies on the plane if

$$2t + 4(1 - t) + 2(-4 + t) - 4 = 0$$
$$2t + 4 - 4t - 8 + 2t - 4 = 0$$
$$0t = 8$$

Since the equation $0t = 8$ is not satisfied by any value of t, there is no point on the line which lies on the plane. Therefore, the line must be parallel to, but distinct from, the plane.

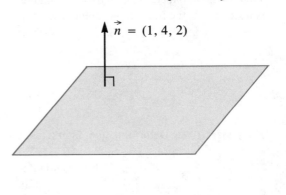

Check. We can show that the line is parallel to the plane by showing that a direction vector of the line is perpendicular to a normal to the plane. The line has direction vector $\vec{m} = (2, -1, 1)$, and the plane has normal $\vec{n} = (1, 4, 2)$, and

$$\vec{m} \cdot \vec{n} = (2, -1, 1) \cdot (1, 4, 2)$$
$$= 2 - 4 + 2$$
$$= 0$$

Example 3. Find the intersection of the line $\dfrac{x + 4}{3} = \dfrac{z}{1}$, $y = 0$ with the plane $x - 2y - 3z + 4 = 0$.

Solution. Any point on the line can be expressed as $(-4 + 3t, 0, t)$, for some parameter t, and this point lies on the plane if

$$(-4 + 3t) - 2(0) - 3t + 4 = 0$$
$$0t = 0$$

The equation $0t = 0$ is satisfied by all values of t. Hence, the point $(-4 + 3t, 0, t)$ lies on the plane for all values of t, and the line lies in the plane. Therefore, the intersection is the line $\dfrac{x + 4}{3} = \dfrac{z}{1}$, $y = 0$.

Check. A direction vector of the line is $\vec{m} = (3, 0, 1)$, and this is perpendicular to the normal to the plane $\vec{n} = (1, -2, -3)$ since
$\vec{m} \cdot \vec{n} = (3, 0, 1) \cdot (1, -2, -3) = 3 - 3 = 0$.
This means that the line is parallel to the plane. However, the point $(-4, 0, 0)$ that lies on the line also lies on the plane, since $-4 - 2(0) - 3(0) + 4 = 0$. Therefore, the line lies in the plane.

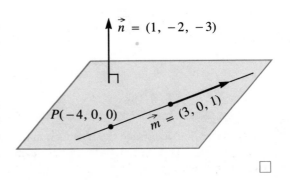

Two lines in 3-space may or may not intersect. If they do not intersect, they are either parallel but distinct, or they are non-parallel. Lines that are distinct and non-parallel are called **skew lines** such lines cannot lie in the same plane.

To determine whether two lines intersect or not, we can use a similar method to that of finding the intersection of a line and a plane. Substitute the parametric equations of one line in the symmetric equations of the other line and solve for the parameter. If there is a solution, the value of the parameter can be used to find the coordinates of the point of intersection. If there is no solution, the lines do not intersect.

Example 4. Determine the intersection of the lines ℓ_1: $\dfrac{x+1}{3} = \dfrac{y-1}{4} = \dfrac{z}{-2}$ and ℓ_2: $\dfrac{x-5}{2} = \dfrac{y-9}{3} = \dfrac{z+4}{1}$. If there is no intersection, determine whether the lines are parallel or skew.

Solution. Any point on ℓ_1 can be represented by $(-1 + 3t, 1 + 4t, -2t)$. This point will lie on ℓ_2 if there is a single value of t satisfying the equations

$$\frac{(-1 + 3t) - 5}{2} = \frac{(1 + 4t) - 9}{3} = \frac{(-2t) + 4}{1}$$

$$\frac{3t - 6}{2} = \frac{4t - 8}{3} = \frac{-2t + 4}{1}$$

If $\dfrac{3t - 6}{2} = \dfrac{4t - 8}{3}$, then $9t - 18 = 8t - 16$, and so $t = 2$. If $\dfrac{4t - 8}{3} = \dfrac{-2t + 4}{1}$, then $4t - 8 = -6t + 12$ and $t = 2$. Hence, the unique value $t = 2$ satisfies both equations and the lines intersect at the point $(-1 + 3(2), 1 + 4(2), -2(2))$, which is $(5, 9, -4)$.

Check. The point $(5, 9, -4)$ lies on ℓ_1 since $\frac{5+1}{3} = \frac{9-1}{4} = \frac{-4}{-2}$. The point $(5, 9, -4)$ lies on ℓ_2 since $\frac{5-5}{2} = \frac{9-9}{3} = \frac{-4+4}{1}$. □

Example 5. Determine the intersection of the lines ℓ_1: $\vec{r} = (2, 1, 0) + t(1, -1, 1)$ and ℓ_2: $\vec{r} = (3, 0, -1) + s(2, 3, -1)$. If there is no intersection, determine whether the lines are parallel or skew.

Solution. Rewrite the equation of ℓ_2 in symmetric form as $\dfrac{x-3}{2} = \dfrac{y}{3} = \dfrac{z+1}{-1}$. Any point on ℓ_1 can be represented by $(2+t, 1-t, t)$, and this point lies on ℓ_2 if there is a single value of t satisfying the equations

$$\frac{(2+t)-3}{2} = \frac{(1-t)}{3} = \frac{(t)+1}{-1}$$

$$\frac{-1+t}{2} = \frac{1-t}{3} = \frac{t+1}{-1}$$

If $\dfrac{-1+t}{2} = \dfrac{1-t}{3}$, then $-3 + 3t = 2 - 2t$ and $t = 1$. If $\dfrac{1-t}{3} = \dfrac{t+1}{-1}$, then $-1 + t = 3t + 3$ and $t = -2$. Since the equations are not satisfied by a single value of t, the lines do not intersect.

The direction vectors of ℓ_1 and ℓ_2 are $(1, -1, 1)$ and $(2, 3, -1)$. Since the direction vectors are not scalar multiples of each other, the lines are not parallel. Hence, ℓ_1 and ℓ_2 are skew lines. $\quad\square$

Another way to determine whether two lines intersect or not is to find the shortest distance between the lines by using the method of section 4.8. If the shortest distance is zero, then the lines intersect.

Exercises 4.1

1. Determine the intersection of the line and the plane.

   a. $(x, y, z) = (4, 6, -2) + t(-1, 2, 1)$ and $2x - y + 6z + 10 = 0$

   b. $\dfrac{x-3}{4} = \dfrac{y+2}{-6} = \dfrac{z-\frac{1}{2}}{-3}$ and $3x + 4y - 7z + 7 = 0$

   c. $x = 5 + t, y = 4 + 2t, z = 7 + 2t$ and $2x + 3y - 4z + 7 = 0$

   d. $(x, y, z) = (2 - t, 14 - t, 1 + t)$ and $3x - y + 2z + 6 = 0$

   e. $(x, y, z) = (5, 7 + t, 3 - t)$ and $z = -5$

2. Where does the line $\vec{r} = (6, 10, 1) + t(3, 4, -1)$ meet

   a. the *xy*-plane?
   $z=0$

   b. the *xz*-plane?
   $y=0$

   c. the *yz*-plane? $x=0$

3. Does the line ℓ lie in the plane π_1?

   a. $\ell: \vec{r} = (-2, 6, 5) + t(3, 2, -1); \quad \pi_1: 3x - 4y + z + 25 = 0$

   b. $\ell: \vec{r} = (4, -1, 2) + t(3, 2, -1); \quad \pi_1: 3x - 4y + z - 17 = 0$

4. Where does the plane $3x - 2y - 7z - 6 = 0$ intersect

   a. the *x*-axis?
   $x=1+t$
   $y=0$
   $z=0$

   b. the *y*-axis?
   $x=0$
   $y=1+1t$
   $z=0$

   c. the *z*-axis?
   $x=0$
   $y=0$
   $z=p+1t$

5. Where does the plane $\vec{r} = (6, -4, 3) + s(-2, 4, 7) + t(-7, 6, -3)$ intersect the z-axis?

6. Find the point of intersection of the plane $3x - 2y + 7z = 31$ with the line that passes through the origin and is perpendicular to the plane.

7. Find the intersection of each pair of lines. If they do not meet, determine whether they are parallel and distinct, or skew.

   a. $\vec{r} = (-2, 0, -3) + t(5, 1, 3)$ and $\vec{r} = (5, 8, -6) + s(-1, 2, -3)$

   b. $\dfrac{x - 3}{4} = y - 2 = z - 2$ and $\dfrac{x - 2}{-3} = \dfrac{y + 1}{2} = \dfrac{z - 2}{-1}$

   c. $\vec{r} = (2, -1, 0) + t(1, 2, -3)$ and $\vec{r} = (-1, 1, 2) + s(-2, 1, 1)$

   d. $\vec{r} = (1, 1, 1) + t(1, 2, -3)$ and $\vec{r} = (3, 5, -5) + s(-2, -4, 6)$

   e. $(x, y, z) = (1 + t, 2 + t, -t)$ and $(x, y, z) = (3 - 2s, 4 - 2s, -1 + 2s)$

8. Show that the lines $\vec{r} = (4, 7, -1) + t(4, 8, -4)$ and $\vec{r} = (1, 5, 4) + s(-1, 2, 3)$ intersect at right angles, and find the point of intersection.

9. Consider the lines $\vec{r} = (1, -1, 1) + t(3, 2, 1)$ and $\vec{r} = (-2, -3, 0) + s(1, 2, 3)$.

   a. Find their point of intersection.

   b. Find a vector equation for the line perpendicular to both of the given lines that passes through their point of intersection.

10. Find the value of c so that the lines $\vec{r} = (1, 3, 0) + t(2, 4, c)$ and $\vec{r} = (2, 4, 2) + s(1, 3, 1)$ intersect.

Problems 4.1

1. Find the intersection of each pair of lines. If they do not meet, determine whether they are parallel or skew.

   a. $(x, y, z) = (1, 1, 1) + t(1, 0, -1)$ and $(x, y, z) = (-1, 1, 0) + s(-2, 0, 2)$

   b. $\vec{r} = (1, 3, 4) + t(1, 2, 0)$ and $\vec{r} = (-2, 5, 5) + s(3, 0, -1)$

2. Find symmetric equations of the line that passes through the point $(0, 1, 2)$ and meets each of the lines $x = y = z + 2$ and $\dfrac{x}{-2} = \dfrac{y + 3}{1} = \dfrac{z}{3}$.

3. Show that the point of intersection of the line $\vec{r} = \vec{p} + t\vec{m}$ with the plane $\vec{n} \cdot \vec{r} + d = 0$ has position vector

$$\vec{p} - \left(\frac{d + \vec{n} \cdot \vec{p}}{\vec{n} \cdot \vec{m}} \right) \vec{m}$$

provided that $\vec{n} \cdot \vec{m} \neq 0$. What happens if $\vec{n} \cdot \vec{m} = 0$?

4. Find a vector equation of the line of intersection of the planes
$3(x - 2) - y + 4(z + 1) = 0$ and $(x - 2) + 6y + 10(z + 1) = 0$.

5. Find the points of intersection of the line $\vec{r} = (0, 5, 3) + t(1, -3, -2)$ with the sphere
$x^2 + y^2 + z^2 = 6$.

6. For what values of k will the line $\dfrac{x - k}{3} = \dfrac{y + 4}{2} = \dfrac{z + 6}{1}$ intersect the plane
$x - 4y + 5z + 5 = 0$ in

a. a single point?

b. an infinite number of points?

c. no point?

4.2 Equivalent Systems of Equations

A plane in R^3 can be represented by one linear equation in the variables x, y, and z. The points of intersection of two or three planes satisfy all of the corresponding linear equations. Hence, the set of points of intersection of planes in R^3 is represented by the solution set of a system of linear equations.

Systems of linear equations occur in many disciplines, such as mathematics, engineering, economics, physics, chemistry, and biology; so it is important that techniques be developed to determine if a given set of linear equations has a solution or not and what that solution is. In this section and the next one, we shall consider methods for solving systems of linear equations in two and three variables. These techniques can be generalized to equations containing more variables.

A **linear equation** in the variables $x_1, x_2, \ldots, x_n$ is an equation of the form

$$a_1x_1 + a_2x_2 + \ldots + a_nx_n = b$$

where $a_1, a_2, \ldots, a_n$, and b are fixed numbers. A line in R^2 can be represented by an equation of the form $Ax + By + C = 0$, which is linear in the variables x and y. A plane in 3-space can be represented by an equation of the form $Ax + By + Cz + D = 0$, which is a linear equation in the three variables x, y, and z. The following equations are linear:

$$x + 5 = 0, \quad x - \sqrt{2}y = 8, \quad x = 2y - \tfrac{3}{2}z + \pi, \quad x_1 + 2x_2 + 7x_3 - x_4 = 0$$

All the variables occur to the first power, and there are no roots or products and no trigonometric, logarithmic, or exponential functions of variables. The following equations are not linear:

$$x - 2y^2 = 8, \quad 2x + 4y - 5xy - 7 = 0, \quad \sqrt{x} - 5y + z = 6, \quad x - \sin y = 0$$

We shall first consider the simplest system, consisting of two equations in two variables. Geometrically, this represents the intersection of two lines in the plane.

Example 1. Find the solution of the linear system.

$$x + 4y = 11$$
$$2x - y = 4$$

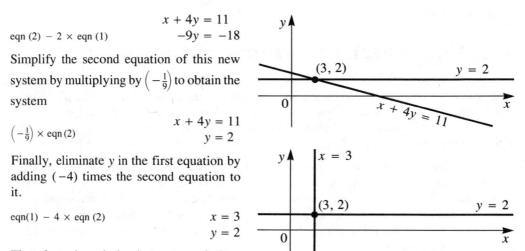

Solution. We have to determine the values of x and the corresponding values of y that satisfy both equations simultaneously. First eliminate a variable, say x, from one of the equations. One way to do this is to retain the first equation and add (-2) times the first equation to the second equation. The result is

$$x + 4y = 11$$

eqn (2) $-$ 2 $\times$ eqn (1) $$-9y = -18$$

Simplify the second equation of this new system by multiplying by $\left(-\frac{1}{9}\right)$ to obtain the system

$$x + 4y = 11$$

$\left(-\frac{1}{9}\right) \times$ eqn (2) $$y = 2$$

Finally, eliminate y in the first equation by adding (-4) times the second equation to it.

eqn(1) $-$ 4 $\times$ eqn (2) $$x = 3$$
$$y = 2$$

Therefore, the solution is $(x, y) = (3, 2)$.

Check. The solution to any system of equations can be easily checked by substituting the solution back in the original equations. In this case $x = 3$ and $y = 2$ satisfy both of the original equations because $3 + 4(2) = 11$ and $2(3) - 2 = 4$. □

Two consistent systems of equations are called **equivalent** if they have the same solution set; that is, every solution to one system is also a solution to the other system. In Example 1, every time we modified a system we obtained an equivalent system with the same solution. Geometrically, each system represented two lines passing through the point (3, 2). Each modification of the system replaced one line with another line through the intersection point, until eventually each of the lines was parallel to a coordinate axis.

Not all systems of two linear equations in two variables have solutions. For example, in the system

$$x + 4y = 11$$
$$2x + 8y = 10$$

subtracting twice the first equation from the second gives

$$x + 4y = 11$$

eqn (2) − 2 × eqn (1) $$0x + 0y = -12$$

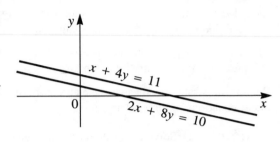

Clearly, the second equation, and therefore the system, has no solutions for x and y. Graphically, this system represents a pair of parallel and distinct lines.

Some systems have an infinite number of solutions. For example, in the system

$$x + 4y = 11$$
$$2x + 8y = 22$$

the second equation is just twice the first equation. All points satisfying the first equation will also satisfy the second.

Geometrically, both these equations represent the same line. We could write the solution parametrically by letting $y = t$ to obtain

$$x = 11 - 4t, \quad y = t$$

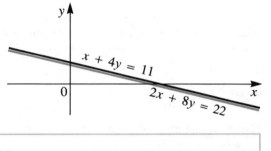

Hence, all the solutions to the system can be written as

$$(x, y) = (11 - 4t, t), \quad t \in R$$

A System of Linear Equations

(i)   has no solutions
(ii) has a unique solution
or   (iii) has an infinite number of solutions.

A system of linear equations that has no solution is called **inconsistent**, whereas a system that has one or more solutions is called **consistent**. If a consistent system has a unique solution, then the solution represents a point. If a system has an infinite number of solutions, then parameters are needed to describe the solution; if one parameter is required, the solution represents a line; if two parameters are required, the solution represents a plane.

The basic idea in solving any system of linear equations in any number of variables is to replace the given system with an equivalent system that is easier to solve. The following three types of elementary operations can be used to manipulate the equations.

Elementary Operations

1. Interchange any two equations in the system.
2. Multiply an equation by a non-zero constant.
3. Replace an equation with the sum of that equation and a multiple of another equation.

If we perform any of these elementary operations, a solution to the original system will also satisfy the modified system. Since the three operations are reversible, any solution to the modified system will also be a solution to the original system. Hence, the original system and the modified system have the same solution set and therefore are equivalent systems.

These elementary operations have a further advantage in that they are readily adaptable for computer use for solving the much larger systems that often occur in practice.

We now illustrate how these three elementary operations can be used to solve a system of three linear equations in three variables.

Example 2. Solve the system of equations.

$$\begin{aligned} x + 2y + 2z &= 6 \\ 3x + 2y + z &= 9 \\ 2x + 5y + 5z &= 14 \end{aligned}$$

Solution. We first use elementary operations to eliminate x from the second and third equations. Retain the first equation, subtract 3 times the first equation from the second, and subtract 2 times the first equation from the third.

	$x + 2y + 2z = 6$
eqn (2) $-$ 3 $\times$ eqn (1)	$-4y - 5z = -9$
eqn (3) $-$ 2 $\times$ eqn (1)	$y + z = 2$

Now that x appears only in the first equation and has a coefficient of 1, we concentrate on the variable y. First obtain a coefficient of 1 in the second equation. We can either multiply the second equation by $\left(-\frac{1}{4}\right)$ or interchange the second and third equations.

	$x + 2y + 2z = 6$
interchange	$y + z = 2$
eqns (2) and (3)	$-4y - 5z = -9$

Now eliminate y from all the equations except the second.

eqn (1) $-$ 2 $\times$ eqn (2)	$x = 2$
	$y + z = 2$
eqn (3) $+$ 4 $\times$ eqn (2)	$-z = -1$

Now consider the variable z. We wish to obtain a coefficient of 1 in the third equation and eliminate z from the other equations.

	$x = 2$
eqn (2) $+$ eqn (3)	$y = 1$
$(-1) \times$ eqn (3)	$z = 1$

The solution to this final system, and therefore to the original system, is $(x, y, z) = (2, 1, 1)$. The original system of three equations has a unique solution. As we shall see in the next section, this solution represents the common point of intersection of three planes in $\boldsymbol{R}^3$.
Check. Substitute the solution in the original system.   □

In the next section, we shall shorten the amount of writing required in this type of solution by using matrix notation.

Exercises 4.2

1. State which equations are linear in x, y, and z.

a. $x - y + \sqrt{2}z = 3$ **b.** $2x + 3y - \sin z = 0$

c. $x - y + 2\sqrt{z} = 3$ **d.** $2x + 3y - z = \sin 60°$

e. $2x + xy + 3z - 4 = 0$ **f.** $4x + y^{-1} + 2z - 9 = 0$

g. $5x + \ln y - z = 4$ **h.** $x = y$

2. a. Graph the lines $4x + 3y + 1 = 0$ and $2x - y - 2 = 0$ on the same set of axes.
    b. Use your graph to find the point of intersection.

3. Consider the system of linear equations.

$$x - y = 0$$
$$x + y = 2$$
$$x + 2y = 2$$

    a. Show graphically that the system has no solution.
    b. Show algebraically, using elementary operations, that the system has no solution.

4. Solve each system.

a. $x - 5y = 2$ **b.** $x + 2y + 3z = 0$
           $y = -1$ $y - 7z = 0$
                                            $z = 0$

5. Solve each system by using elementary operations.

a. $x + 3y = 1$ **b.** $x - 4y = 9$
       $2x - 5y = 13$ $3x - 12y = 25$

c. $x + 2y = 8$ **d.** $x + \frac{3}{2}y = \frac{3}{2}$
      $4x + 8y = 32$ $y = \frac{2}{3}$

e. $x + 2y + 3z = 3$ **f.** $x - 3y - z = 16$
      $x + y + 2z = 1$ $y + 4z = -11$
           $y - 4z = 2$ $z = -2$

g. $x + y + z = 12$
     $2x + y + z = 16$
      $x + 2y + z = 14$

Problems 4.2

1. Solve the system, where a and b are constants.

$$x + 2y = a$$
$$6x + 3y = b$$

2. What conditions must a, b, c, and d satisfy if the only solution to the following system is the trivial solution $(0, 0)$?

$$ax + by = 0$$
$$cx + dy = 0$$

3. For what values of the constant c does the system

$$x \qquad + 6y = 2$$
$$2x + (c^2 - 4)y = c$$

  a. have no solutions?
  b. have an infinite number of solutions?
  c. have a unique solution?

4.3 Gaussian Elimination

In this section we develop efficient methods for solving systems of linear equations using matrix notation. An example of a system of three equations in three variables is

$$x + 2y + z = -4$$
$$x + 4y + 5z = -18$$
$$4x - z = -4$$

By omitting the variables, this system can be abbreviated by the rectangular array of numbers

$$\begin{bmatrix} 1 & 2 & 1 & -4 \\ 1 & 4 & 5 & -18 \\ 4 & 0 & -1 & -4 \end{bmatrix}$$

which is called the **augmented matrix** of the system. The matrix

$$\begin{bmatrix} 1 & 2 & 1 \\ 1 & 4 & 5 \\ 4 & 0 & -1 \end{bmatrix}$$

is called the **coefficient matrix** of the system. Each row of the augmented matrix corresponds to one equation in the system. Each column in the augmented matrix, to the left of the bar, consists of the coefficients of one of the variables. Note that if a variable is absent in an equation, a zero appears as the coefficient. The single column to the right of the bar in the augmented matrix consists of the constants on the right side of the equations. In general, a system of m equations in n variables has an augmented matrix with m rows and $(n + 1)$ columns; this is called an $m \times (n + 1)$ matrix. The coefficient matrix for such a system is an $m \times n$ matrix.

Since the rows of a matrix correspond to the equations of a system, the three elementary operations given in the previous section correspond to the following operations that can be performed on the rows of an augmented matrix.

Elementary Row Operations

1. Interchange any two rows.
2. Multiply a row by a non-zero constant.
3. Replace a row with the sum of that row and a multiple of another row.

The process of using these elementary row operations to simplify a matrix is called **row reduction**.

If we perform a series of elementary row operations on an augmented matrix, we obtain the augmented matrix of an equivalent system that has the same solution set. We shall use the symbol $\sim$ to indicate matrices corresponding to equivalent systems. If we multiply row 2 by $\frac{1}{2}$, then every entry in row 2 is multipled by $\frac{1}{2}$, and we denote this by $\frac{1}{2} \times$ row (2). If we replace row 3 with (-4) times row 1 added to row 3, then every element of row 3 is replaced by that element minus 4 times the corresponding element of row 1, and we denote this by writing row (3) $- 4 \times$ row (1) opposite row 3.

Example 1. Solve the system.

$$\begin{aligned} x + 2y + z &= -4 \\ x + 4y + 5z &= -18 \\ 4x - z &= -4 \end{aligned}$$

Solution. We shall solve the system by performing elementary row operations on the augmented matrix.

<table>
<tr><td></td><td align="center">The augmented matrix is</td><td align="center">The corresponding system of equations is</td></tr>
<tr><td></td><td>$\begin{bmatrix} 1 & 2 & 1 & -4 \\ 1 & 4 & 5 & -18 \\ 4 & 0 & -1 & -4 \end{bmatrix}$</td><td>$\begin{aligned} x + 2y + z &= -4 \\ x + 4y + 5z &= -18 \\ 4x - z &= -4 \end{aligned}$</td></tr>
<tr><td>$\sim$
row (2) $-$ row (1)
row (3) $- 4 \times$ row (1)</td><td>$\begin{bmatrix} 1 & 2 & 1 & -4 \\ 0 & 2 & 4 & -14 \\ 0 & -8 & -5 & 12 \end{bmatrix}$</td><td>$\begin{aligned} x + 2y + z &= -4 \\ 2y + 4z &= -14 \\ -8y - 5z &= 12 \end{aligned}$</td></tr>
<tr><td>$\sim$
row (3) $+ 4 \times$ row (2)</td><td>$\begin{bmatrix} 1 & 2 & 1 & -4 \\ 0 & 2 & 4 & -14 \\ 0 & 0 & 11 & -44 \end{bmatrix}$</td><td>$\begin{aligned} x + 2y + z &= -4 \\ 2y + 4z &= -14 \\ 11z &= -44 \end{aligned}$</td></tr>
</table>

The system can now be solved by **back substitution**. That is, start with the last equation and solve for z to obtain $z = -4$. Substitute $z = -4$ back in the second equation to obtain

$$2y + 4(-4) = -14 \quad \text{or} \quad y = 1$$

Substitute $y = 1$ and $z = -4$ in the first equation to obtain

$$x + 2(1) + (-4) = -4 \quad \text{or} \quad x = -2$$

Therefore, the solution to the system is $(x, y, z) = (-2, 1, -4)$.

Check. Substitute this solution in the original equations. $\qquad\qquad\square$

The method used to solve the system of equations in Example 1 is called **Gaussian elimination**. It is attributed to the great German mathematician Carl Friedrich Gauss. He made profound contributions to complex numbers, the theory of functions, number theory, statistics, probability, and other fields. He has been called the "Prince of Mathematicians."

The final matrix in Example 1 is said to be in row-echelon form and has the following characteristics.

Row-echelon Form

A matrix is in row-echelon form if it satisfies the following properties.

- Any rows consisting entirely of zeros are grouped at the bottom of the matrix.
- The first non-zero element in each row is positioned to the right of the first non-zero element in the previous row.

The word "echelon" is used to describe a formation of troops, ships, etc., in which groups are positioned into parallel rows, each to the right of the row in front of it, so that the whole formation presents the appearance of steps.

The following augmented matrices are in row-echelon form.

$$\left[\begin{array}{ccc|c} 1 & \frac{1}{2} & -3 & 5 \\ 0 & 1 & -8 & 4 \\ 0 & 0 & 0 & 0 \end{array}\right] \qquad \left[\begin{array}{ccc|c} 3 & 1 & -4 & 6 \\ 0 & 0 & 2 & -5 \end{array}\right] \qquad \left[\begin{array}{ccc|c} 0 & 1 & 0 & -3 \\ 0 & 0 & 1 & 4 \\ 0 & 0 & 0 & 3 \end{array}\right]$$

The following augmented matrices are **not** in row-echelon form. How can they be row-reduced so as to appear in row-echelon form?

$$\left[\begin{array}{ccc|c} 1 & -3 & 4 & 6 \\ 0 & 0 & 0 & 0 \\ 0 & 1 & 2 & 7 \end{array}\right] \qquad \left[\begin{array}{ccc|c} 1 & 5 & 4 & -3 \\ 0 & 0 & 1 & 6 \\ 0 & 1 & -3 & 2 \end{array}\right] \qquad \left[\begin{array}{ccc|c} 1 & 4 & 7 & -2 \\ 0 & 3 & 5 & 7 \\ 0 & 4 & 0 & 2 \end{array}\right]$$

Example 2. Solve the system

$$\begin{aligned} 2x + 3y - z &= -2 \\ x - 2y + 3z &= 13 \\ 4x + y + 3z &= 9 \end{aligned}$$

Solution. **Reduce the augmented matrix by using Gaussian elimination.**

$$\begin{bmatrix} 2 & 3 & -1 & | & -2 \\ 1 & -2 & 3 & | & 13 \\ 4 & 1 & 3 & | & 9 \end{bmatrix} \qquad \begin{array}{c} \text{interchange} \\ \text{rows (1) and (2)} \\ \sim \end{array} \qquad \begin{bmatrix} 1 & -2 & 3 & | & 13 \\ 2 & 3 & -1 & | & -2 \\ 4 & 1 & 3 & | & 9 \end{bmatrix}$$

$$\begin{array}{c} \sim \\ \text{row (2)} - 2 \times \text{row (1)} \\ \text{row (3)} - 4 \times \text{row (1)} \end{array} \begin{bmatrix} 1 & -2 & 3 & | & 13 \\ 0 & 7 & -7 & | & -28 \\ 0 & 9 & -9 & | & -43 \end{bmatrix} \qquad \begin{array}{c} \sim \\ \frac{1}{7} \times \text{row (2)} \end{array} \begin{bmatrix} 1 & -2 & 3 & | & 13 \\ 0 & 1 & -1 & | & -4 \\ 0 & 9 & -9 & | & -43 \end{bmatrix}$$

$$\begin{array}{c} \sim \\ \text{row (3)} - 9 \times \text{row (2)} \end{array} \begin{bmatrix} 1 & -2 & 3 & | & 13 \\ 0 & 1 & -1 & | & -4 \\ 0 & 0 & 0 & | & -7 \end{bmatrix}$$

The last matrix is the augmented matrix of the system
$$\begin{aligned} x - 2y + 3z &= 13 \\ y - z &= -4 \\ 0z &= -7 \end{aligned}$$

Since the last equation has no solution, the system has no solution. The original system is inconsistent. □

Example 3. Solve the system

$$\begin{aligned} x + 2y + 7z &= 3 \\ x - y + z &= 4 \\ 3x + 3y + 15z &= 10 \end{aligned}$$

Solution. **Reduce the augmented matrix to its row-echelon form.**

$$\begin{bmatrix} 1 & 2 & 7 & | & 3 \\ 1 & -1 & 1 & | & 4 \\ 3 & 3 & 15 & | & 10 \end{bmatrix} \qquad \begin{array}{c} \sim \\ \text{row (2)} - \text{row (1)} \\ \text{row (3)} - 3 \times \text{row (1)} \end{array} \begin{bmatrix} 1 & 2 & 7 & | & 3 \\ 0 & -3 & -6 & | & 1 \\ 0 & -3 & -6 & | & 1 \end{bmatrix}$$

$$\begin{array}{c} \sim \\ \text{row (3)} - \text{row (2)} \end{array} \begin{bmatrix} 1 & 2 & 7 & | & 3 \\ 0 & -3 & -6 & | & 1 \\ 0 & 0 & 0 & | & 0 \end{bmatrix}$$

The final row-echelon matrix corresponds to the system
$$\begin{aligned} x + 2y + 7z &= 3 \\ -3y - 6z &= 1 \\ 0z &= 0 \end{aligned}$$

The third equation is true for any value of z. Therefore, let $z = t$, where t is any real number, and then solve for the other variables in terms of t. From the second equation, $y = -\frac{1}{3} - 2z = -\frac{1}{3} - 2t$. Substituting the values for y and z in the first equation gives $x + 2\left(-\frac{1}{3} - 2t\right) + 7t = 3$ or $x = \frac{11}{3} - 3t$.

Hence, the solution can be expressed as

$$(x, y, z) = \left(\tfrac{11}{3} - 3t, -\tfrac{1}{3} - 2t, t\right), \quad \text{where } t \in \mathbf{R}$$

Since t is an arbitrary parameter, there are an infinite number of solutions corresponding to different values of t. For example, if $t = 0$, $(x, y, z) = \left(\tfrac{11}{3}, -\tfrac{1}{3}, 0\right)$ is a solution. If $t = -1$, $(x, y, z) = \left(\tfrac{20}{3}, \tfrac{5}{3}, -1\right)$ is a solution, etc.

Check. Substitute the general solution into the original equations.

$$\left(\tfrac{11}{3} - 3t\right) + 2\left(-\tfrac{1}{3} - 2t\right) + 7t = 3$$
$$\left(\tfrac{11}{3} - 3t\right) - \left(-\tfrac{1}{3} - 2t\right) + t = 4$$
$$3\left(\tfrac{11}{3} - 3t\right) + 3\left(-\tfrac{1}{3} - 2t\right) + 15t = 10$$

These equations are satisfied for all values of t. ☐

An augmented matrix in row-echelon form can be further reduced so that back substitution can be avoided.

Reduced Row-echelon Form

A matrix is in reduced row-echelon form if it is in row-echelon form and the following conditions are satisfied.

- The first non-zero element in each row is a 1, called a **leading 1**.
- Any column containing a leading 1 has all its remaining entries equal to zero.

The following matrices are in reduced row-echelon form. The columns indicated with arrows are columns containing leading 1's.

$$\left[\begin{array}{ccc|c} 1 & 0 & 0 & 3 \\ 0 & 1 & 0 & 4 \\ 0 & 0 & 1 & 5 \end{array}\right] \qquad \left[\begin{array}{ccc|c} 1 & 0 & 5 & -2 \\ 0 & 1 & 1 & 4 \end{array}\right] \qquad \left[\begin{array}{ccc|c} 1 & 5 & 0 & 6 \\ 0 & 0 & 1 & 5 \\ 0 & 0 & 0 & 0 \\ 0 & 0 & 0 & 0 \end{array}\right]$$

The following matrices are **not** in reduced row-echelon form. How can they be placed in reduced row-echelon form?

$$\left[\begin{array}{ccc|c} 1 & 6 & 0 & 7 \\ 0 & 1 & 0 & -4 \\ 0 & 0 & 1 & 2 \end{array}\right] \qquad \left[\begin{array}{ccc|c} 1 & 5 & 0 & -1 \\ 0 & 0 & 2 & -1 \\ 0 & 0 & 0 & 0 \end{array}\right]$$

The procedure of putting the augmented matrix of a system of equations into reduced row-echelon form is called **Gauss-Jordan elimination**, named after Gauss and the German geodesist Wilhelm Jordan (1842-1899). Jordan used the method in a textbook he wrote on geodesy, the science of surveying the earth. He needed to find the best linear function to approximate the observed data. The reduced row-echelon form of a matrix is unique, though there are many different ways to reduce a matrix to this form. Gauss-Jordan elimination is used in a number of applications, such as the calculation of the inverse of a matrix, and the simplex method of linear programming. For solving small systems by hand, Gaussian elimination and Gauss-Jordan elimination require about the same amount of work.

Example 4. Solve the system of equations by using Gauss-Jordan elimination.

$$3y - 2z = 19$$
$$x - y + 4z = -13$$
$$x \quad + 3z = -6$$

Solution. **Row reduce the augmented matrix.**

$$\begin{bmatrix} 0 & 3 & -2 & | & 19 \\ 1 & -1 & 4 & | & -13 \\ 1 & 0 & 3 & | & -6 \end{bmatrix} \quad \begin{matrix} \text{interchange} \\ \text{rows (1) and (2)} \\ \sim \end{matrix} \quad \begin{bmatrix} 1 & -1 & 4 & | & -13 \\ 0 & 3 & -2 & | & 19 \\ 1 & 0 & 3 & | & -6 \end{bmatrix}$$

$$\begin{matrix} \\ \sim \\ \text{row (3)} - \text{row (1)} \end{matrix} \quad \begin{bmatrix} 1 & -1 & 4 & | & -13 \\ 0 & 3 & -2 & | & 19 \\ 0 & 1 & -1 & | & 7 \end{bmatrix} \quad \begin{matrix} \sim \\ \text{interchange} \\ \text{rows (2) and (3)} \end{matrix} \quad \begin{bmatrix} 1 & -1 & 4 & | & -13 \\ 0 & 1 & -1 & | & 7 \\ 0 & 3 & -2 & | & 19 \end{bmatrix}$$

$$\begin{matrix} \text{row (1)} + \text{row (2)} \\ \sim \\ \text{row (3)} - 3 \times \text{row (2)} \end{matrix} \quad \begin{bmatrix} 1 & 0 & 3 & | & -6 \\ 0 & 1 & -1 & | & 7 \\ 0 & 0 & 1 & | & -2 \end{bmatrix} \quad \begin{matrix} \text{row (1)} - 3 \times \text{row (3)} \\ \text{row (2)} + \text{row (3)} \\ \sim \end{matrix} \quad \begin{bmatrix} 1 & 0 & 0 & | & 0 \\ 0 & 1 & 0 & | & 5 \\ 0 & 0 & 1 & | & -2 \end{bmatrix}$$

The final reduced row-echelon matrix is the augmented matrix of the system

$$x \quad\quad = 0$$
$$y \quad = 5$$
$$z = -2$$

which is equivalent to the original system. The solution is obvious and no back substitution is necessary. Hence, the solution is $(x, y, z) = (0, 5, -2)$.

Check. Verify that this solution satisfies the original equations. □

Exercises 4.3

1. State the coefficient and augmented matrices for each system of linear equations.

a. $x + 3y = 8$
$2x - 4y = 7$

b. $3x + 4y - z = 1$
$\quad\quad y + 3z = 5$
$\quad x - y \quad = -7$

c. $x + 2y = 0$
$x - 2y = 0$
$x + y = 0$

2. State the system of linear equations corresponding to each augmented matrix.

a. $\begin{bmatrix} 1 & -2 & | & 1 \\ 3 & 4 & | & 0 \end{bmatrix}$

b. $\begin{bmatrix} 2 & 1 & 7 & | & 1 \\ 0 & 3 & 4 & | & 7 \\ 0 & 0 & 6 & | & -5 \end{bmatrix}$

c. $\begin{bmatrix} 1 & 1 & 1 & | & 0 \\ 0 & 5 & 6 & | & 0 \end{bmatrix}$

3. State which of the matrices are in row-echelon form. For those not in row-echelon form, use elementary row operations to reduce them to row-echelon form and state which operations you used.

a. $\begin{bmatrix} 2 & 4 & | & 6 \\ 0 & 1 & | & 9 \end{bmatrix}$

b. $\begin{bmatrix} 1 & 4 & -6 & | & 3 \\ 0 & 0 & 0 & | & 0 \\ 0 & 1 & -7 & | & \frac{1}{2} \end{bmatrix}$

c. $\begin{bmatrix} 1 & 5 & 3 & | & 2 \\ 0 & 1 & -6 & | & 4 \end{bmatrix}$

d. $\begin{bmatrix} 0 & 1 & | & 4 \\ 1 & 3 & | & -3 \end{bmatrix}$

e. $\begin{bmatrix} 1 & -3 & 40 & | & 5 \\ 0 & 1 & 4 & | & 3 \\ 0 & 5 & 1 & | & 3 \end{bmatrix}$

f. $\begin{bmatrix} 1 & 1 & 1 & | & 0 \\ 0 & 2 & 1 & | & 0 \\ 0 & 1 & 2 & | & 0 \end{bmatrix}$

4. Solve the systems of linear equations by Gaussian elimination, indicating which elementary row operations you used at each stage. Check your answers.

a. $\begin{aligned} x - y &= -3 \\ 2x + 3y &= 4 \end{aligned}$

b. $\begin{aligned} x + y + z &= 4 \\ x + 2y + 2z &= 2 \\ x - y + z &= -2 \end{aligned}$

c. $\begin{aligned} x + 2y - z &= 1 \\ x - 5y + 4z &= -4 \\ 3x - y + 2z &= 2 \end{aligned}$

d. $\begin{aligned} x + 2y + 3z &= 0 \\ 2x + y &= 0 \\ x + z &= 0 \end{aligned}$

e. $\begin{aligned} x + y + z &= 3 \\ y + 2z &= 2 \\ 2y + z &= 2 \end{aligned}$

f. $\begin{aligned} x - 3y &= -7 \\ 2x + y - z &= 3 \\ 4x + 2y - 2z &= 8 \end{aligned}$

5. Solve the systems of linear equations. For each case in which there are an infinite number of solutions, give the complete solution in terms of a parameter and also state two particular solutions.

a. $\begin{aligned} x + 2y + z &= 2 \\ x + 3y - z &= 4 \\ 3x + 7y + z &= 8 \end{aligned}$

b. $\begin{aligned} x - y - 3z &= 3 \\ 3x - y - z &= 5 \end{aligned}$

c. $\begin{aligned} 4x - 5y + 5z &= -3 \\ 3x - y + 2z &= 1 \\ 2x + 3y - z &= 5 \end{aligned}$

6. Use Gauss-Jordan elimination to solve each system.

a. $\begin{aligned} x + y + z &= 6 \\ x + 2y &= 4 \\ 2x + y + z &= 6 \end{aligned}$

b. $\begin{aligned} x + y + 3z &= 8 \\ y + 3z &= 6 \\ x + 2y + 6z &= 14 \end{aligned}$

c. $\begin{aligned} x + y - 6z &= -1 \\ 4x - 3y + 2z &= 9 \\ 2x + 9y &= 4 \end{aligned}$

Problems 4.3

1. Solve the system of equations.

$$\frac{1}{x} - \frac{1}{y} + \frac{1}{z} = 4$$

$$\frac{2}{x} + \frac{2}{y} + \frac{1}{z} = 2$$

$$\frac{3}{x} + \frac{1}{y} - \frac{2}{z} = -2$$

2. Find and classify, for all possible values of k, the solutions to the system

$$
\begin{aligned}
x + y - z &= 1 \\
2x - 5y + z &= -1 \\
7x - 7y - z &- k
\end{aligned}
$$

3. For what values of k will the system have a unique solution? Find that solution.

$$
\begin{aligned}
x + 2y + 2z &= 7 \\
3x + y + 5z &= 6 \\
x + 4y + kz &= -20
\end{aligned}
$$

4. Solve the system for x_1, x_2, x_3, and x_4.

$$
\begin{aligned}
x_1 + 2x_2 - x_3 &= 1 \\
x_1 + x_2 - 2x_3 - x_4 &= -8 \\
x_1 + 3x_2 - 4x_3 - x_4 &= -12 \\
2x_1 + 3x_2 &= 8
\end{aligned}
$$

5. Write a computer program that will allow you to perform the three elementary row operations on any given matrix.

4.4 The Intersection of Two Planes

A system of two linear equations in three variables represents two planes in 3-space. The solution to the system describes all the points on the intersection of the two planes. There are three possibilities for the intersection of the planes π_1 and π_2 in 3-space.

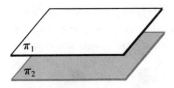

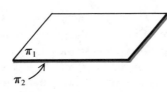

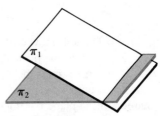

Case I.
The planes are parallel and distinct, in which case there is no intersection.

Case II.
The planes are parallel and coincident; that is, they are the same plane. The intersection consists of all points on this plane.

Case III.
The planes are not parallel and their intersection is a line.

Note that the intersection of two planes can never be a single point. Hence, a system of two linear equations in three unknowns either has no solution or it has an infinite number of solutions; it can never have a unique solution. If the system has an infinite number of solutions, it will require either one parameter to describe the solutions, in which case the intersection is a line, or two parameters, in which case the intersection is a plane.

Example 1. Show that the planes π_1 and π_2 do not intersect.

$$\pi_1: \quad x + 4y - 3z + \ \ 6 = 0$$
$$\pi_2: 2x + 8y - 6z + 11 = 0$$

Solution. The planes have normals $\vec{n}_1 = (1, 4, -3)$ and $\vec{n}_2 = (2, 8, -6)$, respectively. Since $\vec{n}_2 = 2\vec{n}_1$, the normal vectors are parallel and, hence, the planes are parallel. However, the point $(0, 0, 2)$ lies on π_1 but does not lie on π_2, since $2(0) + 8(0) - 6(2) + 11 \neq 0$. Hence, the planes are parallel and distinct and there is no intersection. □

If we were to use Gaussian elimination to solve the system in Example 1, we would obtain the following reduction.

$$\begin{bmatrix} 1 & 4 & -3 & | & -6 \\ 2 & 8 & -6 & | & -11 \end{bmatrix} \quad \underset{\text{row (2)} - 2 \times \text{row (1)}}{\sim} \quad \begin{bmatrix} 1 & 4 & -3 & | & -6 \\ 0 & 0 & 0 & | & 1 \end{bmatrix}$$

The last row of the final matrix corresponds to the equation $0z = 1$, which has no solution. Hence, the system has no solution and the planes do not intersect.

Example 2. Determine the intersection of the planes π_1 and π_2.

$$\pi_1: \quad x - \ \ y + \ \ 5z = 7$$
$$\pi_2: 3x - 3y + 15z = 21$$

Solution. The normal vectors $\vec{n}_1 = (1, -1, 5)$ and $\vec{n}_2 = (3, -3, 15)$ are scalar multiples since $\vec{n}_2 = 3\vec{n}_1$. Hence, the normals are parallel and the planes are parallel. However, the equation of π_2 is just three times the equation of π_1, and so the planes are coincident. Their intersection is the set of points on π_1 (or π_2); that is, $\{(x, y, z) \in \mathbf{R}^3 \,|\, x - y + 5z = 7\}$. We can express the equation of the plane parametrically in terms of two parameters s and t as follows. Let $z = t$ and $y = s$ so that, solving for x, we obtain $x = 7 + s - 5t$. Hence, the solution is $(x, y, z) = (7 + s - 5t, s, t)$, where $s, t, \in \mathbf{R}$. □

Example 3. Find the vector equation of the line of intersection of the planes π_1 and π_2.

$$\pi_1: \quad x + 2y - 4z + \ \ 7 = 0$$
$$\pi_2: 2x - 2y - 5z - 10 = 0$$

Solution. Use Gauss-Jordan elimination to solve the system.

$$\begin{bmatrix} 1 & 2 & -4 & | & -7 \\ 2 & -2 & -5 & | & 10 \end{bmatrix} \quad \underset{\text{row (2) } - 2 \times \text{ row (1)}}{\sim} \quad \begin{bmatrix} 1 & 2 & -4 & | & -7 \\ 0 & -6 & 3 & | & 24 \end{bmatrix}$$

$$\underset{\left(-\frac{1}{6}\right) \times \text{ row (2)}}{\sim} \quad \begin{bmatrix} 1 & 2 & -4 & | & -7 \\ 0 & 1 & -\frac{1}{2} & | & -4 \end{bmatrix} \quad \underset{\sim}{\text{row (1) } - 2 \times \text{ row (2)}} \quad \begin{bmatrix} 1 & 0 & -3 & | & 1 \\ 0 & 1 & -\frac{1}{2} & | & -4 \end{bmatrix}$$

The final reduced row-echelon matrix corresponds to the system

$$x - 3z = 1$$
$$y - \tfrac{1}{2}z = -4$$

Let $z = t$ be the parameter, so that $x = 1 + 3t$ and $y = -4 + \tfrac{1}{2}t$. Therefore, the solution is

$$(x, y, z) = \left(1 + 3t, -4 + \tfrac{1}{2}t, t\right)$$
$$= (1, -4, 0) + t\left(3, \tfrac{1}{2}, 1\right), t \in \mathbf{R}$$

This is the vector equation of the line in the direction $\vec{m} = \left(3, \tfrac{1}{2}, 1\right)$ passing through the point $P(1, -4, 0)$.

Notice that the normals $\vec{n}_1 = (1, 2, -4)$ and $\vec{n}_2 = (2, -2, -5)$, to π_1 and π_2 respectively, are not scalar multiples of each other. Hence, the normals are not parallel and the planes are not parallel.

Check. We could check the solution by substituting the parametric solution in the original equations. Alternatively, we could check that we have the correct line of intersection as follows. The point $P(1, -4, 0)$ lies on both planes since

$$1 + 2(-4) - 4(0) + 7 = 0$$
$$2 - 2(-4) - 5(0) - 10 = 0$$

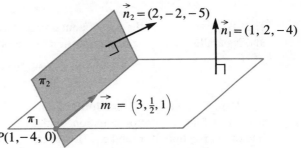

The direction vector of the line of intersection is $\vec{m} = \left(3, \tfrac{1}{2}, 1\right)$, and this is perpendicular to the normal vectors, $\vec{n}_1 = (1, 2, -4)$ and $\vec{n}_2 = (2, -2, -5)$, of both planes since

$$\vec{m} \cdot \vec{n}_1 = \left(3, \tfrac{1}{2}, 1\right) \cdot (1, 2, -4)$$
$$= 3 + 1 - 4$$
$$= 0$$
$$\vec{m} \cdot \vec{n}_2 = \left(3, \tfrac{1}{2}, 1\right) \cdot (2, -2, -5)$$
$$= 6 - 1 - 5$$
$$= 0$$

Two Intersecting Planes, by M.C. Escher.

Example 4. Find the vector equation of the line that passes through the point $(2, -1, 7)$ and is parallel to the line of intersection of the planes π_1 and π_2.

$$\pi_1: \quad x + 2y - 3z = -6$$
$$\pi_2: 3x - \quad y + 2z = 4$$

Solution. We could use Gauss-Jordan elimination to find the vector equation of the line of intersection of π_1 and π_2. However, we only need the direction vector of the line of intersection. This direction vector $\vec{m}$ is perpendicular to both the normals $\vec{n_1}$ of π_1 and $\vec{n_2}$ of π_2. Hence, we can choose $\vec{m}$ to be

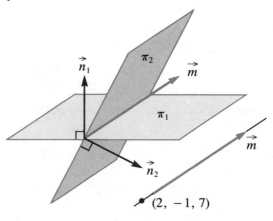

$$\vec{m} = \vec{n_1} \times \vec{n_2}$$
$$= (1, 2, -3) \times (3, -1, 2)$$
$$= (1, -11, -7)$$

Therefore, the vector equation of the required line is

$$\vec{r} = (2, -1, 7) + t(1, -11, -7), t \in \mathbf{R}$$

$\square$

Exercises 4.4

1. Determine which pairs of planes are parallel. For each pair that is not parallel, find parametric equations for the line of intersection.

   a. $x + y - 3z = 4$ and $x + 2y - z = 1$

   b. $5x - 2y + 2z + 1 = 0$ and $5x - 2y + 2z - 3 = 0$

   c. $x - 3y - z + 3 = 0$ and $2x + 4y - z - 5 = 0$

   d. $x + y + z = 1$ and $x = 0$

   e. $x + 3y - z - 4 = 0$ and $2x + 6y - 2z - 8 = 0$

2. Use Gauss-Jordan elimination to find the vector equation of the line of intersection of each pair of planes.

   a. $x + 2y + 7z = 4$ 　　 b. $\quad x - 4y + 3z = 5$ 　　 c. $2x + 8y + 2z = 7$
   $\quad x + 3y - 3z = 1$ 　　　　 $2x + \ y + 6z = 0$ 　　　　 $\quad x + 4y - \ z = 3$

3. Determine the points where the line of intersection of the planes

$$x - 2y + 4z - 8 = 0$$
$$2x + \ y - \ z - 6 = 0$$

   intersects the coordinate planes.

4. Show that the line of intersection of the planes

$$x + 2y - 4z + 8 = 0$$
$$3x - \ y - \ z + 6 = 0$$

   lies in the plane $5x - 11y + 13z - 14 = 0$.

5. Show that the line $\dfrac{x + 2}{3} = \dfrac{y}{1} = \dfrac{z - 1}{-2}$ is parallel to the line of intersection of the planes $x - y + z = 0$ and $x - 5y - z + 8 = 0$.

6. Find the equation of the plane that is perpendicular to the line of intersection of the planes $x + 2y + z = 1$ and $2x + y + 3z = 3$ and also passes through the point $(1, 1, 4)$.

Problems 4.4

1. Find the angle between the plane $x + y = 3$ and the line of intersection of the planes $x - z = -5$ and $x - y + z = 1$.

2. Let ℓ_1 be the line of intersection of the planes $x - 2y = 5$ and $x + z = -1$, and let ℓ_2 be the line of intersection of the planes $4x - 3y = 5$ and $z = 0$. Find the angle between ℓ_1 and ℓ_2.

3. a. Let $\pi_1: a_1x + b_1y + c_1z + d_1 = 0$ and $\pi_2: a_2x + b_2y + c_2z + d_2 = 0$ be two non-parallel planes in 3-space. Show that, for any fixed k,

$$(a_1x + b_1y + c_1z + d_1) + k(a_2x + b_2y + c_2z + d_2) = 0$$

is the equation of a plane through the intersection of π_1 and π_2. As k varies, this equation generates the family of all such planes (except π_2 itself).

b. Find the Cartesian equation of the plane that passes through the origin and the line of intersection of the planes $3x + 4y - 7z - 2 = 0$ and $2x + 3y - 4 = 0$.

c. Find the Cartesian equation of the plane that is parallel to the line $x = 2y = 3z$ and passes through the line of intersection of the planes $4x - 3y - 5z + 10 = 0$ and $4x - y - 3z + 15 = 0$.

4.5   The Intersection of Three Planes

A system of three linear equations in three variables can be represented geometrically by three planes in 3-space, and the solutions to the system represent the intersection of the three planes. The following types of solutions can occur.

Case I. The system has a unique solution, in which case the three planes intersect at only one point.

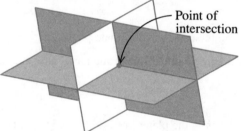

Point of intersection

Case II. The system has an infinite number of solutions described by one parameter, in which case the three planes intersect in a line.

Line of intersection

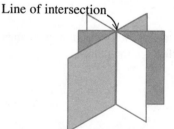

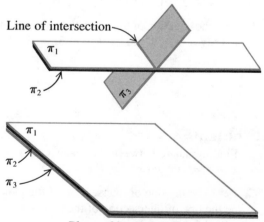

Line of intersection—
π_1
π_2
π_3

Case III. The system has an infinite number of solutions described by two parameters, in which case the three planes are coincident and the solution consists of the coordinates of all the points in the plane.

π_1
π_2
π_3

Plane of intersection

Case IV. The system has no solutions; that is, it is inconsistent. This will happen if at least two of the planes are parallel and distinct. It will also happen if the three lines of intersection of pairs of planes are parallel; in this case the planes bound an infinite triangular prism.

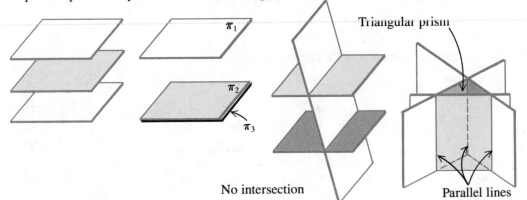

No intersection   Parallel lines

We can find the intersection of any number of planes in 3-space by solving the system of linear equations, using row reduction.

Example 1. Determine the intersection of the three planes.

$$2x + y + z = -4$$
$$3y - 2z = 2$$
$$3x + y + 2z = -7$$

Solution. Use Gaussian elimination on the augmented matrix.

$$\begin{bmatrix} 2 & 1 & 1 & | & -4 \\ 0 & 3 & -2 & | & 2 \\ 3 & 1 & 2 & | & -7 \end{bmatrix} \quad \begin{array}{c} \frac{1}{2} \times \text{row (1)} \\ \sim \end{array} \quad \begin{bmatrix} 1 & \frac{1}{2} & \frac{1}{2} & | & -2 \\ 0 & 3 & -2 & | & 2 \\ 3 & 1 & 2 & | & -7 \end{bmatrix}$$

$$\begin{array}{c} \sim \\ \text{row (3)} - 3 \times \text{row (1)} \end{array} \quad \begin{bmatrix} 1 & \frac{1}{2} & \frac{1}{2} & | & -2 \\ 0 & 3 & -2 & | & 2 \\ 0 & -\frac{1}{2} & \frac{1}{2} & | & -1 \end{bmatrix} \quad \begin{array}{c} (-2) \times \text{row (3)} \\ \sim \end{array} \quad \begin{bmatrix} 1 & \frac{1}{2} & \frac{1}{2} & | & -2 \\ 0 & 3 & -2 & | & 2 \\ 0 & 1 & -1 & | & 2 \end{bmatrix}$$

$$\begin{array}{c} \sim \\ \text{interchange} \\ \text{rows (2) and (3)} \end{array} \quad \begin{bmatrix} 1 & \frac{1}{2} & \frac{1}{2} & | & -2 \\ 0 & 1 & -1 & | & 2 \\ 0 & 3 & -2 & | & 2 \end{bmatrix} \quad \begin{array}{c} \sim \\ \text{row (3)} - 3 \times \text{row (2)} \end{array} \quad \begin{bmatrix} 1 & \frac{1}{2} & \frac{1}{2} & | & -2 \\ 0 & 1 & -1 & | & 2 \\ 0 & 0 & 1 & | & -4 \end{bmatrix}$$

Back substituting $z = -4$, we obtain
$y = 2 + 1(-4) = -2$ and
$x = -2 - \frac{1}{2}(-2) - \frac{1}{2}(-4) = 1$. Hence
the planes intersect in the point
$(x, y, z) = (1, -2, -4)$.

Check. This point lies in all three planes $(1, -2, -4)$
because it satisfies all three equations.

Example 2. Find the intersection of the planes.

$$\begin{aligned} x + y + 2z &= -2 \\ 3x - y + 14z &= 6 \\ x + 2y &= -5 \end{aligned}$$

Solution. Use row reduction of the augmented matrix.

$$\begin{bmatrix} 1 & 1 & 2 & -2 \\ 3 & -1 & 14 & 6 \\ 1 & 2 & 0 & -5 \end{bmatrix} \quad \begin{matrix} \sim \\ \text{row (2)} - 3 \times \text{row (1)} \\ \text{row (3)} - \text{row (1)} \end{matrix} \quad \begin{bmatrix} 1 & 1 & 2 & -2 \\ 0 & -4 & 8 & 12 \\ 0 & 1 & -2 & -3 \end{bmatrix}$$

$$\begin{matrix} \sim \\ \left(-\frac{1}{4}\right) \times \text{row (2)} \end{matrix} \quad \begin{bmatrix} 1 & 1 & 2 & -2 \\ 0 & 1 & -2 & -3 \\ 0 & 1 & -2 & -3 \end{bmatrix} \quad \begin{matrix} \text{row (1)} - \text{row (2)} \\ \sim \\ \text{row (3)} - \text{row (2)} \end{matrix} \quad \begin{bmatrix} 1 & 0 & 4 & 1 \\ 0 & 1 & -2 & -3 \\ 0 & 0 & 0 & 0 \end{bmatrix}$$

This reduced row-echelon form corresponds to the system

$$\begin{aligned} x + 4z &= 1 \\ y - 2z &= -3. \end{aligned}$$

Take $z = t$ as the parameter so that $x = 1 - 4t$ and $y = -3 + 2t$. Hence, the intersection of the planes is the line

$$(x, y, z) = (1 - 4t, -3 + 2t, t), t \in \mathbf{R}$$

The line of intersection passes through the point $(1, -3, 0)$ in the direction of $(-4, 2, 1)$.

Check. The point $(1 - 4t, -3 + 2t, t)$ lies on each plane for all t because

$$\begin{aligned} (1 - 4t) + (-3 + 2t) + 2t &= -2 \\ 3(1 - 4t) - (-3 + 2t) + 14t &= 6 \\ (1 - 4t) + 2(-3 + 2t) &= -5 \end{aligned}$$

The normals to the three planes are $(1, 1, 2)$, $(3, -1, 14)$, and $(1, 2, 0)$. None of the normals are scalar multiples of one another, and so there are no parallel planes. Hence, the intersection must be as shown in the figure.

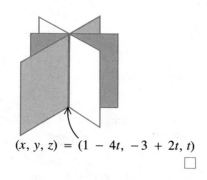

$$(x, y, z) = (1 - 4t, -3 + 2t, t)$$

When you are studying the intersection of planes, it is sometimes helpful to determine the normal vectors to the planes and find out if there are any relations between them. If you notice a relation between the normal vectors, there is often no need to do the row reduction.

Example 3. Determine the intersection of the planes π_1, π_2, and π_3.

$$\pi_1: \quad x - 2y + 3z = 9$$
$$\pi_2: \quad x + y - z = 4$$
$$\pi_3: 2x - 4y + 6z = 5$$

Solution. The normal vectors to the planes are $\vec{n}_1 = (1, -2, 3)$, $\vec{n}_2 = (1, 1, -1)$, and $\vec{n}_3 = (2, -4, 6)$, respectively.

Since $\vec{n}_3 = 2\vec{n}_1$, but the third equation is not twice the first, the planes π_1 and π_3 are parallel and distinct. The plane π_2 is not parallel to the others, and so it intersects them in parallel lines, as shown in the figure. The three planes have no common points of intersection, and so the system has no solution.

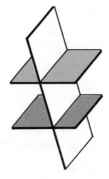

Alternatively, we could have used row reduction.

$$\begin{bmatrix} 1 & -2 & 3 & | & 9 \\ 1 & 1 & -1 & | & 4 \\ 2 & -4 & 6 & | & 5 \end{bmatrix} \quad \underset{\substack{\text{row (2)} - \text{row (1)} \\ \text{row (3)} - 2\ \text{row (1)}}}{\sim} \quad \begin{bmatrix} 1 & -2 & 3 & | & 9 \\ 0 & 3 & -4 & | & -5 \\ 0 & 0 & 0 & | & -13 \end{bmatrix}$$

Without proceeding further, we see that the last row of the final matrix corresponds to the equation $0z = -13$, which has no solution. □

Example 4. Determine the intersection of the planes.

$$\pi_1: \quad x - y - 3z = 1$$
$$\pi_2: \quad 2x - 2y - 6z = 2$$
$$\pi_3: -4x + 4y + 12z = -4$$

Solution. The normal vectors to the three planes are $\vec{n}_1 = (1, -1, -3)$, $\vec{n}_2 = (2, -2, -6)$, and $\vec{n}_3 = (-4, 4, 12)$, which are all scalar multiples of one another; hence, the three planes are parallel. However, the second equation is twice the first, and the third equation is -4 times the first; therefore, all three equations represent the same plane. Hence, the three planes intersect in a plane and there are an infinite number of solutions to the system. The solution set could be written as

$$\{(x, y, z) \in R^3 \mid x - y - 3z = 1\}$$

Alternatively, we could take $y = s$ and $z = t$ as parameters, so that $x = 1 + s + 3t$, and the solution would, therefore, be written as

$$(x, y, z) = (1 + s + 3t, s, t), \ s, t, \in R$$ □

Example 5. Determine the intersection of the planes.

$$\pi_1: \ x - y + 4z = 5$$
$$\pi_2: \ 3x + y + \ z = -2$$
$$\pi_3: \ 5x - y + 9z = 1$$

Solution. Row reduce the augmented matrix.

$$\begin{bmatrix} 1 & -1 & 4 & | & 5 \\ 3 & 1 & 1 & | & -2 \\ 5 & -1 & 9 & | & 1 \end{bmatrix} \quad \begin{array}{c} \sim \\ \text{row (2)} - 3 \times \text{row (1)} \\ \text{row (3)} - 5 \times \text{row (1)} \end{array} \quad \begin{bmatrix} 1 & -1 & 4 & | & 5 \\ 0 & 4 & -11 & | & -17 \\ 0 & 4 & -11 & | & -24 \end{bmatrix}$$

$$\begin{array}{c} \sim \\ \text{row (3)} - \text{row (2)} \end{array} \quad \begin{bmatrix} 1 & -1 & 4 & | & 5 \\ 0 & 4 & -11 & | & -17 \\ 0 & 0 & 0 & | & 7 \end{bmatrix}$$

Without proceeding further, we see that the last row of the final matrix has corresponding equation $0z = 7$, which has no solution. Hence, the planes have no common intersection.

Since none of the normals, $\vec{n_1} = (1, -1, 4)$, $\vec{n_2} = (3, 1, 1)$, and $\vec{n_3} = (5, -1, 9)$, are scalar multiples of one another, there are no parallel planes. Pairs of planes intersect in lines, but since there is no common intersection, these lines must be parallel, as shown in the sketch.

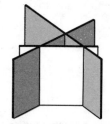

Check. We can check that these lines of intersection are parallel. Planes π_1 and π_2 intersect in a line having direction $\vec{n_1} \times \vec{n_2} = (1, -1, 4) \times (3, 1, 1) = (-5, 11, 4)$. Planes π_1 and π_3 intersect in a line having direction $\vec{n_1} \times \vec{n_3} = (1, -1, 4) \times (5, -1, 9) = (-5, 11, 4)$. Planes π_2 and π_3 intersect in a line having direction
$$\vec{n_2} \times \vec{n_3} = (3, 1, 1) \times (5, -1, 9) = (10, -22, -8) = (-2)(-5, 11, 4). \qquad \square$$

A system of linear equations is said to be **homogeneous** if all of the constant terms are zero. An example of a homogeneous system is

$$2x + 3y - \ z = 0$$
$$x + 4z = 0$$
$$6x + 2y + \ z = 0$$
$$\qquad\qquad \uparrow \quad \text{All constants are zero.}$$

If at least one of the constant terms is non-zero, the system is **non-homogeneous**.

A homogeneous system is always consistent because it always has the trivial solution, in which all the variables equal zero. A homogeneous system either

　　　　(i) has only the trivial solution

or　　　(ii) has infinitely many non-trivial solutions in addition to the trivial solution.

A homogeneous system in three variables represents a system of planes through the origin. Geometrically, the solution of the system is the origin only, or a line through the origin, or a plane through the origin.

Exercises 4.5

1. Each matrix is in row-echelon form and has resulted from reducing the augmented matrix of a system of three equations in three variables in x, y, and z. What geometric properties can you infer about the original system?

a. $\begin{bmatrix} 1 & 4 & 3 & | & 0 \\ 0 & 1 & -1 & | & 0 \\ 0 & 0 & 1 & | & 0 \end{bmatrix}$
     b. $\begin{bmatrix} 1 & -1 & 2 & | & 3 \\ 0 & 0 & 0 & | & 0 \\ 0 & 0 & 0 & | & 0 \\ 0 & 0 & 0 & | & 0 \end{bmatrix}$
     c. $\begin{bmatrix} 1 & 0 & 3 & | & 2 \\ 0 & 1 & 4 & | & 7 \\ 0 & 0 & 0 & | & 0 \end{bmatrix}$

2. Determine the intersection, if any, of each set of planes in 3-space. In each case give a geometrical interpretation of the system and its solution, and also state whether the system has no solutions, a unique solution, or an infinite number of solutions.

a. $\begin{aligned} x + 2y + z &= 12 \\ 2x - y + z &= 5 \\ 3x + y - 2z &= 1 \end{aligned}$
   b. $\begin{aligned} x - y + 2z &= 4 \\ 2x - 2y + 4z &= 7 \\ 3x - 3y + 6z &= 11 \end{aligned}$
   c. $\begin{aligned} x + y - z &= 5 \\ 2x + 2y - 4z &= 6 \\ x + y - 2z &= 3 \end{aligned}$

d. $\begin{aligned} -2x + 4y + 6z &= -2 \\ 4x - 8y - 12z &= 4 \\ x - 2y - 3z &= 1 \end{aligned}$
   e. $\begin{aligned} x + y + 2z &= 2 \\ x - y - 2z &= 5 \\ 3x + 3y + 6z &= 5 \end{aligned}$
   f. $\begin{aligned} x + 3y + 5z &= 10 \\ 2x + 6y + 10z &= 18 \\ x + 3y + 5z &= 9 \end{aligned}$

g. $\begin{aligned} x - 3y - 2z &= 9 \\ x + 11y + 5z &= -5 \\ 2x + 8y + 3z &= 4 \end{aligned}$
   h. $\begin{aligned} x + y + 2z &= 6 \\ x - y - 4z &= -2 \\ 3x + 5y + 12z &= 27 \end{aligned}$
   i. $\begin{aligned} 2x + y + z &= 0 \\ x - 2y - 3z &= 0 \\ 3x + 2y + 4z &= 0 \end{aligned}$

Problems 4.5

1. Let $\vec{n}_1$, $\vec{n}_2$, and $\vec{n}_3$ be normals to three planes in 3-space such that $\vec{n}_1$, $\vec{n}_2$, and $\vec{n}_3$ are linearly dependent.

a. What can be said about the three lines of intersection of pairs of these planes?

b. What can be said about the intersection of the three planes?

2. For what value of k will the set of planes intersect in a line?

$$\begin{aligned} x + 2y - z &= 0 \\ x + 9y - 5z &= 0 \\ kx - y + z &= 0 \end{aligned}$$

4.6 The Distance from a Point to a Line

In this section we begin developing various methods of finding distances in the plane and in 3-space.

Consider the problem of finding the distance from a point to a line in the plane.

Let $Ax + By + C = 0$ be the equation of the line ℓ, and let $Q(x_1, y_1)$ be a point in R^2. The shortest distance, d, from the point Q to the line will be the length of the perpendicular QR from Q to the line.

One method of finding the distance QR is to find the equation of the line through Q perpendicular to the line ℓ, calculate the coordinates of the point of intersection R, and then calculate the distance QR. However, the following method is less work.

Let $P(x_0, y_0)$ be any point on the line ℓ. Since RQ is perpendicular to ℓ, it is in the direction of the normal vector $\vec{n} = (A, B)$ to the line ℓ. Then the distance d equals the length of the scalar projection of $\overrightarrow{PQ}$ on $\vec{n}$. Using the properties of scalar projection discussed in section 1.9, we have

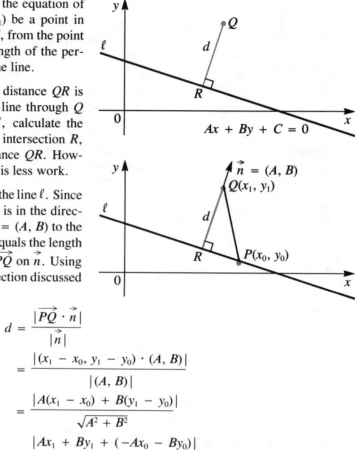

$$d = \frac{|\overrightarrow{PQ} \cdot \vec{n}|}{|\vec{n}|}$$

$$= \frac{|(x_1 - x_0, y_1 - y_0) \cdot (A, B)|}{|(A, B)|}$$

$$= \frac{|A(x_1 - x_0) + B(y_1 - y_0)|}{\sqrt{A^2 + B^2}}$$

$$= \frac{|Ax_1 + By_1 + (-Ax_0 - By_0)|}{\sqrt{A^2 + B^2}}$$

Since $P(x_0, y_0)$ lies on ℓ, it satisfies the equation $Ax + By + C = 0$; that is, $Ax_0 + By_0 + C = 0$ or $C = -Ax_0 - By_0$. Substitute this in the equation above to obtain the following result.

The distance from the point $Q(x_1, y_1)$ to the line $Ax + By + C = 0$ is

$$d = \frac{|Ax_1 + By_1 + C|}{\sqrt{A^2 + B^2}}$$

If the expression $Ax_1 + By_1 + C$ is positive, then Q lies on one side of the line, and if it is negative, then Q lies on the other side of the line; of course, if it is zero, then Q lies on the line. If we let Q be the origin $(0, 0)$, we obtain the following result.

The distance from the origin to the line $Ax + By + C = 0$ **is**

$$d = \frac{|C|}{\sqrt{A^2 + B^2}}$$

Example 1. Find the distance from the point $Q(2, -3)$ to the line $4x + 5y - 6 = 0$.

Solution. Using the formula for the distance from a point to a line, we can calculate the required distance:

$$d = \frac{|4(2) + 5(-3) - 6|}{\sqrt{4^2 + 5^2}}$$

$$= \frac{|8 - 15 - 6|}{\sqrt{16 + 25}}$$

$$= \frac{13}{\sqrt{41}}$$

$\square$

Example 2. Find the distance from the origin to the line $\vec{r} = (-4, 2) + t(-3, 4), t \in \mathbf{R}$.

Solution. The equation of the line can be written as $\frac{x + 4}{-3} = \frac{y - 2}{4}$; that is,

$4x + 16 = -3y + 6$ or $4x + 3y + 10 = 0$. Using the formula for the distance from the origin to a line, we can calculate the distance from the origin to this line:

$$d = \frac{|10|}{\sqrt{3^2 + 4^2}}$$

$$= \frac{10}{5}$$

$$= 2$$

$\square$

Example 3. Find the distance between the lines $\ell_1\colon 3x + 4y - 8 = 0$ and $\ell_2\colon 6x + 8y - 7 = 0$.

Solution. The normals are $\vec{n}_1 = (3, 4)$ and $\vec{n}_2 = (6, 8)$ and satisfy $\vec{n}_2 = 2\vec{n}_1$. Hence, the lines are parallel. They are distinct since the second equation is not twice the first equation.

The distance between these parallel lines is the shortest distance from any point P_1 on ℓ_1 to ℓ_2. Now $P_1(0, 2)$ lies on ℓ_1 and its distance to ℓ_2 is

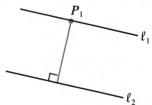

$$d = \frac{|6(0) + 8(2) - 7|}{\sqrt{6^2 + 8^2}}$$

$$= \tfrac{9}{10}$$

Hence, the parallel lines are $\tfrac{9}{10}$ units apart.

$\square$

Now consider the problem of finding the distance from a point to a line in R^3.

Let $\vec{r} = \vec{r_1} + t\vec{m}$ be the vector equation of a line ℓ and let Q be a point in R^3. The shortest distance d from Q to the line ℓ is the length of the perpendicular QR to the line. We give two general methods for finding this perpendicular distance.

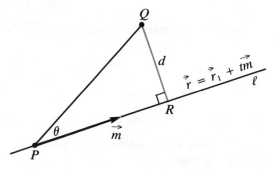

Method 1. Let P be a point on ℓ and let θ be the angle between PQ and $\vec{m}$, the direction vector of the line. Then

$$d = |\vec{PQ}| \sin \theta$$

Recall that the magnitude of the cross product, $|\vec{PQ} \times \vec{m}|$, is $|\vec{PQ}||\vec{m}| \sin \theta$. Therefore,

$$d = \frac{|\vec{PQ} \times \vec{m}|}{|\vec{m}|}$$

Method 2. As in method 1, let P be a point on the line ℓ. Calculate the length of PR, which is the length of the scalar projection of $\vec{PQ}$ on $\vec{m}$, and then use Pythagoras' Theorem in triangle PQR to find $d = QR$. Hence,

$$PR = \frac{|\vec{PQ} \cdot \vec{m}|}{|\vec{m}|}$$

$$d = QR = \sqrt{(PQ)^2 - (PR)^2}$$

Example 4. Find the distance from the point $Q(6, 3, -1)$ to the line $r = (3, -2, 0) + t(4, 3, -2)$

Solution. The point $P(3, -2, 0)$ lies on the line whose direction vector is $\vec{m} = (4, 3, -2)$. The vector $\vec{PQ}$ is $(6, 3, -1) - (3, -2, 0) = (3, 5, -1)$.
By Method 1,

$$d = \frac{|(3, 5, -1) \times (4, 3, -2)|}{|(4, 3, -2)|}$$

$$= \frac{|(-7, 2, -11)|}{|(4, 3, -2)|}$$

$$= \sqrt{\frac{49 + 4 + 121}{16 + 9 + 4}}$$

$$= \sqrt{\frac{174}{29}}$$

$$= \sqrt{6}$$

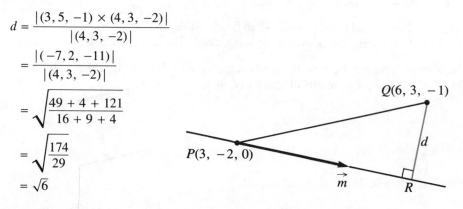

Check. Check the answer using Method 2. Using projections, we obtain

$$PR = \frac{|(3, 5, -1) \cdot (4, 3, -2)|}{|(4, 3, -2)|}$$

$$= \frac{|12 + 15 + 2|}{\sqrt{16 + 9 + 4}}$$

$$= \sqrt{29}$$

Now $|\vec{PQ}| = |(3, 5, -1)| = \sqrt{9 + 25 + 1} = \sqrt{35}$. Hence, by Pythagoras' Theorem,

$$d = QR$$
$$= \sqrt{(PQ)^2 - (PR)^2}$$
$$= \sqrt{35 - 29}$$
$$= \sqrt{6} \qquad \square$$

Method 2 can also be used for finding the distance from a point to a line in the plane. However, Method 1 can only be used in 3-space because the cross product is only defined for vectors in 3-space.

[handwritten: 45 4 + 16 + 25 81 53 134 81 + 49 + 4]

Exercises 4.6

1. Find the distance from the point $Q(3, -2)$ to each line.

   a. $3x - 2y - 6 = 0$
   b. $x - y - 5 = 0$
   c. $\dfrac{x - 3}{2} = \dfrac{y - 4}{7}$
   d. $x = 3t + 5, y = t - 7, \ t \in R$
   e. $x = 5$
   f. $\vec{r} = (-3, 4) + t(0, 1), \ t \in R$

2. Find the distance from the point $Q(1, -2, -3)$ to each line.

   a. $\vec{r} = (3, 1, 0) + t(1, 1, 2)$
   b. the line through $(-1, -1, 1)$ and $(0, 0, 2)$
   c. $\dfrac{x - 1}{2} = \dfrac{y + 1}{2} = \dfrac{z - 1}{5}$
   d. $x = 2 + 2t, y = -2 + 2t, z = 3$

3. Find the distance from the origin to each line.

   a. $3x - 4y - 7 = 0$
   b. $(x, y) = (2 + t, -5 + 3t)$
   c. $(x, y, z) = (1 + 2t, 3 + 4t, 6 + 5t)$ *[handwritten: Cannot use short formula for 3-space.]*

   [handwritten: P, ℓ, N, ∴ use pythagoras. proven in class.]

4. Let PN be the perpendicular from a point P to a line ℓ. If N lies on ℓ, prove that N is the closest point on the line to P.

5. Find the distance from the point $(-1, 2, 1)$ to the line of intersection of the planes $x + y + z = 1$ and $x - y - 2z = 0$.

[handwritten: → do matrices for point and a vector of the int line.]

6. Find the distance between the pairs of parallel lines.

   a. $x + y - 7 = 0$ and $2x + 2y + 15 = 0$

   b. $2x - 3y - 6 = 0$ and $2x - 3y - 8 = 0$

   c. $\vec{r} = (-2, 2, 1) + t(7, 3, -4)$ and $\vec{r} = (2, -1, -2) + s(7, 3, -4)$

   d. $\dfrac{x - 2}{3} = \dfrac{y - 1}{1} = \dfrac{z}{2}$ and $\dfrac{x + 1}{3} = \dfrac{y}{1} = \dfrac{z + 2}{2}$

7. Find the equation of all lines in the plane that are 3 units from the line $5x - 3y = 0$.

8. What point on the y-axis is $\dfrac{12\sqrt{13}}{13}$ units from the line $3x - 2y + 6 = 0$?

9. In the unit cube shown in the diagram, find the distance from the vertex A to the diagonal BH.

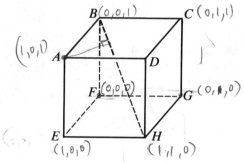

Problems 4.6

1. a. Show that the distance d between the parallel lines $Ax + By + C_1 = 0$ and $Ax + By + C_2 = 0$ in the plane is

$$d = \frac{|C_1 - C_2|}{\sqrt{A^2 + B^2}}$$

   b. Use this result to find the distance between the parallel lines $2x + 3y + 17 = 0$ and $4x + 6y + 31 = 0$.

2. Find the equation satisfied by the set of all points in the plane that are equidistant from the lines $x - 2y + 6 = 0$ and $2x - y - 2 = 0$. What is the geometric interpretation of this result?

3. Find the equation satisfied by the set of all points in the plane that are equidistant from the point $(2, 0)$ and the line $x + 2 = 0$. What curve does this equation represent?

4. Use calculus to find the minimum distance from the point $Q(2, 3, -1)$ to the line $\vec{r} = (2, -3, 5) + t(1, -1, 7)$. (Hint: Set up the distance function from the point Q to the point with parameter t on the line and then minimize the square of this distance.)

4.7 The Distance from a Point to a Plane

The shortest distance from a point Q to a plane in 3-space is the length of the perpendicular QR to the plane.

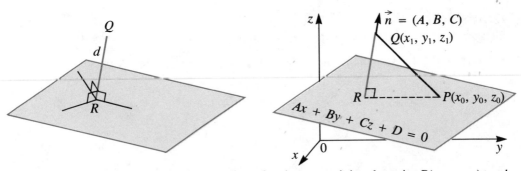

Let $Ax + By + Cz + D = 0$ be the equation of a plane containing the point $P(x_0, y_0, z_0)$, and let $Q(x_1, y_1, z_1)$ be a point in 3-space. Since RQ is perpendicular to the plane, it is in the direction of the normal vector $\vec{n} = (A, B, C)$ to the plane. Hence, the distance $d = |\overrightarrow{RQ}|$ equals the length of the scalar projection of $\overrightarrow{PQ}$ on $\vec{n}$. That is,

$$d = \frac{|\overrightarrow{PQ} \cdot \vec{n}|}{|\vec{n}|}$$

$$= \frac{|(x_1 - x_0, y_1 - y_0, z_1 - z_0) \cdot (A, B, C)|}{|(A, B, C)|}$$

$$= \frac{|A(x_1 - x_0) + B(y_1 - y_0) + C(z_1 - z_0)|}{\sqrt{A^2 + B^2 + C^2}}$$

$$= \frac{|Ax_1 + By_1 + Cz_1 + (-Ax_0 - By_0 - Cz_0)|}{\sqrt{A^2 + B^2 + C^2}}$$

Since P lies on the plane, $Ax_0 + By_0 + Cz_0 + D = 0$ or $D = -Ax_0 - By_0 - Cz_0$. Substitute this in the above equation to obtain the following result.

The distance from the point $Q(x_1, y_1, z_1)$ to the plane $Ax + By + Cz + D = 0$ is

$$d = \frac{|Ax_1 + By_1 + Cz_1 + D|}{\sqrt{A^2 + B^2 + C^2}}$$

If the expression $Ax_1 + By_1 + Cz_1 + D$ is positive, then Q lies on one side of the plane, and if it is negative, then Q lies on the other side of the plane. If $Ax_1 + By_1 + Cz_1 + D = 0$, then $Q(x_1, y_1, z_1)$ lies on the plane and $d = 0$. If we let Q be the origin $(0, 0, 0)$, we obtain the following result.

The distance from the origin to the plane $Ax + By + Cz + D = 0$ is

$$d = \frac{|D|}{\sqrt{A^2 + B^2 + C^2}}$$

Example 1.

Find the distance from the point $Q(1, 3, -2)$ to the plane $4x - y - z + 6 = 0$.

Solution. Using the formula for the distance from a point to a plane, we obtain

$$d = \frac{|4(1) - (3) - (-2) + 6|}{\sqrt{16 + 1 + 1}}$$

$$= \frac{9}{\sqrt{18}}$$

$$= \frac{3}{\sqrt{2}}$$

$\square$

Example 2. Find the distance between the planes π_1: $2x + 2y - z - 3 = 0$ and π_2: $4x + 4y - 2z + 9 = 0$.

Solution. The normals to the planes are $\vec{n}_1 = (2, 2, -1)$ and $\vec{n}_2 = (4, 4, -2)$, and since $\vec{n}_2 = 2\vec{n}_1$, the normals are parallel and the planes are parallel. Since the second equation is not twice the first, the planes are distinct.

The distance between these parallel planes is the distance from a point P_1 on π_1 to the plane π_2. Now $P_1(0, 0, -3)$ lies on π_1. The distance from P_1 to π_2: $4x + 4y - 2z + 9 = 0$ is

$$d = \frac{|4(0) + 4(0) - 2(-3) + 9|}{\sqrt{4^2 + 4^2 + (-2)^2}}$$

$$= \frac{|15|}{\sqrt{36}}$$

$$= \tfrac{5}{2}$$

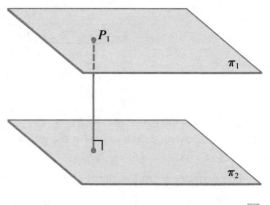

Hence, the planes are $\tfrac{5}{2}$ units apart.

$\square$

Example 3. Find the foot of the perpendicular from $Q(2, 0, -1)$ to the plane π_1: $3x - y - 2z - 1 = 0$, and also find the reflection of Q in π_1.

Solution. Let R be the foot of the perpendicular from Q to the plane π_1 and let S be the reflection of Q in π_1. The line QR lies in the direction of the normal, $(3, -1, -2)$, to π_1 and passes through Q $(2, 0, -1)$. Hence, the vector equation of the line containing QR is

$(x, y, z) = (2, 0, -1) + t(3, -1, -2)$

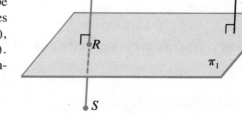

and the parametric equations are
$x = 2 + 3t$, $y = -t$, and $z = -1 + 2t$.
The intersection of this line with the plane
π_1 will be the point R. The point on the line
QR with parameter t lies on the plane
$3x - y - 2z - 1 = 0$ if

$$3(2 + 3t) - (-t) - 2(-1 - 2t) - 1 = 0$$
$$7 + 14t = 0$$

Hence, the parameter for the foot of the perpendicular, R, is $t = -\frac{7}{14} = -\frac{1}{2}$. Therefore, the

coordinates of R are $(2, 0, -1) - \frac{1}{2}(3, -1, -2)$ or $\left(\frac{1}{2}, \frac{1}{2}, 0\right)$.

If S is the reflection of Q in π_1, then S lies on the line through Q and R, and $QR = RS$. Since

the parameter of Q is $t = 0$ and the parameter of R is $t = -\frac{1}{2}$, the parameter of S must be

$t = -1$. Therefore, the coordinates of S are $(2, 0, -1) - (3, -1, -2)$ or $(-1, 1, 1)$.

Check. Check that the distance QS is twice the distance from Q to the plane π_1. We have
$\overrightarrow{QS} = (-1, 1, 1) - (2, 0, -1) = (-3, 1, 2)$, and so

$$\begin{aligned}|\overrightarrow{QS}| &= \sqrt{(-3)^2 + 1^2 + 2^2} \\ &= \sqrt{14}\end{aligned}$$

Now the distance from $Q(2, 0, -1)$ to the plane $3x - y - 2z - 1 = 0$ is

$$\begin{aligned}d &= \frac{|3(2) - (0) - 2(-1) - 1|}{\sqrt{3^2 + (-1)^2 + (-2)^2}} \\ &= \frac{|7|}{\sqrt{14}} \\ &= \frac{\sqrt{14}}{2}\end{aligned}$$

Hence, $2|\overrightarrow{QR}| = |\overrightarrow{QS}|$. □

Exercises 4.7

1. Find the distance from the given point to the given plane.

   a. $(1, 1, -1)$; $x + y - z - 3 = 0$

   b. $(1, 2, 3)$; $2x + y - 2z - 4 = 0$

   c. $(7, -3, 2)$; $2x - 3z - 1 = 0$

   d. $(0, 0, 0)$; $y = 7$

   e. $(1, 2, -3)$; $2x - 3y - 6z + 14 = 0$

2. a. Find the Cartesian equation of the plane that contains the point $P(7, -3, 4)$, and that is perpendicular to the vector $(1, -2, 5)$.

   b. How far is this plane from the origin?

3. Find the distance from the origin to the plane that has an x-intercept of 2, a y-intercept of -3, and a z-intercept of 5.

4. Find the distance from the point Q $(2, -3, 1)$ to the plane containing the points $A(2, 2, -3)$, $B(2, 7, -1)$, and $C(4, -2, 3)$.

5. The rectangular box shown has sides FG of length 2, CG of length 1, and EF of length 3. Find the distance from C to the plane AFH.

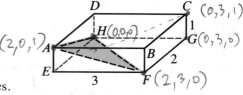

6. Find the distance between the pairs of planes.

   a. $2x - 4y + 2z - 1 = 0$ and $2x - 4y + 2z - 3 = 0$

   b. $x + 2y + z = 4$ and $x + 2y + z = -8$

   c. $4x - 12y + 6z + 7 = 0$ and $2x - 6y + 3z - 6 = 0$

7. Find the Cartesian equation of a plane, with normal $(4, -3, 2)$, that is a distance of 3 units from the origin.

8. Find the distance of each point from the plane $2x - 2y + z - 3 = 0$ and state whether the point lies on the same side of the plane as the origin, on the opposite side of the plane from the origin, or in the plane.

   a. $(1, 0, 0)$ **b.** $(-1, 0, 0)$ **c.** $(-2, -1, 5)$

   d. $(2, 1, 2)$ **e.** $(1, 0, 1)$ **f.** $(3, 7, 9)$

9. Find the foot of the perpendicular from $Q(-3, 3, 1)$ to the plane π_1: $2x + z - 5 = 0$, and also find the reflection of Q in π_1.

Problems 4.7

1. a. Show that the distance between the parallel planes $Ax + By + Cz + D_1 = 0$ and $Ax + By + Cz + D_2 = 0$ in 3-space is

$$d = \frac{|D_1 - D_2|}{\sqrt{A^2 + B^2 + C^2}}$$

   b. Use this result to find the distance between the parallel planes $3x - 9y - 12z + 5 = 0$ and $x - 3y - 4z + 6 = 0$.

2. If a, b, and c are the x-intercept, y-intercept, and z-intercept of a plane, respectively, and d is the distance from the origin to the plane, show that

$$\frac{1}{d^2} = \frac{1}{a^2} + \frac{1}{b^2} + \frac{1}{c^2}$$

3. Find the equation of the reflection of the line $\vec{r} = (0, 2, 5) + t(-1, 1, 3)$ in the plane $x + y + z = 1$.

4.8 The Distance between Skew Lines (Optional)

Recall that two lines in 3-space that do not intersect and are not parallel are called **skew lines**. Intersecting lines and parallel lines lie in a plane. Skew lines are pairs of lines that do not lie in a plane.

Let ℓ_1 and ℓ_2 be skew lines in 3-space. To find the shortest distance, d, between the lines ℓ_1 and ℓ_2, we need to find points R_1 on ℓ_1 and R_2 on ℓ_2 so that the distance R_1R_2 is a minimum. This shortest distance will occur when R_1R_2 is perpendicular to both lines. The proof of the fact that the common perpendicular is unique and that the mini-

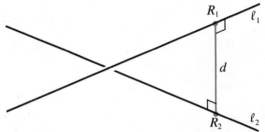

mum distance occurs along the common perpendicular is left as a problem. The length of R_1R_2 is then called the shortest distance, or simply the distance, between the lines, and R_1R_2 is called the **common perpendicular**.

If $\vec{r} = \vec{r_1} + t_1\vec{m_1}$ and $\vec{r} = \vec{r_2} + t_2\vec{m_2}$ are the **vector** equations of the skew lines ℓ_1 and ℓ_2, respectively, then the common perpendicular is at right angles to both $\vec{m_1}$ and $\vec{m_2}$ and so must be in the direction of $\vec{m_1} \times \vec{m_2}$. Let π_1 and π_2 be parallel planes, both with normal $\vec{m_1} \times \vec{m_2}$, that contain the lines ℓ_1 and ℓ_2, respectively. The shortest distance, R_1R_2, between the skew lines is the distance between the planes π_1 and π_2.

Let P_1 be a point on ℓ_1 and let P_2 be a point on ℓ_2. Let S be the point on π_1 for which SP_2 is parallel to R_1R_2. Then the length of R_1R_2 is equal to that of SP_2 and this is the length of the scalar projection of $\overrightarrow{P_1P_2}$ on the normal $\vec{m_1} \times \vec{m_2}$. Hence, the shortest distance between the skew lines is

$$
\begin{aligned}
d &= |\overrightarrow{R_1R_2}| \\
&= |\overrightarrow{SP_2}| \\
&= \frac{|\overrightarrow{P_1P_2} \cdot (\vec{m_1} \times \vec{m_2})|}{|\vec{m_1} \times \vec{m_2}|}
\end{aligned}
$$

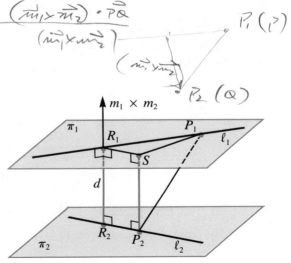

This method will still work if the lines intersect. However, if we tried to apply it to parallel lines ℓ_1 and ℓ_2, we would find that $\vec{m_1} \times \vec{m_2} = \vec{0}$.

Example 1. Find the distance between the lines ℓ_1: $\vec{r} = (-1, -9, 5) + t(-2, 1, 3)$ and ℓ_2: $r = (2, 7, 9) + s(1, 2, 3)$.

Solution. The direction of the common perpendicular is

$$(-2, 1, 3) \times (1, 2, 3) = (-3, 9, -5)$$

The point $P_1(-1, -9, 5)$ lies on ℓ_1, and $P_2(2, 7, 9)$ lies on ℓ_2 so that

$$\overrightarrow{P_1P_2} = (2, 7, 9) - (-1, -9, 5) = (3, 16, 4)$$

The shortest distance between the lines ℓ_1 and ℓ_2 is the length of the scalar projection of $(3, 16, 4)$ on $(-3, 9, -5)$; this is

$$d = \frac{|(3, 16, 4) \cdot (-3, 9, -5)|}{|(-3, 9, -5)|}$$
$$= \frac{|-9 + 144 - 20|}{\sqrt{9 + 81 + 25}}$$
$$= \frac{115}{\sqrt{115}}$$
$$= \sqrt{115} \qquad\qquad \square$$

Example 2. Find the distance between the lines ℓ_1: $\dfrac{x + 1}{3} = \dfrac{y - 1}{4} = \dfrac{z}{-2}$ and ℓ_2: $\dfrac{x - 5}{2} = \dfrac{y - 9}{3} = \dfrac{z + 4}{1}$.

Solution. The direction of the common perpendicular is

$$(3, 4, -2) \times (2, 3, 1) = (10, -7, 1)$$

The point $P_1(-1, 1, 0)$ lies on ℓ_1, and $P_2(5, 9, -4)$ lies on ℓ_2. Therefore, $\overrightarrow{P_1P_2} = (5, 9, -4) - (-1, 1, 0) = (6, 8, -4)$. The distance between the lines is the length of the scalar projection of $(6, 8, -4)$ on $(10, -7, 1)$, and this is

$$d = \frac{|(6, 8, -4) \cdot (10, -7, 1)|}{|(10, -7, 1)|}$$
$$= \frac{|60 - 56 - 4|}{\sqrt{100 + 49 + 1}}$$
$$= 0$$

Hence, the given lines intersect.

Check. The point of intersection of these two lines was found in Example 4 of section 4.1.

$\square$

Exercises 4.8

1. Find the shortest distance between the lines.

   a. $\vec{r} = (0, -2, 6) + t_1(2, 1, -1)$ and $\vec{r} = (0, -5, 0) + t_2(-1, 1, 2)$

   b. $x = 6, y = -4 - t, z = t$ and $x = -2s, y = 5, z = 3 + s$

   c. $(x, y, z) = (-2, 4, -6) + t(3, -6, 9)$ and $(x, y, z) = (0, 0, 0) + s(2, -2, 1)$

   d. $\dfrac{x - 1}{2} = \dfrac{y}{4} = \dfrac{z + 1}{3}$ and $x = y - 1 = z$

2. Given the points $A(-2, 1, 3)$, $B(1, 0, -4)$, $C(2, 2, 2)$, and $D(4, 1, 0)$, find the shortest distance between the lines AB and CD.

3. A tetrahedron has vertices $O(0, 0, 0)$, $A(1, 0, 0)$, $B(2, 3, 0)$, and $C(0, 0, 4)$. Find the shortest distance between the edges

   a. OA and BC b. OC and AB

Problems 4.8

1. For each pair of lines, find the points of intersection of the common perpendicular with the lines, and also find the distance between the lines.

   a. $(x, y, z) = (0, -1, 0) + t(1, 2, 1)$ and $(x, y, z) = (-2, 2, 0) + s(2, -1, 2)$

   b. $\dfrac{x}{2} = \dfrac{y + 1}{1} = \dfrac{z + 2}{3}$, and $\dfrac{x - 7}{4} = \dfrac{y - 1}{-3} = \dfrac{z + 5}{-4}$

2. Find the equations of the common perpendicular of the lines $\dfrac{x + 1}{1} = \dfrac{y - 1}{2} = \dfrac{z - 1}{2}$ and $\dfrac{x + 1}{1} = \dfrac{y - 2}{-1} = \dfrac{z - 2}{1}$.

3. a. Prove that each pair of skew lines has a common perpendicular and that the perpendicular is unique.

   b. Prove that the minimum distance between the lines occurs along this common perpendicular.

4. Find the Cartesian equation of the plane parallel to, and equidistant from, the skew lines $(x, y, z) = (2, -4, 3) + t(3, 5, 1)$ and $(x, y, z) = (0, -6, 5) + s(5, 1, 0)$.

5. Let ℓ_1: $\vec{r} = (3, 4, 1) + t(2, 1, 2)$ and ℓ_2: $\vec{r} = (4, 17, -3) + s(4, 2, -1)$ be two lines. Find the Cartesian equation of the plane that contains ℓ_1 and the point R_2 on ℓ_2 that is at a minimum distance from ℓ_1.

Review Exercises

1. Find the intersection, if any, of

   a. the line $\vec{r} = (0, 0, 2) + t(4, 3, 4)$ and the line $\vec{r} = (-4, 1, 0) + s(-4, 1, -2)$.

   b. the line $x = t$, $y = 1 + 2t$, $z = 3 - t$ and the line $x = -3$, $y = -6 + 2s$, $z = 3 - 6s$.

   c. the line $(x, y, z) = (2, 1, 4) + t(1, 0, 1)$ and the plane $3x - 4y - 3z - 9 = 0$.

   d. the line $\dfrac{x - 1}{2} = \dfrac{y + 4}{-1} = \dfrac{z}{3}$ and the plane $5x - y - 4z = 2$.

   e. the plane $x + 3y - 2z - 4 = 0$ and the plane $2x + 3y + z + 5 = 0$.

   f. the plane $x + 2y - 5z - 3 = 0$ and the plane $3x + 6y - 10z - 1 = 0$.

2. Show that the line $(x, y, z) = (-5 - 3t, 3 - 4t, 1 + 5t)$ lies in the plane $2x + y + 2z + 5 = 0$.

3. Show that the lines $\vec{r} = (2, 4, 3) + t(1, -3, 0)$ and $\vec{r} = (0, 2, 2) + s(2, 1, 3)$ are skew lines.

4. For what values of k will the planes $2x - 6y + 4z + 3 = 0$ and $3x - 9y + 6z + k = 0$

   a. not intersect?   **b.** intersect in a line?   **c.** intersect in a plane?

5. A plane passes through the points $(1, 0, 2)$ and $(-1, 1, 0)$ and is parallel to the vector $(-1, 1, 1)$.

   a. Find the Cartesian equation of the plane.

   b. Find the equation of a line through the point $Q(0, 3, 3)$ that is perpendicular to the plane.

   c. Find the foot of the perpendicular, R, from Q to the plane.

   d. Use a distance formula to check your answer to part **c**.

6. Find the equation of the plane that passes through the point $(3, 0, -4)$ and is perpendicular to the line of intersection of the planes $x + 2y - 7z = 3$ and $x - 5y + 4z = 1$.

7. Let ℓ be the line of intersection of the two planes $x + y + z = 1$ and $2x - 3y + z + 2 = 0$.

   a. Find the Cartesian equation of the plane, π_1, that contains the line ℓ and passes through the origin.

   b. Show that the plane π_1 make an angle of $60°$ with the plane $x - z = 0$.

8. Solve each system of equations and give the geometric interpretation in 3-space of each system and its solutions.

   a. $x + 5y - 8 = 0$ **b.** $2x - 2y + 4z = 5$ **c.** $3x + 2y - 4z + 1 = 0$
   $\quad\ 5x - 7y + 8 = 0$ $\quad\ \ x - y + 2z = 2$ $\quad\ \ 2x - y - z + 3 = 0$

d. $x + 2y - 3z = 11$
$2x + y = 7$
$3x + 6y - 8z = 32$

e. $x - y + 3z = 4$
$x + y + 2z = 2$
$3x + y + 7z = 9$

f.
$2x$

g. $x + 2y + z = -3$
$x + 7y + 4z = -13$
$2x - y - z = 4$

h. $3x - 3z = 12$
$2x - 2z = 8$
$x - z = 4$

i. $x +$
$x + 2y$
$2x + 2y + z$

9. Solve each system of equations and state whether the system has no solution, solution, or an infinite number of solutions. For systems having an infinite number solutions, give three particular solutions besides the general solution.

a. $x - 2y - 2z = 6$
$2x - 5y + 3z = -10$
$3x - 4y + z = -1$

b. $x + 3y + 2z = 6$
$3x - y + z = -2$
$2x + 2y - 3z = 14$

c. $2x + y - z = 3$
$x + y = 2$
$x - z = 1$

10. Find the intersection, if any, of the following four planes and sketch a geometrical representation of the system and its solution.

$$x + 2y + z = 1$$
$$2x - 3y - z = 6$$
$$3x + 5y + 4z = 5$$
$$4x + y + z = 8$$

11. Find the shortest distance between

   a. the points $(2, 1, 3)$ and $(0, -4, 7)$.
   b. the point $(3, 7)$ and the line $2x - 3y = 7$.
   c. the point $(4, 0, 1)$ and the line $\vec{r} = (2, -2, 1) + t(1, 2, -1)$.
   d. the point $(1, 3, 2)$ and the line $\dfrac{x - 1}{-1} = \dfrac{y - 3}{1} = \dfrac{z - 7}{2}$.
   e. the point $(7, 7, -7)$ and the plane $6y - z + 5 = 0$.
   f. the point $(3, 2, 1)$ and the plane $3x + 2y + z = 10$.
   g. the line $\vec{r} = (1, 3, 2) + t(1, 2, -1)$ and the plane $y + 2z = 5$.
   h. the planes $x + 2y - 5z - 10 = 0$ and $2x + 4y - 10z - 17 = 0$.

12. Find the distance from the point $(1, -2, -2)$ to the plane having an x-intercept of -1, a y-intercept of 2, and a z-intercept of 3.

13. The rectangular box shown has sides
   EH of length 2, EF of length 4, and HD
   of length 5. Let M be the midpoint of
   CD. Find

   a. the distance from B to the plane
      AGM.

   b. the distance from B to the line GM.

14. Find the coordinates of the foot of the perpendicular from $Q(3, 2, 4)$ to the line
   $\vec{r} = (-6, -7, -3) + t(5, 3, 4)$.

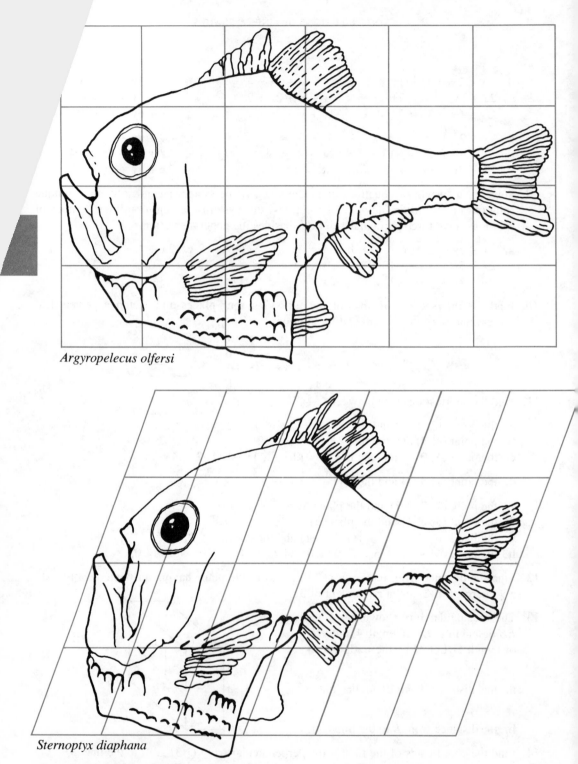

Argyropelecus olfersi

Sternoptyx diaphana

One species of fish is a linear transformation of the other.

Linear Transformations and Matrices

Many quantities in nature vary "linearly" in relation to other quantities. For example, Sir Isaac Newton discovered that acceleration varies linearly with force. Linear functions are the simplest of functions, but they often occur in applications and are important. Linear functions of two or more variables are usually called linear transformations, and they can be represented very naturally by using matrices. In this chapter, we shall study the meaning of linearity and illustrate it by examining linear transformations in two dimensions and their corresponding matrices.

Many "linear problems" can be reduced to problems involving matrices and linear equations. Moreover, matrix problems can often be conveniently solved with computers. In real applications of mathematics, non-linear problems are often impossible to solve exactly and they are approximated by linear problems that can be solved. For example, a mathematical model of the Canadian economy may consist of many non-linear equations involving hundreds of variables. These would be approximated by a linear system of equations and solved with a computer.

5.1 Linear Functions

Let us investigate the characteristics of a linear function or linear relationship by examining a linear scale such as a ruler. A ruler acts as a linear function that translates real numbers to directed distances from a fixed origin on a line.

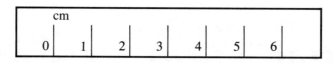

If the number 1 is 1 cm from the origin O, then the number 3 is three times that distance from O. The number 6 is twice as far from O as 3 is from O. The ruler is designed so that the multiple ka of the number a is placed at a distance k times as far from O as a is placed. That is, if $T(x)$ is the distance of the number x from O, then

$$T(ka) = kT(a)$$

Moreover, if a and b are two numbers, the distance of $a + b$ from O is the same as the sum of the distances of a from O and b from O; that is

$$T(a + b) = T(a) + T(b)$$

These are the two crucial properties of linear functions.

A function $T(x)$ is called **linear** if, for all a, b in the domain, and for each scalar k,

$$T(a + b) = T(a) + T(b)$$
$$\text{and} \qquad T(ka) = kT(a)$$

The nature of the quantities a and $T(a)$ can vary a great deal. The only requirement is that the quantities can be added and have scalar multiples. They may represent numbers, distances, voltages, forces, velocities, vectors, and so on.

A sales tax is normally a linear tax on goods sold; each dollar is taxed at a constant rate, say 8%. However, an income tax is usually non-linear. People with low incomes pay no tax, but the rate for the others depends on their tax bracket — the more you earn, the higher the percentage that goes to tax.

Here are some further examples to illustrate the notion of linearity.

- The process of tripling a number is linear because

$$3(a + b) = 3a + 3b \quad \text{and} \quad 3(ka) = k(3a)$$

for any numbers a, b, and k.

- In calculus, the process of differentiation is linear because

$$\frac{d}{dx}(u + v) = \frac{du}{dx} + \frac{dv}{dx} \quad \text{and} \quad \frac{d}{dx}(ku) = k\frac{du}{dx}$$

for any functions u and v and any real number k.

- Since $\sin(a + b) = \sin a \cos b + \cos a \sin b$, the process of taking the sine of an angle is **not** a linear function because

$$\sin(a + b) \neq \sin a + \sin b$$

- The quadratic function $f(x) = x^2$ is **not** linear because

$$(a + b)^2 \neq a^2 + b^2$$

- For each constant m, the real function $T(x) = mx$ is linear. We have

$$T(a + b) = m(a + b) = ma + mb = T(a) + T(b)$$

for any numbers a and b. Also, for any numbers a and k,

$$T(ka) = m(ka) = k(ma) = kT(a)$$

The following theorem shows that the only possible linear functions from R to R are of the above form.

Theorem. If $T:R \to R$ is linear, then there is a constant m such that

$$T(x) = mx, \quad \text{for all } x$$

Proof. Let $m = T(1)$. Then, for any x, we have

$$
\begin{aligned}
T(x) &= T(x1) \\
&= xT(1) \quad \text{(since T is linear and x is a scalar)} \\
&= mx \quad \text{(since $T(1) = m$)}
\end{aligned}
$$
$\square$

Hence, the graph of a linear function $T:R \to R$ is a straight line through the origin.

Sometimes all the functions $f(x) = mx + b$, of degree 1, are called "linear," because their graphs are straight lines. However, if b is not zero, they do not qualify for linearity according to the definition used in this chapter. This somewhat contradictory usage of mathematical terms is a problem we have to bear on occasion.

Now consider an example in which the quantities are vectors.

Example. If $\vec{u}$ is a vector in the plane, let $T(\vec{u}) = 2\vec{u}$, so that T is the function that doubles the length of a vector but leaves its direction unchanged. Show that T is a linear function.

Solution. Let $\vec{u}$ and $\vec{v}$ be any vectors in the plane. Then

$$\begin{aligned}
T(\vec{u}) + T(\vec{v}) &= 2\vec{u} + 2\vec{v} \quad \text{(by the definition of } T) \\
&= 2(\vec{u} + \vec{v}) \\
&= T(\vec{u} + \vec{v}) \quad \text{(by the definition of } T)
\end{aligned}$$

If k is any scalar, then

$$\begin{aligned}
T(k\vec{u}) &= 2(k\vec{u}) \quad \text{(by the definition of } T) \\
&= k(2\vec{u}) \\
&= kT(\vec{u}) \quad \text{(by the definition of } T)
\end{aligned}$$

This shows that T satisfies both conditions and is, therefore, linear. $\quad\square$

Though most rulers have linear scales, non-linear scales also have specific uses. For example, examine the abandoned slide rule up in your attic; it uses a logarithmic scale.

The intensity of an earthquake is measured on a logarithmic scale called the Richter scale. An increase of 1 on this scale means that an earthquake is 10 times as powerful. For example, an earthquake measuring 8.0 on the Richter scale is 1000 times as powerful as one measuring 5.0.

The effective acidity or alkalinity of a solution is measured by the pH scale and is the negative logarithm of the hydrogen ion concentration. Pure water has a hydrogen ion concentration of 10^{-7} moles per litre and therefore has a pH of 7. A pH of 7 is considered neutral, whereas solutions with a pH below 7 are acidic and those with a pH above 7 are alkaline. For example, lemon juice, which has a hydrogen ion concentration of approximately 10^{-2} moles per litre, has a pH of 2.

Exercises 5.1

1. Which of the following functions $T:R \to R$ is linear? Give reasons.

a. $T(x) = x^2 - x$

b. $T(x) = 3x + 4$

c. $T(x) = -7x$

d. $T(x) = 0$

e. $T(x) = |x|$

f. $T(x) = 1$

g. $T(x) = 2^x$

h. $T(x) = x$

i. $T(x) = \dfrac{5x}{4}$

2. a. Newton's Law of Gravity implies that a mass at a distance r from the earth is attracted towards the earth with a force $\dfrac{k}{r^2}$, where k is a constant. Is this force linear as a function of the distance r?

 b. Ohm's Law states that the voltage drop V across a resistor of R ohms is $V = IR$, where I is the current in amperes. If a voltage is applied across a fixed resistor, does the resulting current vary linearly with the voltage?

3. The strength of sound is measured in decibels (dB). This is a logarithmic scale such that the difference in decibels of two sounds of intensities I_1 and I_2 is

$$10 \log_{10} \frac{I_1}{I_2}$$

 a. If one sound is 1 dB more than another, how do their intensities compare?

 b. If one sound is 10 dB (or 1 bel) more than another, how do their intensities compare?

 c. If one sound is twice as loud as another, what is the difference in their decibel levels?

4. Describe three correspondences in science or nature that are linear and three that are not.

Problems 5.1

1. If f is a positive real function defined on the interval from 0 to 1, let $A(f)$ be the area under the graph of f between $x = 0$ and $x = 1$. Is A a linear function of f?

2. What relationship would a straight line imply if it were drawn on

 a. semi-logarithmic graph paper? **b.** log-log graph paper?

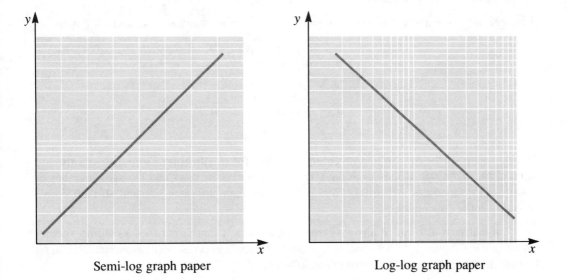

Semi-log graph paper   Log-log graph paper

5.2 Matrices

In this section we shall study some general properties of matrices. Matrices are the natural objects to use for studying linear transformations of two or more variables, and this will be done in subsequent sections.

We have already used matrices in solving systems of linear equations. Recall that a 2×2 **matrix** is an array of four numbers $A = \begin{bmatrix} a & b \\ c & d \end{bmatrix}$, arranged in two rows and two columns.

Some examples of 2×2 matrices are $\begin{bmatrix} 5 & 2 \\ -1 & 3 \end{bmatrix}, \begin{bmatrix} \frac{1}{4} & 0 \\ -15 & \sqrt{6} \end{bmatrix}, \begin{bmatrix} 0 & 1 \\ 1 & 0 \end{bmatrix}$ and $\begin{bmatrix} \cos\theta & -\sin\theta \\ \sin\theta & \cos\theta \end{bmatrix}$

Two matrices that play distinguished roles are the **zero matrix** $\begin{bmatrix} 0 & 0 \\ 0 & 0 \end{bmatrix}$ and the **identity matrix** $\begin{bmatrix} 1 & 0 \\ 0 & 1 \end{bmatrix}$. As we shall see, these matrices play the same role in the algebra of matrices as the numbers 0 and 1 play in the algebra of numbers.

A matrix can be any rectangular array of numbers. For example, $\begin{bmatrix} 5 & \sqrt{2} & -1 \\ 0 & -7 & 6 \\ \pi & 3 & 21 \end{bmatrix}$ is a 3×3 matrix. The matrix $[x \quad y]$ has one row and two columns and is called a 1×2 matrix. This 1×2 matrix can be identified with a vector in R^2 and is often called a **row vector**. The 2×1 matrix $\begin{bmatrix} x \\ y \end{bmatrix}$ has two rows and one column and is often called a **column vector**. Again, this 2×1 matrix can be identified with a vector in R^2.

A general $m \times n$ **matrix** A is a rectangular array of numbers with m rows and n columns:

$$A = \begin{bmatrix} a_{11} & a_{12} & a_{13} & \cdots & a_{1n} \\ a_{21} & a_{22} & a_{23} & \cdots & a_{2n} \\ \cdot & \cdot & \cdot & & \cdot \\ \cdot & \cdot & \cdot & & \cdot \\ \cdot & \cdot & \cdot & & \cdot \\ a_{m1} & a_{m2} & a_{m3} & \cdots & a_{mn} \end{bmatrix}$$

The element a_{ij} in the ith row and jth column is called the (i, j)th **entry**. Two matrices are said to be of the same **size** if they each have the same number of rows and the same number of columns. Two matrices are **equal** if and only if they have the same size and all their corresponding entries are equal.

A $1 \times n$ matrix is also called a **row vector**, and an $m \times 1$ matrix is called a **column vector**. As we saw in Chapter 1, two vectors can be added by adding corresponding entries. We extend this addition to matrices of any size in the following definition.

Matrix Addition

If A and B are matrices **of the same size**, their **sum** $A + B$ is a matrix of the same size formed by adding corresponding entries in A and B.

In particular, addition of 2×2 matrices is defined by

$$\begin{bmatrix} a_{11} & a_{12} \\ a_{21} & a_{22} \end{bmatrix} + \begin{bmatrix} b_{11} & b_{12} \\ b_{21} & b_{22} \end{bmatrix} = \begin{bmatrix} a_{11} + b_{11} & a_{12} + b_{12} \\ a_{21} + b_{21} & a_{22} + b_{22} \end{bmatrix}$$

Addition of matrices of different sizes is **not** defined.

Example. If $A = \begin{bmatrix} 3 & -2 \\ 7 & 1 \end{bmatrix}$, $B = \begin{bmatrix} -4 & 6 \\ 0 & -5 \end{bmatrix}$, and $C = \begin{bmatrix} 2 & 3 & -2 \\ 1 & 7 & 0 \end{bmatrix}$, calculate $A + B, A + A$ and $B + C$.

Solution. **We have**

$$A + B = \begin{bmatrix} 3 & -2 \\ 7 & 1 \end{bmatrix} + \begin{bmatrix} -4 & 6 \\ 0 & -5 \end{bmatrix} = \begin{bmatrix} -1 & 4 \\ 7 & -4 \end{bmatrix}$$

and

$$A + A = \begin{bmatrix} 3 & -2 \\ 7 & 1 \end{bmatrix} + \begin{bmatrix} 3 & -2 \\ 7 & 1 \end{bmatrix} = \begin{bmatrix} 6 & -4 \\ 14 & 2 \end{bmatrix}$$

The sum $B + C$ does not exist, since B and C have different sizes. □

If a vector is multiplied by a scalar, each entry is multiplied by that scalar. We extend this notion to a matrix of any size.

Scalar Multiplication

If A is a matrix and m is a scalar, the product mA is a matrix of the same size as A in which every entry is multiplied by m. In particular, for 2×2 matrices,

$$m \begin{bmatrix} a_{11} & a_{12} \\ a_{21} & a_{22} \end{bmatrix} = \begin{bmatrix} ma_{11} & ma_{12} \\ ma_{21} & ma_{22} \end{bmatrix}$$

For example, $(-3) \begin{bmatrix} 2 & 0 \\ -3 & -5 \end{bmatrix} = \begin{bmatrix} -6 & 0 \\ 9 & 15 \end{bmatrix}$. Notice that $2A = A + A$, for any matrix A, and zero times any matrix is the zero matrix of the same size, with all the entries zero.

Matrix addition and scalar multiplication satisfy exactly the same laws as vector addition and scalar multiplication that were given in section 1.4. The proofs are all easy to verify.

Properties of Matrix Addition and Scalar Multiplication

If the matrices A, B, C, and the zero matrix, O, are of the same size, and m and n are real numbers, the following properties are valid.

- $A + B = B + A$ (Commutative Law)
- $A + (B + C) = (A + B) + C$ (Associative Law)
- $A + O = A$
- Each matrix A has a negative, $-A$, such that $A + (-A) = O$
- $m(nA) = (mn)A$ (Associative Law)
- $m(A + B) = mA + mB$ (Distributive Law)
- $(m + n)A = mA + nA$ (Distributive Law)
- $1A = A$

Therefore, when they are needed to solve problems, matrices of the same size can be manipulated just like any other algebraic quantity by using addition and scalar multiplication. Note that $(-1)A = -A$, the negative of A.

Let $A = \begin{bmatrix} a & b \\ c & d \end{bmatrix}$ be a 2 × 2 matrix and let $X = \begin{bmatrix} x \\ y \end{bmatrix}$ be a **column** vector in $\mathbf{R}^2$. The matrix A **acts on** X to produce another column vector, AX in $\mathbf{R}^2$, according to the definition

$$AX = \begin{bmatrix} a & b \\ c & d \end{bmatrix}\begin{bmatrix} x \\ y \end{bmatrix} = \begin{bmatrix} ax + by \\ cx + dy \end{bmatrix}$$

For example, $\begin{bmatrix} 1 & -1 \\ 6 & 2 \end{bmatrix}$ acts on $\begin{bmatrix} 4 \\ -5 \end{bmatrix}$ to produce

$$\begin{bmatrix} 1 & -1 \\ 6 & 2 \end{bmatrix}\begin{bmatrix} 4 \\ -5 \end{bmatrix} = \begin{bmatrix} 1(4) + (-1)(-5) \\ 6(4) + 2(-5) \end{bmatrix} = \begin{bmatrix} 9 \\ 14 \end{bmatrix}$$

The identity matrix $\begin{bmatrix} 1 & 0 \\ 0 & 1 \end{bmatrix}$ acts on the vector $\begin{bmatrix} x \\ y \end{bmatrix}$ to produce the same vector

$$\begin{bmatrix} 1 & 0 \\ 0 & 1 \end{bmatrix}\begin{bmatrix} x \\ y \end{bmatrix} = \begin{bmatrix} 1(x) + 0(y) \\ 0(x) + 1(y) \end{bmatrix} = \begin{bmatrix} x \\ y \end{bmatrix}$$

When the zero matrix $\begin{bmatrix} 0 & 0 \\ 0 & 0 \end{bmatrix}$ acts on any vector $\begin{bmatrix} x \\ y \end{bmatrix}$, it always produces the zero vector:

$$\begin{bmatrix} 0 & 0 \\ 0 & 0 \end{bmatrix}\begin{bmatrix} x \\ y \end{bmatrix} = \begin{bmatrix} 0(x) + 0(y) \\ 0(x) + 0(y) \end{bmatrix} = \begin{bmatrix} 0 \\ 0 \end{bmatrix}$$

This action of A on X to produce AX is a special case of the product of two matrices, which will be discussed in section 5.4.

The **matrix product** of $A = \begin{bmatrix} a & b \\ c & d \end{bmatrix}$ and $\begin{bmatrix} x \\ y \end{bmatrix}$ is

$$\begin{bmatrix} a & b \\ c & d \end{bmatrix}\begin{bmatrix} x \\ y \end{bmatrix} = \begin{bmatrix} ax + by \\ cx + dy \end{bmatrix}$$

Notice that the result is a 2×1 matrix or column vector. The top entry $ax + by$, is the dot product of the first row of A, $[a \ \ b]$, with $\begin{bmatrix} x \\ y \end{bmatrix}$. The bottom entry, $cx + dy$, is the dot product of the second row of A, $[c \ \ d]$, with $\begin{bmatrix} x \\ y \end{bmatrix}$.

Eac: 2 × 2 matrix A acts on any column vector in $\mathbf{R}^2$ to give another column vector in $\mathbf{R}^2$, and so A defines a function from $\mathbf{R}^2$ to $\mathbf{R}^2$. We shall see that it is linear and its geometric implications will be explored in the next section.

Any system of two **linear** equations in two variables, such as

$$2x + 5y = 3$$
$$3x - y = -2$$

can be written as a matrix equation

$$\begin{bmatrix} 2 & 5 \\ 3 & -1 \end{bmatrix}\begin{bmatrix} x \\ y \end{bmatrix} = \begin{bmatrix} 3 \\ -2 \end{bmatrix}$$

because the matrix product on the left side is $\begin{bmatrix} 2x + 5y \\ 3x - y \end{bmatrix}$.

Exercises 5.2

1. Calculate each quantity.

   a. $\begin{bmatrix} 2 & -3 \\ 1 & 0 \end{bmatrix} + \begin{bmatrix} 4 & 3 \\ -4 & 2 \end{bmatrix}$

   b. $\begin{bmatrix} 1 & -\sqrt{2} & 7 \\ 2 & \sqrt{3} & -5 \end{bmatrix} + \begin{bmatrix} 5 & 2\sqrt{2} & -1 \\ 2 & 3\sqrt{3} & 5 \end{bmatrix}$

2. If $A = \begin{bmatrix} 1 & 4 \\ -2 & 5 \end{bmatrix}$, $B = \begin{bmatrix} 0 & -3 \\ 7 & 2 \end{bmatrix}$, $I = \begin{bmatrix} 1 & 0 \\ 0 & 1 \end{bmatrix}$ and $O = \begin{bmatrix} 0 & 0 \\ 0 & 0 \end{bmatrix}$, compute each quantity.

   a. $3A$
   b. $A - I$
   c. $A + 2B$
   d. $B + O$

   e. $-B$
   f. $4A - 3B$
   g. $5I$
   h. $A + B + I$

3. Explain why you cannot add the matrices $\begin{bmatrix} 1 & 2 & 3 \\ -3 & 0 & 0 \end{bmatrix}$ and $\begin{bmatrix} -3 & 1 \\ 4 & 0 \end{bmatrix}$.

4. Write down three 2×2 matrices A, B, and C and calculate $(A + B) + C$ and $A + (B + C)$.

5. For any 2×2 matrices A and B, and any real number m, prove that

$$m(A + B) = mA + mB$$

6. Find a, b, and c if $\begin{bmatrix} a+b & c \\ b & a-b \end{bmatrix} + \begin{bmatrix} 4 & b \\ c & c \end{bmatrix} = \begin{bmatrix} 1 & 3 \\ 3 & 10 \end{bmatrix}$.

7. Find p and q if $p\begin{bmatrix} 1 & 3 \\ 4 & -1 \end{bmatrix} + q\begin{bmatrix} 1 & -5 \\ 2 & -3 \end{bmatrix} = \begin{bmatrix} -1 & 9 \\ -1 & 4 \end{bmatrix}$.

8. If $A = \begin{bmatrix} 2 & 1 \\ -5 & 7 \end{bmatrix}$, $B = \begin{bmatrix} 2 & -3 \\ -4 & 6 \end{bmatrix}$, $X = \begin{bmatrix} 3 \\ 2 \end{bmatrix}$, and $V = \begin{bmatrix} 0 \\ -3 \end{bmatrix}$, calculate each quantity.

    a. AX **b.** AV **c.** BX **d.** BV

9. Find the value of x and y if

$$\begin{bmatrix} 4 & -2 \\ 5 & 3 \end{bmatrix}\begin{bmatrix} x \\ y \end{bmatrix} = \begin{bmatrix} 10 \\ 1 \end{bmatrix}$$

Problems 5.2

1. Find the 2×2 matrices A and B such that

$$3A + 4B = \begin{bmatrix} 1 & 0 \\ 0 & 1 \end{bmatrix}$$

and

$$2A + 3B = \begin{bmatrix} 5 & -1 \\ 2 & 2 \end{bmatrix}$$

2. Find the 2×2 matrix A if it acts on $X_1 = \begin{bmatrix} 4 \\ 5 \end{bmatrix}$ to give $X_2 = \begin{bmatrix} 3 \\ 4 \end{bmatrix}$ and acts on X_2 to give X_1.

5.3 Linear Transformations

A linear function of vectors is usually called a linear transformation. In this section we concentrate on vectors in the plane, which may be represented by ordered pairs in $\boldsymbol{R}^2$. We look at linear transformations of the form $T{:}\boldsymbol{R}^2 \to \boldsymbol{R}^2$.

In section 5.1 we saw that a linear function $T{:}\boldsymbol{R} \to \boldsymbol{R}$ of one variable was determined by one number m, and that T could be written as $T(x) = mx$. We now show that a linear transformation $T{:}\boldsymbol{R}^2 \to \boldsymbol{R}^2$ of two variables is determined by four numbers that can be conveniently specified by the elements of a 2×2 matrix A. The transformation can then be written as $T(X) = AX$, where AX is the action of A on the column vector X.

The notion of linearity for transformations of vectors in the plane is the same as that given in section 5.1.

A function $T:R^2 \to R^2$ is called a **linear transformation** if
$$T(\vec{u} + \vec{v}) = T(\vec{u}) + T(\vec{v})$$
$$\text{and} \quad T(k\vec{u}) = kT(\vec{u})$$
for all vectors $\vec{u}, \vec{v}$ in R^2 and all scalars k.

Example 1. Let $T:R^2 \to R^2$ be the transformation that takes a vector to its reflection in the x-axis. Show that T is a linear transformation.

Solution. The reflection of the vector $\vec{u} = (x, y)$ in the x-axis is $(x, -y)$, and so the transformation is

$$T(x, y) = (x, -y)$$

If $\vec{x} = (a_1, b_1)$ and $\vec{v} = (a_2, b_2)$ are any two vectors, then

$$\begin{aligned}
T(\vec{u} + \vec{v}) &= T((a_1, b_1) + (a_2, b_2)) \\
&= T(a_1 + a_2, b_1 + b_2) \\
&= (a_1 + a_2, -(b_1 + b_2)) \\
&= (a_1, -b_1) + (a_2, -b_2) \\
&= T(\vec{u}) + T(\vec{v})
\end{aligned}$$

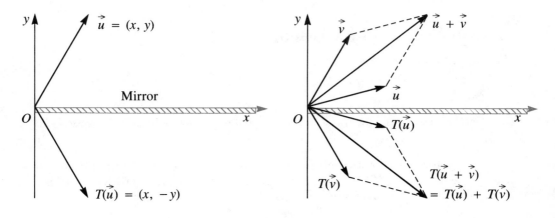

Also, if k is a scalar

$$\begin{aligned}
T(k\vec{u}) &= T(k(a_1, b_1)) \\
&= T(ka_1, kb_1) \\
&= (ka_1, -kb_1) \\
&= k(a_1, -b_1) \\
&= kT(\vec{u})
\end{aligned}$$

This shows that T is a linear transformation. The first calculation above shows that the reflection of the sum of two vectors is the sum of their reflections. The second calculation shows that the reflection of the magnification of a vector is the magnification of its reflection.   □

In fact, all reflections about lines through the origin are linear transformations, and all rotations about the origin are linear. However, as the following example shows, translations are not linear.

Example 2. Show that the translation of the plane defined by $T(x, y) = (x + 1, y)$ is **not** linear.

Proof. To show that T is not linear we need only **one** instance where either of the conditions for linearity fails. For example,

$$T((3, 0) + (0, 5)) = T(3, 5)$$
$$= (4, 5)$$

whereas
$$T(3, 0) + T(0, 5) = (4, 0) + (1, 5)$$
$$= (5, 5)$$

Hence,
$$T((3, 0) + (0, 5)) \neq T(3, 0) + T(0, 5)$$

and T is not linear.   □

An important property of a linear transformation is that it must transform the origin $\vec{0}$ in the domain to the origin in the range. Indeed, if $\vec{u}$ is any vector in the domain of a linear transformation T, then

$$T(\vec{0}) = T(0\vec{u}) = 0T(\vec{u}) = \vec{0}$$

Transformation of the Origin

For any linear transformation T,

$$T(\vec{0}) = \vec{0}$$

Hence, another reason why the translation in Example 2 cannot be linear is because $T(0, 0) = (1, 0)$.

Any 2×2 matrix A acts on column vectors X in $\mathbf{R}^2$ to give rise to a transformation of the plane defined by $T(X) = AX$. We also write the transformation as $X \rightarrow AX$ where "$\rightarrow$" is read "is mapped to." We now show that this transformation is always linear.

In particular, the identity matrix $I = \begin{bmatrix} 1 & 0 \\ 0 & 1 \end{bmatrix}$ gives rise to the **identity transformation** that maps every vector to itself:

$$\begin{bmatrix} x \\ y \end{bmatrix} \rightarrow \begin{bmatrix} 1 & 0 \\ 0 & 1 \end{bmatrix} \begin{bmatrix} x \\ y \end{bmatrix} = \begin{bmatrix} x \\ y \end{bmatrix}$$

The zero matrix gives rise to the **zero transformation** that maps every vector to the zero vector:

$$\begin{bmatrix} x \\ y \end{bmatrix} \rightarrow \begin{bmatrix} 0 & 0 \\ 0 & 0 \end{bmatrix} \begin{bmatrix} x \\ y \end{bmatrix} = \begin{bmatrix} 0 \\ 0 \end{bmatrix}$$

Theorem 1. If A is a 2×2 matrix, then A represents a linear transformation $T:\mathbf{R}^2 \to \mathbf{R}^2$ where

$$T(X) = AX \quad \text{for all column vectors } X = \begin{bmatrix} x \\ y \end{bmatrix}$$

Proof. Let $A = \begin{bmatrix} a & b \\ c & d \end{bmatrix}$, and let $X_1 = \begin{bmatrix} x_1 \\ y_1 \end{bmatrix}$ and $X_2 = \begin{bmatrix} x_2 \\ y_2 \end{bmatrix}$ be two column vectors. Since we have seen that $T:\mathbf{R}^2 \to \mathbf{R}^2$ defines a transformation, we have to verify that T is linear. The first requirement for linearity is that $T(X_1 + X_2) = T(X_1) + T(X_2)$. The sum of the column vectors X_1 and X_2 is the column vector $X_1 + X_2 = \begin{bmatrix} x_1 + x_2 \\ y_1 + y_2 \end{bmatrix}$; hence, we have

$$
\begin{aligned}
T(X_1 + X_2) &= A(X_1 + X_2) \\
&= \begin{bmatrix} a & b \\ c & d \end{bmatrix} \begin{bmatrix} x_1 + x_2 \\ y_1 + y_2 \end{bmatrix} \\
&= \begin{bmatrix} a(x_1 + x_2) + b(y_1 + y_2) \\ c(x_1 + x_2) + d(y_1 + y_2) \end{bmatrix} \\
&= \begin{bmatrix} (ax_1 + by_1) + (ax_2 + by_2) \\ (cx_1 + dy_1) + (cx_2 + dy_2) \end{bmatrix} \\
&= \begin{bmatrix} ax_1 + by_1 \\ cx_1 + dy_1 \end{bmatrix} + \begin{bmatrix} ax_2 + by_2 \\ cx_2 + dy_2 \end{bmatrix} \\
&= \begin{bmatrix} a & b \\ c & d \end{bmatrix} \begin{bmatrix} x_1 \\ y_1 \end{bmatrix} + \begin{bmatrix} a & b \\ c & d \end{bmatrix} \begin{bmatrix} x_2 \\ y_2 \end{bmatrix} \\
&= AX_1 + AX_2 \\
&= T(X_1) + T(X_2)
\end{aligned}
$$

The second requirement for linearity is that $T(kX_1) = kT(X_1)$, for each scalar k. The column vector kX_1, being a scalar multiple of X_1, is $\begin{bmatrix} kx_1 \\ ky_1 \end{bmatrix}$. Hence,

$$
\begin{aligned}
T(kX_1) &= A(kX_1) \\
&= \begin{bmatrix} a & b \\ c & d \end{bmatrix} \begin{bmatrix} kx_1 \\ ky_1 \end{bmatrix} \\
&= \begin{bmatrix} akx_1 + bky_1 \\ ckx_1 + dky_1 \end{bmatrix} \\
&= \begin{bmatrix} k(ax_1 + by_1) \\ k(cx_1 + dy_1) \end{bmatrix} \\
&= k\begin{bmatrix} ax_1 + by_1 \\ cx_1 + dy_1 \end{bmatrix} \\
&= kAX_1 \\
&= kT(X_1)
\end{aligned}
$$

Hence, T is a linear transformation. □

Therefore, if we define a transformation $T:\mathbf{R}^2 \to \mathbf{R}^2$ by $T(X) = AX$, where A is any 2×2 matrix, we can be sure that T is a **linear** transformation.

Example 3. Find the image of the points $P(2, 3)$ and $Q(3, -2)$ under the linear transformation represented by the matrix $\begin{bmatrix} 1 & 0 \\ 0 & 0 \end{bmatrix}$. Describe this transformation in geometric terms.

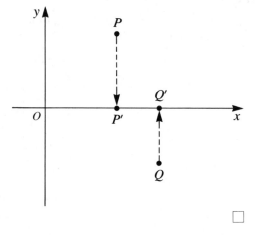

Solution. **Since**

$$\begin{bmatrix} 1 & 0 \\ 0 & 0 \end{bmatrix}\begin{bmatrix} 2 \\ 3 \end{bmatrix} = \begin{bmatrix} 2 \\ 0 \end{bmatrix} \text{ and } \begin{bmatrix} 1 & 0 \\ 0 & 0 \end{bmatrix}\begin{bmatrix} 3 \\ -2 \end{bmatrix} = \begin{bmatrix} 3 \\ 0 \end{bmatrix}$$

the image of P is the point $P'(2, 0)$ and the image of Q is the point $Q'(3, 0)$. In general

$$\begin{bmatrix} 1 & 0 \\ 0 & 0 \end{bmatrix}\begin{bmatrix} x \\ y \end{bmatrix} = \begin{bmatrix} x \\ 0 \end{bmatrix}$$

so that the point (x, y) is mapped to the point $(x, 0)$. Hence, the transformation is the vertical **projection** onto the x-axis. □

Example 4. Find the equation of the image of the circle $x^2 + y^2 = 1$ under the linear transformation T represented by the matrix $\begin{bmatrix} 2 & 0 \\ 0 & 1 \end{bmatrix}$.

Solution. Let (u, v) be the image of the general point (x, y). Then

$$\begin{bmatrix} u \\ v \end{bmatrix} = T\begin{bmatrix} x \\ y \end{bmatrix}$$
$$= \begin{bmatrix} 2 & 0 \\ 0 & 1 \end{bmatrix}\begin{bmatrix} x \\ y \end{bmatrix}$$
$$= \begin{bmatrix} 2x \\ y \end{bmatrix}$$

Hence, $u = 2x$ and $v = y$, or

$$x = \frac{u}{2} \quad \text{and} \quad y = v$$

The point (x, y) lies on the original circle $x^2 + y^2 = 1$ if and only if the point (u, v) lies on the image curve with equation

$$\frac{u^2}{4} + v^2 = 1$$

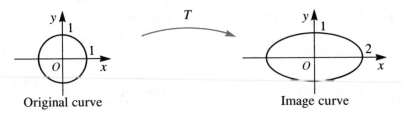

Original curve   Image curve

The image curve is an ellipse with semi-axes of length 2 and 1. The transformation T is a **horizontal stretch** by a factor of two. ☐

Note that we write $T\left(\begin{bmatrix} x \\ y \end{bmatrix}\right)$ as just $T\begin{bmatrix} x \\ y \end{bmatrix}$ to avoid a proliferation of brackets.

A linear transformation will transform a circle into an ellipse (or a circle). In fact, hyperbolas can be transformed into other hyperbolas and parabolas into other parabolas. Occasionally the image of any of these curves may degenerate into a line segment. This would happen in the vertical projection of Example 3.

Example 5. Find the image of the unit square, with vertices $O(0, 0)$, $A(0, 1)$, $B(1, 1)$, and $C(1, 0)$, under the linear transformation represented by the matrix $\begin{bmatrix} 1 & 0 \\ 2 & 1 \end{bmatrix}$.

Solution. The images of the vertices are

$$\begin{bmatrix} 1 & 0 \\ 2 & 1 \end{bmatrix}\begin{bmatrix} 0 \\ 0 \end{bmatrix} = \begin{bmatrix} 0 \\ 0 \end{bmatrix} \quad \begin{bmatrix} 1 & 0 \\ 2 & 1 \end{bmatrix}\begin{bmatrix} 0 \\ 1 \end{bmatrix} = \begin{bmatrix} 0 \\ 1 \end{bmatrix}$$

$$\begin{bmatrix} 1 & 0 \\ 2 & 1 \end{bmatrix}\begin{bmatrix} 1 \\ 1 \end{bmatrix} = \begin{bmatrix} 1 \\ 3 \end{bmatrix} \quad \begin{bmatrix} 1 & 0 \\ 2 & 1 \end{bmatrix}\begin{bmatrix} 1 \\ 0 \end{bmatrix} = \begin{bmatrix} 1 \\ 2 \end{bmatrix}$$

Hence, the vertices O and A are fixed while B maps to $B'(1, 3)$ and C maps to $C'(1, 2)$.

The vector equation of the line AB is $(x, y) = (0, 1) + t(1, 0)$, so that any point on this line has coordinates $(t, 1)$. The image of this point under the transformation is

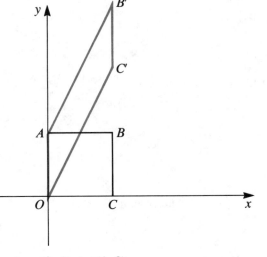

$$\begin{bmatrix} 1 & 0 \\ 2 & 1 \end{bmatrix}\begin{bmatrix} t \\ 1 \end{bmatrix} = \begin{bmatrix} t \\ 2t + 1 \end{bmatrix}$$

Thus, the vector equation of the line AB' is $(x, y) = (0, 1) + t(1, 2)$.

Hence, the straight line segment AB transforms to the straight line segment AB'. Similarly, the other sides of the square $OABC$ are transformed into the corresponding sides of the parallelogram $OAB'C'$.

This transformation is an example of a **vertical shear**. The x-coordinates remain fixed, but the y-coordinates are changed, so that points are shifted in a vertical direction. However, points on the y-axis are fixed. ☐

Illustrations of Some Linear Transformations of the Plane

Matrix	Transformation	Image of	
$\begin{bmatrix} 1 & 0 \\ 0 & 1 \end{bmatrix}$	identity		
$\begin{bmatrix} 0 & 0 \\ 0 & 1 \end{bmatrix}$	projection onto the y-axis		
$\begin{bmatrix} a & 0 \\ 0 & a \end{bmatrix}$	dilatation or magnification		
$\begin{bmatrix} a & 0 \\ 0 & d \end{bmatrix}$	two-way stretch		
$\begin{bmatrix} 0 & 1 \\ 1 & 0 \end{bmatrix}$	reflection in the line $y = x$		
$\begin{bmatrix} -1 & 0 \\ 0 & -1 \end{bmatrix}$	reflection in the origin		
$\begin{bmatrix} 1 & b \\ 0 & 1 \end{bmatrix}$	horizontal shear		
$\begin{bmatrix} a & b \\ c & d \end{bmatrix}$	arbitrary linear transformation		

The above table illustrates some of the geometric effects that can arise when we interpret 2×2 matrices as transformations. Try drawing some other examples yourself.

We showed in Theorem 1 that every 2×2 matrix represents a linear transformation. Are there some linear transformations of the plane that cannot be represented in this way? We now show that the answer is no — every linear transformation can be represented by a matrix. Moreover, each linear transformation is represented by a unique matrix, so that there is a one-to-one correspondence between linear transformations and matrices. This is why matrices are the ideal objects for handling linear transformations.

Theorem 2. If $T: \mathbf{R}^2 \rightarrow \mathbf{R}^2$ is a linear transformation, then there is exactly one matrix $A = \begin{bmatrix} a & b \\ c & d \end{bmatrix}$ such that

$$T(X) = AX = \begin{bmatrix} ax + by \\ cx + dy \end{bmatrix}, \quad \text{for all column vectors } X = \begin{bmatrix} x \\ y \end{bmatrix}$$

If we knew that the linear transformation T were represented by a matrix, how could we construct this matrix? Notice what happens to the images of the standard basis vectors under a transformation represented by the matrix A. We have

$$\begin{bmatrix} a & b \\ c & d \end{bmatrix} \begin{bmatrix} 1 \\ 0 \end{bmatrix} = \begin{bmatrix} a \\ c \end{bmatrix} \quad \text{and} \quad \begin{bmatrix} a & b \\ c & d \end{bmatrix} \begin{bmatrix} 0 \\ 1 \end{bmatrix} = \begin{bmatrix} b \\ d \end{bmatrix}$$

Hence, we can build the matrix that represents T from the column vectors $T\begin{bmatrix} 1 \\ 0 \end{bmatrix}$ and $T\begin{bmatrix} 0 \\ 1 \end{bmatrix}$.

The Matrix Representing a Linear Transformation

Given any linear transformation $T: \mathbf{R}^2 \rightarrow \mathbf{R}^2$, we can construct the matrix A representing T as follows.

- The image of $\begin{bmatrix} 1 \\ 0 \end{bmatrix}$ is the first column of A.

- The image of $\begin{bmatrix} 0 \\ 1 \end{bmatrix}$ is the second column of A.

We now use this idea in the formal proof of Theorem 2.

Proof. Given the linear transformation T, let $\begin{bmatrix} a \\ c \end{bmatrix}$ be the vector obtained when T is applied

to $\begin{bmatrix} 1 \\ 0 \end{bmatrix}$, and let $\begin{bmatrix} b \\ d \end{bmatrix}$ be the image of $\begin{bmatrix} 0 \\ 1 \end{bmatrix}$. That is,

$$\begin{bmatrix} a \\ c \end{bmatrix} = T\begin{bmatrix} 1 \\ 0 \end{bmatrix} \quad \text{and} \quad \begin{bmatrix} b \\ d \end{bmatrix} = T\begin{bmatrix} 0 \\ 1 \end{bmatrix}$$

Then, if $\begin{bmatrix} x \\ y \end{bmatrix}$ is any column vector,

$$\begin{aligned}
T\begin{bmatrix} x \\ y \end{bmatrix} &= T\left(x\begin{bmatrix} 1 \\ 0 \end{bmatrix} + y\begin{bmatrix} 0 \\ 1 \end{bmatrix} \right) \\
&= T\left(x\begin{bmatrix} 1 \\ 0 \end{bmatrix} \right) + T\left(y\begin{bmatrix} 0 \\ 1 \end{bmatrix} \right) \\
&= xT\begin{bmatrix} 1 \\ 0 \end{bmatrix} + yT\begin{bmatrix} 0 \\ 1 \end{bmatrix} \\
&= x\begin{bmatrix} a \\ c \end{bmatrix} + y\begin{bmatrix} b \\ d \end{bmatrix} \\
&= \begin{bmatrix} ax \\ cx \end{bmatrix} + \begin{bmatrix} by \\ dy \end{bmatrix} \\
&= \begin{bmatrix} ax + by \\ cx + dy \end{bmatrix} \\
&= \begin{bmatrix} a & b \\ c & d \end{bmatrix}\begin{bmatrix} x \\ y \end{bmatrix}
\end{aligned}$$

We have found a unique matrix $A = \begin{bmatrix} a & b \\ c & d \end{bmatrix}$ such that the action of T on any column vector is exactly the same as the product of A with that column vector. Hence, the linear transformation T can be represented by the matrix A. $\square$

Example 6. Find the matrix representing the linear transformation of the plane that reflects each point in the x-axis.

Solution. We showed in Example 1 that the transformation T that reflects each point in the x-axis is linear. Therefore, by Theorem 2, there is a unique matrix A representing T.

Since the vector $\begin{bmatrix} 1 \\ 0 \end{bmatrix}$ is fixed under the reflection T, $T\begin{bmatrix} 1 \\ 0 \end{bmatrix} = \begin{bmatrix} 1 \\ 0 \end{bmatrix}$. The vector $\begin{bmatrix} 0 \\ 1 \end{bmatrix}$ is taken to $\begin{bmatrix} 0 \\ -1 \end{bmatrix}$

under T. Hence, the columns of A must be $\begin{bmatrix} 1 \\ 0 \end{bmatrix}$ and $\begin{bmatrix} 0 \\ -1 \end{bmatrix}$; that is $A = \begin{bmatrix} 1 & 0 \\ 0 & -1 \end{bmatrix}$.

Check. $A\begin{bmatrix} x \\ y \end{bmatrix} = \begin{bmatrix} 1 & 0 \\ 0 & -1 \end{bmatrix}\begin{bmatrix} x \\ y \end{bmatrix} = \begin{bmatrix} x \\ -y \end{bmatrix}$

This agrees with the formula for T given in Example 1. $\square$

0 — explain

Exercises 5.3

1. Describe, in geometric terms, what each of the transformations of the plane does to the point (x, y). Which transformations are linear and which are non-linear? Give reasons.

   a. $T(x, y) = (0, y)$ **b.** $T(x, y) = (y, x)$

   c. $T(x, y) = (0, 0)$ **d.** $T(x, y) = (4, 2)$

   e. $T(x, y) = (x - 3, y - 2)$ **f.** $T(x, y) = (\sqrt{x^2 + y^2}, 0)$

2. Find the linear transformation $T: \mathbf{R}^2 \to \mathbf{R}^2$ represented by each matrix. Then describe each transformation in geometric terms.

   a. $\begin{bmatrix} 0 & 0 \\ 0 & 1 \end{bmatrix}$ **b.** $\begin{bmatrix} 3 & 0 \\ 0 & 3 \end{bmatrix}$ **c.** $\begin{bmatrix} 1 & 0 \\ 0 & 4 \end{bmatrix}$ **d.** $\begin{bmatrix} 1 & -1 \\ 0 & 1 \end{bmatrix}$

   e. $\begin{bmatrix} -1 & 0 \\ 0 & 1 \end{bmatrix}$ **f.** $\begin{bmatrix} \frac{1}{2} & \frac{1}{2} \\ \frac{1}{2} & \frac{1}{2} \end{bmatrix}$ **g.** $\begin{bmatrix} 5 & 0 \\ 0 & 2 \end{bmatrix}$ **h.** $\begin{bmatrix} -1 & 0 \\ 0 & 4 \end{bmatrix}$

3. Find the images of the points $P(2, 1)$ and $Q(-3, -3)$ under each of the transformations in Exercise 2.

4. Determine which functions define a linear transformation of the plane. For each T that is linear, find the 2×2 matrix representing T.

   a. $T\begin{bmatrix} x \\ y \end{bmatrix} = \begin{bmatrix} x + 1 \\ y \end{bmatrix}$ **b.** $T\begin{bmatrix} x \\ y \end{bmatrix} = \begin{bmatrix} x + 2y \\ x + 2y \end{bmatrix}$

   c. $T\begin{bmatrix} x \\ y \end{bmatrix} = \begin{bmatrix} 3y - 2x \\ 7y \end{bmatrix}$ **d.** $T\begin{bmatrix} x \\ y \end{bmatrix} = \begin{bmatrix} xy \\ x - y \end{bmatrix}$

5. Find the matrix of the linear transformation that represents a clockwise rotation of the plane through $90°$ about the origin.

6. Find the image of the x-axis, the y-axis, and the line $3x + 2y = 6$ under the transformation represented by each matrix.

   a. $\begin{bmatrix} 5 & 0 \\ 0 & -1 \end{bmatrix}$ **b.** $\begin{bmatrix} 4 & -3 \\ 7 & 1 \end{bmatrix}$ **c.** $\begin{bmatrix} 1 & 2 \\ 2 & 4 \end{bmatrix}$

7. Find the image of the circle $x^2 + y^2 = k^2$, of radius k, under the transformation with matrix $\begin{bmatrix} 7 & 0 \\ 0 & -3 \end{bmatrix}$.

8. Describe and sketch the image of the square with vertices $O(0, 0)$, $A(0, 1)$, $B(1, 1)$, and $C(1, 0)$ under the linear transformation represented by each matrix.

   a. $\begin{bmatrix} 0 & 1 \\ -1 & 0 \end{bmatrix}$ **b.** $\begin{bmatrix} 3 & 0 \\ 1 & -1 \end{bmatrix}$ **c.** $\begin{bmatrix} 4 & 3 \\ 1 & 2 \end{bmatrix}$

9. Find the linear transformation $T: \mathbf{R}^2 \to \mathbf{R}^2$ that maps $(0, 2)$ to $(7, 6)$ and maps $(-1, -1)$ to $(0, 1)$.

10. In each case, is it possible to have a linear transformation T satisfying the given conditions? If so, describe one such transformation.

  a. $T\begin{bmatrix} 1 \\ 0 \end{bmatrix} = \begin{bmatrix} 2 \\ 1 \end{bmatrix}$, $T\begin{bmatrix} 0 \\ 1 \end{bmatrix} = \begin{bmatrix} 5 \\ -3 \end{bmatrix}$ and $T\begin{bmatrix} 2 \\ 3 \end{bmatrix} = \begin{bmatrix} 19 \\ -7 \end{bmatrix}$ $\begin{bmatrix} 2 & 5 \\ 1 & -3 \end{bmatrix}\begin{bmatrix} 2 \\ 3 \end{bmatrix} = \begin{bmatrix} 19 \\ -7 \end{bmatrix}$ ✓

  b. $T\begin{bmatrix} 1 \\ 0 \end{bmatrix} = \begin{bmatrix} 2 \\ 1 \end{bmatrix}$, $T\begin{bmatrix} 0 \\ 1 \end{bmatrix} = \begin{bmatrix} 5 \\ -3 \end{bmatrix}$ and $T\begin{bmatrix} 2 \\ 3 \end{bmatrix} = \begin{bmatrix} 5 \\ 4 \end{bmatrix}$ (c) T is linear 2×2 matrix.

  c. $T\begin{bmatrix} -1 \\ 2 \end{bmatrix} = \begin{bmatrix} 5 \\ 0 \end{bmatrix}$, $T\begin{bmatrix} 5 \\ 1 \end{bmatrix} = \begin{bmatrix} 1 \\ 1 \end{bmatrix}$ and $T\begin{bmatrix} 1 \\ 1 \end{bmatrix} = \begin{bmatrix} 2 \\ 2 \end{bmatrix}$ $T\begin{bmatrix} -1 & 5 \\ 2 & 1 \end{bmatrix} = \begin{bmatrix} 5 & 1 \\ 0 & 1 \end{bmatrix}$ $det\frac{-1}{11}$

  $T = \begin{bmatrix} 5 & 1 \\ 0 & 1 \end{bmatrix}\begin{bmatrix} 1 & -5 \\ -2 & -1 \end{bmatrix}$

11. For each linear transformation T represented by the given matrix, describe geometrically the set of points that transform to the origin; that is, solve $T\begin{bmatrix} x \\ y \end{bmatrix} = \begin{bmatrix} 0 \\ 0 \end{bmatrix}$.

  (This set is called the null space of T.)

  a. $\begin{bmatrix} 0 & 0 \\ 0 & 0 \end{bmatrix}$ **b.** $\begin{bmatrix} 1 & 1 \\ -2 & -2 \end{bmatrix}$ **c.** $\begin{bmatrix} 3 & 1 \\ -1 & 0 \end{bmatrix}$ **d.** $\begin{bmatrix} 3 & -2 \\ -6 & 4 \end{bmatrix}$

  $=-\frac{1}{11}$ $=\begin{bmatrix} 3 \\ -2 \end{bmatrix}$ $T\begin{bmatrix} -23 \\ 11 \\ -3 \\ 11 \end{bmatrix}$

12. If you draw a graph with linear scales on the coordinate axes so that one unit on the x-axis is 1 cm and one unit on the y-axis is 3 cm, will the graph of $y = mx + b$ be a straight line? Will the graph of $x^2 + y^2 = a^2$ be a circle? Explain.

Problems 5.3

1. Prove that a linear transformation $T:\mathbf{R}^2 \to \mathbf{R}^2$ transforms a line to either a line or a point. That is, if X is a point on the line passing through P and Q, show that $T(X)$ is a point on the line passing through $T(P)$ and $T(Q)$. Also prove that, if X lies on the segment between P and Q, then $T(X)$ lies on the segment between $T(P)$ and $T(Q)$.

2. What is the image of the parabola $y^2 = x$ under the linear transformation with matrix $\begin{bmatrix} 3 & -4 \\ 4 & 3 \end{bmatrix}$? Sketch the parabola and its transformed image.

3. a. Show how a 3×3 matrix can act on a column vector in $\mathbf{R}^3$.

  b. Describe geometrically the linear transformation $T:\mathbf{R}^3 \to \mathbf{R}^3$ represented by the matrix $\begin{bmatrix} 1 & 0 & 0 \\ 0 & 1 & 0 \\ 0 & 0 & 0 \end{bmatrix}$.

  c. Can a 2×3 matrix act on column vectors in $\mathbf{R}^3$? What would the result of this action be?

4. Write a computer program that displays the image of the cube with vertices $(0, 0, 0)$, $(1, 0, 0)$, $(1, 1, 0)$, $(0, 1, 0)$, $(0, 0, 1)$, $(1, 0, 1)$, $(1, 1, 1)$, $(0, 1, 1)$ under the linear transformation $\mathbf{R}^3 \to \mathbf{R}^2$ represented by an arbitrary 2×3 matrix A.

5.4 Matrix Multiplication

The result of composing two linear transformations of the plane to itself is a third transformation of the plane that is also linear. We shall use this idea to define multiplication of matrices. The product of two matrices will represent the composition of their corresponding transformations.

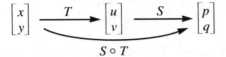

Let $S: R^2 \to R^2$ and $T: R^2 \to R^2$ be two linear transformations. Suppose that

$$T\begin{bmatrix} x \\ y \end{bmatrix} = \begin{bmatrix} u \\ v \end{bmatrix} \quad \text{and} \quad S\begin{bmatrix} u \\ v \end{bmatrix} = \begin{bmatrix} p \\ q \end{bmatrix}.$$

The **composite** of S and T, denoted by $S \circ T$, is the transformation defined by

$$(S \circ T)\begin{bmatrix} x \\ y \end{bmatrix} = S\left(T\begin{bmatrix} x \\ y \end{bmatrix}\right) = S\begin{bmatrix} u \\ v \end{bmatrix} = \begin{bmatrix} p \\ q \end{bmatrix}$$

Notice the order of the transformations in $S \circ T$. First apply T and then apply S. We can remember this by reading $S \circ T$ as "S following T."

Example 1. Let S and T be linear transformations represented by the matrices

$A = \begin{bmatrix} -2 & 5 \\ 4 & -7 \end{bmatrix}$ and $B = \begin{bmatrix} 3 & 1 \\ 1 & -2 \end{bmatrix}$, respectively.

a. Find the transformation $S \circ T$. **b.** Find the transformation $T \circ S$.

Solution.
a. To calculate $S \circ T$, we have to perform T first. Now

$$T\begin{bmatrix} x \\ y \end{bmatrix} = B\begin{bmatrix} x \\ y \end{bmatrix} = \begin{bmatrix} 3 & 1 \\ 1 & -2 \end{bmatrix}\begin{bmatrix} x \\ y \end{bmatrix} = \begin{bmatrix} 3x + y \\ x - 2y \end{bmatrix}$$

Let $u = 3x + y$ and $v = x - 2y$, so that $T\begin{bmatrix} x \\ y \end{bmatrix} = \begin{bmatrix} u \\ v \end{bmatrix}$. The composite $S \circ T$ is the trans-

formation defined by

$$(S \circ T)\begin{bmatrix} x \\ y \end{bmatrix} = S\left(T\begin{bmatrix} x \\ y \end{bmatrix}\right) = S\begin{bmatrix} u \\ v \end{bmatrix}$$

Since S is represented by the matrix A,

$$S\begin{bmatrix} u \\ v \end{bmatrix} = A\begin{bmatrix} u \\ v \end{bmatrix} = \begin{bmatrix} -2 & 5 \\ 4 & -7 \end{bmatrix}\begin{bmatrix} u \\ v \end{bmatrix} = \begin{bmatrix} -2u + 5v \\ 4u - 7v \end{bmatrix}$$

Hence, the composite is

$$(S \circ T)\begin{bmatrix} x \\ y \end{bmatrix} = \begin{bmatrix} -2u + 5v \\ 4u - 7v \end{bmatrix}$$

$$= \begin{bmatrix} -2(3x + y) + 5(x - 2y) \\ 4(3x + y) - 7(x - 2y) \end{bmatrix}$$

$$= \begin{bmatrix} -x - 12y \\ 5x + 18y \end{bmatrix}$$

This composite $S \circ T$ is the linear transformation represented by the matrix $\begin{bmatrix} -1 & -12 \\ 5 & 18 \end{bmatrix}$.

b. To calculate $T \circ S$ we have to perform S first, followed by T. We have

$$(T \circ S)\begin{bmatrix} x \\ y \end{bmatrix} = T\left(S\begin{bmatrix} x \\ y \end{bmatrix}\right)$$

$$= T\begin{bmatrix} -2x + 5y \\ 4x - 7y \end{bmatrix}$$

$$= \begin{bmatrix} 3(-2x + 5y) + (4x - 7y) \\ (-2x + 5y) - 2(4x - 7y) \end{bmatrix}$$

$$= \begin{bmatrix} -2x + 8y \\ -10x + 19y \end{bmatrix}$$

Hence, the composite $S \circ T$ is the linear transformation represented by the matrix $\begin{bmatrix} -2 & 8 \\ -10 & 19 \end{bmatrix}$. □

We shall define the matrix product of A and B to be the matrix $AB = \begin{bmatrix} -1 & -12 \\ 5 & 18 \end{bmatrix}$

that represents the transformation $S \circ T$. The product of B and A will be the matrix $BA = \begin{bmatrix} -2 & 8 \\ -10 & 19 \end{bmatrix}$ that represents the transformation $T \circ S$. Notice that since AB and BA are different, matrix multiplication is **not commutative** but depends on the order of the matrices being multiplied.

Theorem. If $A = \begin{bmatrix} a_{11} & a_{12} \\ a_{21} & a_{22} \end{bmatrix}$ and $B = \begin{bmatrix} b_{11} & b_{12} \\ b_{21} & b_{22} \end{bmatrix}$ are matrices representing the linear transformations S and T, respectively, then the composite $S \circ T$ is a linear transformation represented by the matrix

$$AB = \begin{bmatrix} a_{11}b_{11} + a_{12}b_{21} & a_{11}b_{12} + a_{12}b_{22} \\ a_{21}b_{11} + a_{22}b_{21} & a_{21}b_{12} + a_{22}b_{22} \end{bmatrix}$$

Proof. The composite transformation is

$$(S \circ T)\begin{bmatrix} x \\ y \end{bmatrix} = S\left(T\begin{bmatrix} x \\ y \end{bmatrix}\right)$$

$$= S\begin{bmatrix} b_{11}x + b_{12}y \\ b_{21}x + b_{22}y \end{bmatrix}$$

$$= \begin{bmatrix} a_{11}(b_{11}x + b_{12}y) + a_{12}(b_{21}x + b_{22}y) \\ a_{21}(b_{11}x + b_{12}y) + a_{22}(b_{21}x + b_{22}y) \end{bmatrix}$$

$$= \begin{bmatrix} (a_{11}b_{11} + a_{12}b_{21})x + (a_{11}b_{12} + a_{12}b_{22})y \\ (a_{21}b_{11} + a_{22}b_{21})x + (a_{21}b_{12} + a_{22}b_{22})y \end{bmatrix}$$

Hence,

$$\begin{bmatrix} a_{11}b_{11} + a_{12}b_{21} & a_{11}b_{12} + a_{12}b_{22} \\ a_{21}b_{11} + a_{22}b_{21} & a_{21}b_{12} + a_{22}b_{22} \end{bmatrix}$$

represents $S \circ T$. Therefore, by Theorem 1 of section 5.3, the transformation $S \circ T$ is linear. We now define this matrix to be the matrix product AB.   □

Matrix Multiplication for 2 × 2 Matrices

$$\begin{bmatrix} a_{11} & a_{12} \\ a_{21} & a_{22} \end{bmatrix}\begin{bmatrix} b_{11} & b_{12} \\ b_{21} & b_{22} \end{bmatrix} = \begin{bmatrix} a_{11}b_{11} + a_{12}b_{21} & a_{11}b_{12} + a_{12}b_{22} \\ a_{21}b_{11} + a_{22}b_{21} & a_{21}b_{12} + a_{22}b_{22} \end{bmatrix}$$

At first sight this seems very complicated. However, there is a simple pattern to matrix multiplication. Notice that the entry in the **first row** and **first column** of the product AB is $a_{11}b_{11} + a_{12}b_{21}$ and that this is the dot product of the **first row** of A, $[a_{11} \;\; a_{12}]$, with the **first column** of B, $\begin{bmatrix} b_{11} \\ b_{21} \end{bmatrix}$.

$$\begin{bmatrix} a_{11} & a_{12} \\ * & * \end{bmatrix}\begin{bmatrix} b_{11} & * \\ b_{21} & * \end{bmatrix} = \begin{bmatrix} a_{11}b_{11} + a_{12}b_{21} & * \\ * & * \end{bmatrix}$$

The entry in the **first row** and **second column** of AB is the ''dot product'' of the **first row** of A with the **second column** of B.

$$\begin{bmatrix} a_{11} & a_{12} \\ * & * \end{bmatrix}\begin{bmatrix} * & b_{12} \\ * & b_{22} \end{bmatrix} = \begin{bmatrix} * & a_{11}b_{12} + a_{12}b_{22} \\ * & * \end{bmatrix}$$

In general the element in the ith row and jth column of AB is the dot product of the ith row of A with the jth column of B.

Example 2. If $A = \begin{bmatrix} 2 & 0 \\ 1 & -3 \end{bmatrix}$ and $B = \begin{bmatrix} -7 & 1 \\ -4 & 2 \end{bmatrix}$ find AB, BA, and B^2.

Solution.

$$AB = \begin{bmatrix} 2 & 0 \\ 1 & -3 \end{bmatrix}\begin{bmatrix} -7 & 1 \\ -4 & 2 \end{bmatrix}$$

$$= \begin{bmatrix} 2(-7) + 0(-4) & 2(1) + 0(2) \\ 1(-7) - 3(-4) & 1(1) - 3(2) \end{bmatrix}$$

$$= \begin{bmatrix} -14 & 2 \\ 5 & -5 \end{bmatrix}$$

$$BA = \begin{bmatrix} -7 & 1 \\ -4 & 2 \end{bmatrix}\begin{bmatrix} 2 & 0 \\ 1 & -3 \end{bmatrix}$$

$$= \begin{bmatrix} -7(2) + 1(1) & -7(0) + 1(-3) \\ -4(2) + 2(1) & -4(0) + 2(-3) \end{bmatrix}$$

$$= \begin{bmatrix} -13 & -3 \\ -6 & -6 \end{bmatrix}$$

$$B^2 = BB$$

$$= \begin{bmatrix} -7 & 1 \\ -4 & 2 \end{bmatrix}\begin{bmatrix} -7 & 1 \\ -4 & 2 \end{bmatrix}$$

$$= \begin{bmatrix} -7(-7) + 1(-4) & -7(1) + 1(2) \\ -4(-7) + 2(-4) & -4(1) + 2(2) \end{bmatrix}$$

$$= \begin{bmatrix} 45 & -5 \\ 20 & 0 \end{bmatrix}$$

Notice that $AB \neq BA$. $\qquad\qquad\qquad\qquad\qquad\qquad\qquad\qquad\qquad\qquad\qquad\qquad\qquad$ □

Example 3.

a. Find the matrix representing the linear transformation that consists of a counterclockwise rotation, T, about the origin through $90°$ followed by a reflection, S, in the line $x + y = 0$.

b. What would happen if the reflection were applied first?

Solution.

a. Recall from section 5.3 that the columns of the matrix representing a linear transformation are the images of $\begin{bmatrix} 1 \\ 0 \end{bmatrix}$ and $\begin{bmatrix} 0 \\ 1 \end{bmatrix}$. The rotation T maps $\begin{bmatrix} 1 \\ 0 \end{bmatrix}$ to $\begin{bmatrix} 0 \\ 1 \end{bmatrix}$ and maps $\begin{bmatrix} 0 \\ 1 \end{bmatrix}$ to $\begin{bmatrix} -1 \\ 0 \end{bmatrix}$.

Hence, the matrix representing T is

$$B = \begin{bmatrix} 0 & -1 \\ 1 & 0 \end{bmatrix}$$

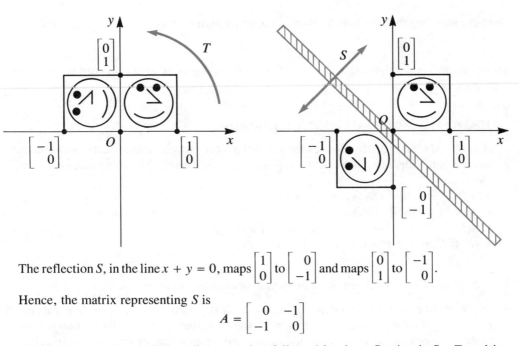

The reflection S, in the line $x + y = 0$, maps $\begin{bmatrix} 1 \\ 0 \end{bmatrix}$ to $\begin{bmatrix} 0 \\ -1 \end{bmatrix}$ and maps $\begin{bmatrix} 0 \\ 1 \end{bmatrix}$ to $\begin{bmatrix} -1 \\ 0 \end{bmatrix}$.

Hence, the matrix representing S is

$$A = \begin{bmatrix} 0 & -1 \\ -1 & 0 \end{bmatrix}$$

The transformation consisting of the rotation followed by the reflection is $S \circ T$, and its matrix is

$$AB = \begin{bmatrix} 0 & -1 \\ -1 & 0 \end{bmatrix}\begin{bmatrix} 0 & -1 \\ 1 & 0 \end{bmatrix} = \begin{bmatrix} -1 & 0 \\ 0 & 1 \end{bmatrix}$$

The matrix AB represents a reflection in the y-axis.

b. If the reflection is applied first and then the rotation, the transformation is $T \circ S$ with matrix

$$BA = \begin{bmatrix} 0 & -1 \\ 1 & 0 \end{bmatrix}\begin{bmatrix} 0 & -1 \\ -1 & 0 \end{bmatrix} = \begin{bmatrix} 1 & 0 \\ 0 & -1 \end{bmatrix}$$

The matrix BA represents a reflection in the x-axis. ☐

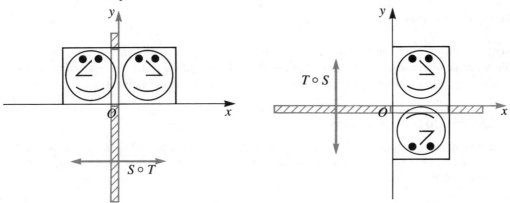

We have seen that matrix multiplication is not commutative; that is,

$$AB \neq BA$$

However, matrix multiplication does satisfy the other properties we would normally expect of a product.

Properties of Matrix Multiplication

If A, B, and C are matrices of sizes for which the following operations can be performed, and if I is the identity matrix of the appropriate size, then the following properties are valid.

- $A(BC) = (AB)C$ (Associative Law)
- $AI = A$, $IA = A$ (Identity)
- $A(B + C) = AB + AC$ (Distributive Law)
- $(B + C)A = BA + CA$ (Distributive Law)

If A, B, C and I are 2×2 matrices, then these operations are always defined.

Proof. It would be possible, though tedious, to verify the Associative Law for 2×2 matrices by multiplying three general matrices together. However, since matrix multiplication is derived from the composition of linear transformations, and composition of functions is associative, it is preferable to proceed as follows.

Let R, S, and T be linear transformations with matrices A, B, and C, respectively. For a vector $\vec{u}$ in the domain of T,

$$
\begin{aligned}
(R \circ (S \circ T))(\vec{u}) &= R(S \circ T(\vec{u})) \\
&= R(S(T(\vec{u}))) \\
&= (R \circ S)(T(\vec{u})) \\
&= ((R \circ S) \circ T)(\vec{u})
\end{aligned}
$$

Since composition of functions is associative, the matrices of $R \circ (S \circ T)$ and $(R \circ S) \circ T$ must be the same; that is, $A(BC) = (AB)C$.

The other properties can be proved directly.   □

Matrix multiplication can be defined for two matrices A and B of arbitrary size provided that **the number of columns** of A **equals the number of rows** of B. If the number of columns of A is not equal to the number of rows of B, then their product is **not** defined.

Matrix Multiplication

If A is an $m \times n$ matrix and B is an $n \times k$ matrix, their product AB is defined to be the $m \times k$ matrix whose (i, j)th entry is the dot product of the ith row of A with the jth column of B.

For example, if A is a 2×2 matrix and X is a 2×1 matrix (or column vector), the product AX is defined to be a 2×1 matrix and agrees with the action of A on X given in section 5.2.

Example 4. If $A = \begin{bmatrix} 2 & 0 & -1 \\ 1 & 7 & 3 \end{bmatrix}$ and $B = \begin{bmatrix} 4 & 2 \\ -1 & 1 \\ -5 & 3 \end{bmatrix}$, find, if possible, AB, BA and A^2.

Solution. The size of A is 2×3, and the size of B is 3×2. Hence, AB is defined and is a 2×2 matrix, and BA is defined and is a 3×3 matrix, but $A^2 = AA$ is **not defined**.

$$AB = \begin{bmatrix} 2 & 0 & -1 \\ 1 & 7 & 3 \end{bmatrix}_{2 \times 3} \begin{bmatrix} 4 & 2 \\ -1 & 1 \\ -5 & 3 \end{bmatrix}_{3 \times 2} = \begin{bmatrix} 13 & 1 \\ -18 & 18 \end{bmatrix}$$

$$BA = \begin{bmatrix} 4 & 2 \\ -1 & 1 \\ -5 & 3 \end{bmatrix} \begin{bmatrix} 2 & 0 & -1 \\ 1 & 7 & 3 \end{bmatrix} = \begin{bmatrix} 10 & 14 & 2 \\ -1 & 7 & 4 \\ -7 & 21 & 14 \end{bmatrix}$$

Note that, not only are AB and BA different, but they are not even the same size. □

Example 5. If $A = \begin{bmatrix} 1 & -2 \\ -2 & 5 \end{bmatrix}$, $X = \begin{bmatrix} x \\ y \end{bmatrix}$, and $Z = [x \ \ y]$, calculate ZAX.

Solution. Since Z has size 1×2, A has size 2×2, and X has size 2×1, their product is defined. Since matrix multiplication is associative, we can calculate either $Z(AX)$ or $(ZA)X$ and obtain the same answer. We have

$$ZAX = [x \ \ y] \begin{bmatrix} 1 & -2 \\ -2 & 5 \end{bmatrix} \begin{bmatrix} x \\ y \end{bmatrix}$$

$$= [x \ \ y] \begin{bmatrix} x - 2y \\ -2x + 5y \end{bmatrix}$$

$$= [x(x - 2y) + y(-2x + 5y)]$$

$$= [x^2 - 4xy + 5y^2]$$

Notice that the final product is a 1×1 matrix. Often 1×1 matrices are considered to be real numbers. □

Exercises 5.4

1. Write down any two 2×2 matrices A and B and calculate $A + B$, AB, BA, A^2, and B^2.

2. If $A = \begin{bmatrix} 2 & 1 \\ -1 & 0 \end{bmatrix}$, $B = \begin{bmatrix} 7 & -3 \\ 1 & 2 \end{bmatrix}$, $C = \begin{bmatrix} 0 & 1 \\ 2 & 3 \end{bmatrix}$, and I and O are the 2×2 identity and zero matrices, respectively, calculate each matrix.

a. $A + B + C$ **b.** AB **c.** BA **d.** $AB + BA$

e. $A(B + C)$ **f.** $AB + AC$ **g.** AI **h.** BO

i. $A(BC)$ **j.** $(AB)C$ **k.** A^3 **l.** $(A - I)^2$

3. Find the matrix representing the linear transformation that consists of a rotation of one half revolution about the origin followed by a reflection in the line $x = y$.

4. Let $A = \begin{bmatrix} 2 & -1 \\ -4 & 2 \end{bmatrix}$, $B = \begin{bmatrix} 1 & 0 \\ -1 & -4 \end{bmatrix}$, and $C = \begin{bmatrix} 2 & 3 \\ 1 & 2 \end{bmatrix}$. Verify that $AB = AC$. Note that since $B \neq C$, cancellation of the matrix A is not valid.

5. If A is a 2×2 matrix, B is a 3×1 matrix, C is a 3×2 matrix, and D is a 1×2 matrix, which of the following operations are defined?

   a. BCA **b.** $CA + 4C$ **c.** $A^2 + C^2$ **d.** $BD + C$

   e. $3A - A^2$ **f.** $C - BDA^2$ **g.** A^3 **h.** ACA

6. If $A = \begin{bmatrix} 3 \\ -5 \end{bmatrix}$, $B = \begin{bmatrix} 1 & 0 & 2 \\ 4 & -1 & -6 \end{bmatrix}$, $C = \begin{bmatrix} 8 & -1 \\ 3 & -4 \end{bmatrix}$, and $D = [7 \ \ 1 \ \ 2]$, calculate the following, if they are defined.

   a. AD **b.** DA **c.** $A + D$ **d.** DB

   e. AB **f.** $BC + 3B$ **g.** CB **h.** $CAD + B$

7. For each of the following transformations T, find $T \circ T \circ \ldots \circ T$ (composed n times).

   a. The dilatation with matrix $\begin{bmatrix} a & 0 \\ 0 & a \end{bmatrix}$

   b. The rotation with matrix $\begin{bmatrix} 0 & -1 \\ 1 & 0 \end{bmatrix}$

   c. The projection with matrix $\begin{bmatrix} 0 & 0 \\ 0 & 1 \end{bmatrix}$

   d. The shear with matrix $\begin{bmatrix} 1 & b \\ 0 & 1 \end{bmatrix}$

Problems 5.4

1. If $A = \begin{bmatrix} 2 & -1 \\ -6 & 3 \end{bmatrix}$, show that $A^2 = 5A$. Calculate A^n for any positive integer n.

2. Find each 2×2 matrix whose square is the zero matrix.

3. If A and B are 2×2 matrices, is it always true that

$$(A - B)(A + B) = A^2 - B^2?$$

4. If AB is the zero matrix, does BA have to be the zero matrix?

5. Write a computer program to calculate the nth power of any 2×2 or 3×3 matrix.

6. a. Find a matrix P such that $PA = P\begin{bmatrix} a & b \\ c & d \end{bmatrix} = \begin{bmatrix} c & d \\ a & b \end{bmatrix}$ for any matrix A. Such a matrix P is called a permutation matrix because it permutes the rows when P is multiplied on the left of A.

b. What is the effect of multiplying A on the right by P?

5.5 Determinants (Optional)

In this section, we shall determine the conditions under which a system of n linear equations in n variables has a unique solution. Such systems have square coefficient matrices, and to each square matrix we shall associate a number, called its determinant. Determinants will also be useful for determining whether sets of vectors are linearly dependent, whether a square matrix has an inverse, and for various vector geometry problems. In this book we shall only deal with determinants of 2×2 and 3×3 matrices.

The **determinant** of the 2×2 matrix $A = \begin{bmatrix} a_1 & b_1 \\ a_2 & b_2 \end{bmatrix}$ is

$$\det A = \begin{vmatrix} a_1 & b_1 \\ a_2 & b_2 \end{vmatrix} = a_1 b_2 - a_2 b_1$$

Note that $\det A$ is just a real number.

Example 1. Find the determinants of the matrices $\begin{bmatrix} 2 & -3 \\ 1 & 4 \end{bmatrix}$ and $\begin{bmatrix} -6 & 15 \\ 10 & -25 \end{bmatrix}$.

Solution.

$$\begin{vmatrix} 2 & -3 \\ 1 & 4 \end{vmatrix} = 2(4) - 1(-3)$$

$$= 11$$

$$\begin{vmatrix} -6 & 15 \\ 10 & -25 \end{vmatrix} = (-6)(-25) - 15(10)$$

$$= 150 - 150$$

$$= 0 \qquad \square$$

> **Theorem.** The two vectors (a_1, b_1) and (a_2, b_2) in the plane are linearly dependent (that is, parallel) if and only if
> $$\begin{vmatrix} a_1 & b_1 \\ a_2 & b_2 \end{vmatrix} = 0$$

Proof. The non-zero vectors (a_1, b_1) and (a_2, b_2) are parallel if and only if $(a_1, b_1) = k(a_2, b_2)$, for some real number k. This happens if $a_1 = ka_2$ and $b_1 = kb_2$. Thus,
$$\begin{vmatrix} a_1 & b_1 \\ a_2 & b_2 \end{vmatrix} = a_1 b_2 - a_2 b_1$$
$$= 0$$

Conversely, it follows that if $\begin{vmatrix} a_1 & b_1 \\ a_2 & b_2 \end{vmatrix} = 0$, then (a_1, b_1) and (a_2, b_2) are parallel.   □

It follows that (a_1, b_1) and (a_2, b_2) are linearly independent if and only if $\begin{vmatrix} a_1 & b_1 \\ a_2 & b_2 \end{vmatrix} \neq 0$.

We see, from Example 1, that the vectors $(2, -3)$ and $(1, 4)$ are linearly independent but that $(-6, 15)$ and $(10, -25)$ are linearly dependent.

Determinants can be used to determine whether a system of two linear equations in two variables has a unique solution and to find the solution in that case. This method is named after the Swiss mathematician, Gabriel Cramer (1704-1754).

> ## Cramer's Rule
>
> The system
> $$a_1 x + b_1 y = c_1$$
> $$a_2 x + b_2 y = c_2$$
>
> has a unique solution if and only if
> $$D = \begin{vmatrix} a_1 & b_1 \\ a_2 & b_2 \end{vmatrix} \neq 0$$
>
> If $D \neq 0$, the unique solution is
> $$x = \frac{D_1}{D}, \quad y = \frac{D_2}{D}$$
>
> where $D_1 = \begin{vmatrix} c_1 & b_1 \\ c_2 & b_2 \end{vmatrix}$, and $D_2 = \begin{vmatrix} a_1 & c_1 \\ a_2 & c_2 \end{vmatrix}$

Note that D is just the determinant of coefficients in the system of equations and that D_1 is obtained from D by replacing the first column by the constants on the right-hand side of the system; D_2 is obtained from D by replacing the second column by the constants.

Proof. Two lines in the plane will intersect in a unique point if they are not parallel. If they are parallel, they will either be distinct or will intersect in a whole line. The two given lines will be parallel if and only if their normal vectors (a_1, b_1) and (a_2, b_2) are parallel. Hence, the given system will have a unique solution if and only if the normal vectors are linearly independent; that is, if and only if

$$D = \begin{vmatrix} a_1 & b_1 \\ a_2 & b_2 \end{vmatrix} \neq 0$$

To find the solution, multiply the first equation by b_2 and the second equation by b_1 to obtain

$$a_1 b_2 x + b_1 b_2 y = b_2 c_1$$
$$a_2 b_1 x + b_1 b_2 y = b_1 c_2$$

Subtracting, we have $(a_1 b_2 - a_2 b_1)x = b_2 c_1 - b_1 c_2$. Now if $D = a_1 b_2 - a_2 b_1 \neq 0$, there is a unique solution and we can divide by D to obtain

$$x = \frac{b_2 c_1 - b_1 c_2}{a_1 b_2 - a_2 b_1} = \frac{\begin{vmatrix} c_1 & b_1 \\ c_2 & b_2 \end{vmatrix}}{\begin{vmatrix} a_1 & b_1 \\ a_2 & b_2 \end{vmatrix}} = \frac{D_1}{D}$$

Similarly, by eliminating x we obtain

$$y = \frac{a_1 c_2 - a_2 c_1}{a_1 b_2 - a_2 b_1} = \frac{\begin{vmatrix} a_1 & c_1 \\ a_2 & c_2 \end{vmatrix}}{\begin{vmatrix} a_1 & b_1 \\ a_2 & b_2 \end{vmatrix}} = \frac{D_2}{D} \qquad \square$$

Example 2. Determine whether the following systems have a unique solution; if they do, find the solution by Cramer's Rule.

a. $2x - 3y = 7$
    $5x + y = 9$

b. $4x - 2y = 7$
    $-6x + 3y = 1$

Solution.

a. The determinant of the coefficients is

$$D = \begin{vmatrix} 2 & -3 \\ 5 & 1 \end{vmatrix} = 2 + 15 = 17$$

Since $D \neq 0$, the system has a unique solution and we can use Cramer's Rule to obtain

$$x = \frac{D_1}{D} = \frac{\begin{vmatrix} 7 & -3 \\ 9 & 1 \end{vmatrix}}{17} = \frac{34}{17} = 2$$

$$y = \frac{D_2}{D} = \frac{\begin{vmatrix} 2 & 7 \\ 5 & 9 \end{vmatrix}}{17} = -\frac{17}{17} = -1$$

Check. The solution $x = 2$, $y = -1$ satisfies the system.

b. The second system has determinant

$$D = \begin{vmatrix} 4 & -2 \\ -6 & 3 \end{vmatrix} = 12 - 12 = 0$$

Hence, the system has either no solution or an infinite number of solutions and Cramer's rule cannot be used. In this case there is no solution since the system represents two distinct parallel lines. □

The **determinant** of the 3×3 matrix $A = \begin{bmatrix} a_1 & a_2 & a_3 \\ b_1 & b_2 & b_3 \\ c_1 & c_2 & c_3 \end{bmatrix}$ is

$$\det A = \begin{vmatrix} a_1 & a_2 & a_3 \\ b_1 & b_2 & b_3 \\ c_1 & c_2 & c_3 \end{vmatrix} = a_1 \begin{vmatrix} b_2 & b_3 \\ c_2 & c_3 \end{vmatrix} - a_2 \begin{vmatrix} b_1 & b_3 \\ c_1 & c_3 \end{vmatrix} + a_3 \begin{vmatrix} b_1 & b_2 \\ c_1 & c_2 \end{vmatrix}$$

The right side of this formula could be expanded by using the definition of a 2×2 determinant, but it is probably easier to remember in the above form. There are many other ways to evaluate a 3×3 determinant, but this will suffice for our purposes, and it also can be generalized to higher dimensions.

For example,

$$\begin{vmatrix} -2 & 3 & 4 \\ 1 & 0 & -1 \\ -3 & 5 & 2 \end{vmatrix} = -2 \begin{vmatrix} 0 & -1 \\ 5 & 2 \end{vmatrix} - 3 \begin{vmatrix} 1 & -1 \\ -3 & 2 \end{vmatrix} + 4 \begin{vmatrix} 1 & 0 \\ -3 & 5 \end{vmatrix}$$

$$= -2(0 + 5) - 3(2 - 3) + 4(5 - 0)$$

$$= 13$$

The test for linear dependence can be generalized to R^3.

Theorem. The three vectors (a_1, a_2, a_3), (b_1, b_2, b_3), and $(c_1, c_2, c_3) \in R^3$ are linearly dependent (that is, coplanar) if and only if

$$\begin{vmatrix} a_1 & a_2 & a_3 \\ b_1 & b_2 & b_3 \\ c_1 & c_2 & c_3 \end{vmatrix} = 0$$

Proof. The three vectors $\vec{a} = (a_1, a_2, a_3)$, $\vec{b} = (b_1, b_2, b_3)$ and $\vec{c} = (c_1, c_2, c_3)$ in 3-space are linearly dependent if and only if they are coplanar. The normal to the plane of $\vec{b}$ and $\vec{c}$ is $\vec{b} \times \vec{c}$. The three vectors are coplanar if and only if $\vec{a}$ also lies in this plane, that is, if $\vec{a} \cdot (\vec{b} \times \vec{c}) = 0$. The expression $\vec{a} \cdot (\vec{b} \times \vec{c})$ is the determinant of the 3×3 matrix whose rows are the components of $\vec{a}$, $\vec{b}$, and $\vec{c}$. $\quad\square$

Cramer's Rule can also be generalized.

Cramer's Rule

A system of three equations in three variables x, y, and z has a unique solution if and only if the 3×3 determinant D of the coefficients is non-zero. If $D \neq 0$, the unique solution is

$$x = \frac{D_1}{D}, \quad y = \frac{D_2}{D}, \quad z = \frac{D_3}{D}$$

where D_i is the determinant obtained from D by replacing the ith column by the constants on the right-hand side of the system.

Example 3. Determine whether the following systems have a unique solution, and if they do, find the solution by Cramer's Rule.

a. $2x + 3y + z = 0$
$\quad x - y - z = 0$
$\quad 3x + y + z = 0$

b. $2x - 3y + z = 7$
$\quad x + 4y - z = 2$
$\quad -x + 2z = 5$

Solution.

a. Note that this is a homogeneous system and it has the trivial solution, $x = 0$, $y = 0$, $z = 0$. The determinant of the coefficients will determine if this is the only solution. We have

$$D = \begin{vmatrix} 2 & 3 & 1 \\ 1 & -1 & -1 \\ 3 & 1 & 1 \end{vmatrix}$$

$$= 2(0) - 3(4) + 1(4)$$

$$= -8$$

$$\neq 0$$

Since D is non-zero, the system has a unique solution, which must be $x = 0$, $y = 0$, and $z = 0$.

b. Calculate the determinants D, D_1, D_2, and D_3.

$$D = \begin{vmatrix} 2 & -3 & 1 \\ 1 & 4 & -1 \\ -1 & 0 & 2 \end{vmatrix} \qquad D_1 = \begin{vmatrix} 7 & -3 & 1 \\ 2 & 4 & -1 \\ 5 & 0 & 2 \end{vmatrix}$$

$$= 2(8) + 3(1) + 4 \qquad\qquad = 7(8) + 3(9) + (-20)$$

$$= 23 \qquad\qquad\qquad\qquad = 63$$

$$\neq 0$$

$$D_2 = \begin{vmatrix} 2 & 7 & 1 \\ 1 & 2 & -1 \\ -1 & 5 & 2 \end{vmatrix} \qquad D_3 = \begin{vmatrix} 2 & -3 & 7 \\ 1 & 4 & 2 \\ -1 & 0 & 5 \end{vmatrix}$$

$$= 2(9) - 7(1) + 7 \qquad\qquad = 2(20) + 3(7) + 7(4)$$

$$= 18 \qquad\qquad\qquad\qquad = 89$$

Hence, the unique solution is

$$x = \frac{D_1}{D} = \frac{63}{23} \qquad y = \frac{D_2}{D} = \frac{18}{23} \qquad z = \frac{D_3}{D} = \frac{89}{23}$$

Check. The solution can be checked using a calculator.   □

Cramer's Rule can be generalized to a system of n equations in n variables, but is too unwieldy for practical computations, even on a computer. It is much more efficient to use Gaussian elimination. However, Cramer's rule is a useful theoretical tool that is helpful in proving theorems about systems of equations.

Exercises 5.5

1. Evaluate each determinant.

a. $\begin{vmatrix} 5 & -11 \\ 6 & 3 \end{vmatrix}$
b. $\begin{vmatrix} 6 & -\frac{1}{2} \\ 48 & -4 \end{vmatrix}$
c. $\begin{vmatrix} 2 & 1 & 0 \\ 0 & 5 & -1 \\ 4 & 3 & -3 \end{vmatrix}$

d. $\begin{vmatrix} 5 & -6 & -2 \\ 1 & 1 & 1 \\ 4 & 3 & 7 \end{vmatrix}$
e. $\begin{vmatrix} 1 & 2 & -1 \\ 5 & 2 & -2 \\ 3 & -1 & 0 \end{vmatrix} + \begin{vmatrix} 4 & 0 & -1 \\ 7 & 6 & 2 \\ 1 & 3 & -1 \end{vmatrix}$

2. Prove the following properties of determinants for a 2×2 matrix A.

   a. If B is the 2×2 matrix obtained by interchanging the rows of A, then $\det B = -\det A$.

   b. If B is obtained from A by multiplying the second row by k, then $\det B = k \det A$.

   c. If the two rows of A are equal, $\det A = 0$.

   d. If A is the triangular matrix $\begin{bmatrix} a_1 & a_2 \\ 0 & b_2 \end{bmatrix}$, then $\det A = a_1 b_2$, the product of the diagonal elements.

   e. The transpose of $A = \begin{bmatrix} a_1 & a_2 \\ b_1 & b_2 \end{bmatrix}$ is $A^t = \begin{bmatrix} a_1 & b_1 \\ a_2 & b_2 \end{bmatrix}$, where the rows and columns are interchanged. Prove that $\det A^t = \det A$. This equality means that all the previous properties apply to the columns of a determinant as well as the rows.

3. Find two matrices A and B for which $\det(A + B) \neq \det A + \det B$.

4. Find all values of x such that $\begin{vmatrix} x - 1 & 1 \\ -2 & x - 4 \end{vmatrix} = 0$.

5. Determine whether each system has a unique solution. Solve the systems that do have a unique solution using Cramer's Rule.

   a. $5x + y = 11$
      $2x - y = 1$

   b. $kx + 2y = 1$
      $8x + ky = 2, \quad k \neq \pm 4$

   c. $2x + y - z = 4$
      $-x + 2y + 3z = 3$
      $-2x + 7y + 4z = 7$

   d. $3x + 2y - z = 4$
      $x + y - 5z = -3$
      $-2x - y + 4z = 0$

   e. $x + y - z = 2$
      $2x - y + z = 3$
      $5x - y + z = 8$

   f. $x + 3y - z = 0$
      $2x - y + 5z = 0$
      $-x + 4y + 3z = 0$

6. Show that, for all real numbers t, the only solution to the following system of equations is the trivial solution $x = 0$, $y = 0$.

$$(t - 2)x \quad - y = 0$$
$$9x + (t + 2)y = 0$$

Problems 5.5

1. Prove the properties in Exercise 2 for determinants of 3×3 matrices. Then use these properties to evaluate the determinants.

a. $\begin{vmatrix} 5 & -1 & 4 \\ 3 & 3 & 2 \\ -25 & 5 & -20 \end{vmatrix}$ **b.** $\begin{vmatrix} 2 & 5 & 9 \\ 0 & 10 & 3 \\ 0 & 0 & -6 \end{vmatrix}$ **c.** $\begin{vmatrix} 3 & 1 & 0 \\ 2 & 5 & 0 \\ -1 & -1 & 0 \end{vmatrix}$

2. Evaluate $\begin{vmatrix} a+b & a+b & a^2-b^2 \\ 1 & 1 & a-b \\ a & 1 & b \end{vmatrix}$.

3. Write a computer program to evaluate a 3×3 determinant.

4. Use Cramer's Rule to find the quadratic function $f(x)$ for which $f(1) = 4$, $f(2) = 13$, and $f(3) = 26$.

5. a. In the triangle ABC prove that

$$a = b \cos C + c \cos B$$

b. Use Cramer's Rule to solve the system

$$c \cos B + b \cos C = a$$
$$c \cos A + a \cos C = b$$
$$b \cos A + a \cos B = c$$

for $\cos A$ and deduce the Cosine Law

$$a^2 = b^2 + c^2 - 2bc \cos A$$

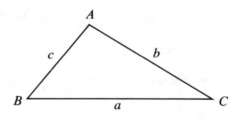

5.6 Geometric Applications of Determinants (Optional)

We shall show that the area of a parallelogram in the plane, cross products, and the volume of a parallelepiped in 3-space can be expressed conveniently as determinants.

The **area of the parallelogram** in the plane with sides along the vectors (a_1, a_2) and (b_1, b_2) is the absolute value of $\begin{vmatrix} a_1 & a_2 \\ b_1 & b_2 \end{vmatrix}$.

Proof. Let $\vec{a} = (a_1, a_2)$, let $\vec{b} = (b_1, b_2)$, and let θ be the angle between them. Take $\vec{a}$ as the base of the parallelogram and let h be its height. Then the area of the parallelogram is

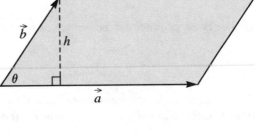

$$A = |\vec{a}|\, h$$
$$= |\vec{a}|\,|\vec{b}|\, \sin \theta$$

Hence,

$$A^2 = |\vec{a}|^2|\vec{b}|^2(1 - \cos^2 \theta)$$
$$= |\vec{a}|^2|\vec{b}|^2 - |\vec{a}|^2|\vec{b}|^2 \cos^2 \theta$$
$$= |\vec{a}|^2|\vec{b}|^2 - (\vec{a} \cdot \vec{b})^2$$
$$= (a_1^2 + a_2^2)(b_1^2 + b_2^2) - (a_1 b_1 + a_2 b_2)^2$$
$$= a_1^2 b_2^2 + a_2^2 b_1^2 - 2a_1 b_1 a_2 b_2$$
$$= (a_1 b_2 - a_2 b_1)^2$$

Therefore, the area is the absolute value of $\begin{vmatrix} a_1 & a_2 \\ b_1 & b_2 \end{vmatrix}$. $\qquad\square$

If the determinant is zero, then the parallelogram collapses and $\vec{a}$ is parallel to $\vec{b}$. This agrees with our original idea that a determinant is zero if and only if the vectors represented by the rows are linearly dependent.

Example 1. Find the area of the triangle in the plane with vertices $P(2, -1)$, $Q(-3, 7)$, and $R(-1, 5)$.

Solution. Two sides of the triangle are along the vectors $\overrightarrow{PQ} = (-3, 7) - (2, -1) = (-5, 8)$ and $\overrightarrow{PR} = (-1, 5) - (2, -1) = (-3, 6)$. The area of the triangle with these vectors as sides is half the area of the parallelogram with these sides. Now

$$\tfrac{1}{2}\begin{vmatrix} -5 & 8 \\ -3 & 6 \end{vmatrix} = \tfrac{1}{2}[-5(6) - 8(-3)]$$
$$= -3$$

Hence, the area of the triangle is $|-3|$ or 3 square units. $\qquad\square$

If we recall the formula for the cross product from section 2.5, we see that its components can be written in terms of 2×2 determinants.

$$\vec{b} \times \vec{c} = (b_2 c_3 - b_3 c_2, b_3 c_1 - b_1 c_3, b_1 c_2 - b_2 c_1)$$
$$= \vec{i}\begin{vmatrix} b_2 & b_3 \\ c_2 & c_3 \end{vmatrix} - \vec{j}\begin{vmatrix} b_1 & b_3 \\ c_1 & c_3 \end{vmatrix} + \vec{k}\begin{vmatrix} b_1 & b_2 \\ c_1 & c_2 \end{vmatrix}$$

Comparing this formula with the definition of a 3×3 determinant given in the previous section, we see that we should be able to write the cross product as a 3×3 determinant whose first row consists of the standard basis vectors $\vec{i}, \vec{j}$, and $\vec{k}$.

The **cross product** can be written as $\vec{b} \times \vec{c} = \begin{vmatrix} \vec{i} & \vec{j} & \vec{k} \\ b_1 & b_2 & b_3 \\ c_1 & c_2 & c_3 \end{vmatrix}$.

This is not a proper determinant because the entries in the first row are vectors, not scalars. However, this expression is very useful for remembering the components of a cross product.

Example 2. Compute $(2, -3, 1) \times (5, 1, 2)$.

Solution.

$$(2, -3, 1) \times (5, 1, 2) = \begin{vmatrix} \vec{i} & \vec{j} & \vec{k} \\ 2 & -3 & 1 \\ 5 & 1 & 2 \end{vmatrix}$$

$$= \vec{i} \begin{vmatrix} -3 & 1 \\ 1 & 2 \end{vmatrix} - \vec{j} \begin{vmatrix} 2 & 1 \\ 5 & 2 \end{vmatrix} + \vec{k} \begin{vmatrix} 2 & -3 \\ 5 & 1 \end{vmatrix}$$

$$= -7\vec{i} + \vec{j} + 17\vec{k}$$

$$= (-7, 1, 17)$$

Check. $(2, -3, 1) \cdot (-7, 1, 17) = -14 - 3 + 17 = 0$, and
$(5, 1, 2) \cdot (-7, 1, 17) = -35 + 1 + 34 = 0$.   ☐

A **parallelepiped** in 3-space is a box-like solid whose opposite faces are parallel and are congruent parallelograms. It is determined by three non-coplanar vectors $\vec{a}$, $\vec{b}$ and $\vec{c}$, representing the edges. Its volume, V, is obtained by taking the product of the area of one of its faces and the perpendicular distance from that face to the opposite face.

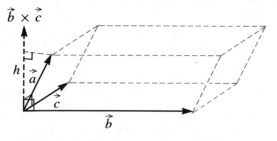

The **volume of the parallelepiped** with sides along the vectors $\vec{a} = (a_1, a_2, a_3)$, $\vec{b} = (b_1, b_2, b_3)$, and $\vec{c} = (c_1, c_2, c_3)$ is

$V = |\vec{a} \cdot (\vec{b} \times \vec{c})|$, which is the absolute value of $\begin{vmatrix} a_1 & a_2 & a_3 \\ b_1 & b_2 & b_3 \\ c_1 & c_2 & c_3 \end{vmatrix}$.

Proof. The area of the parallelogram face determined by $\vec{b}$ and $\vec{c}$ is $|\vec{b} \times \vec{c}|$. The perpendicular distance, h, to the opposite face is the length of the projection of $\vec{a}$ on the normal $\vec{b} \times \vec{c}$, to the plane of $\vec{b}$ and $\vec{c}$. Hence,

$$h = \frac{|\vec{a} \cdot (\vec{b} \times \vec{c})|}{|\vec{b} \times \vec{c}|}$$

The volume is therefore,

$$V = h|\vec{b} \times \vec{c}|$$
$$= |\vec{a} \cdot (\vec{b} \times \vec{c})|$$

Now

$$\vec{a} \cdot (\vec{b} \times \vec{c}) = (a_1, a_2, a_3) \cdot \left(\begin{vmatrix} b_2 & b_3 \\ c_2 & c_3 \end{vmatrix}, -\begin{vmatrix} b_1 & b_3 \\ c_1 & c_3 \end{vmatrix}, \begin{vmatrix} b_1 & b_2 \\ c_1 & c_2 \end{vmatrix} \right)$$

$$= a_1 \begin{vmatrix} b_2 & b_3 \\ c_2 & c_3 \end{vmatrix} - a_2 \begin{vmatrix} b_1 & b_3 \\ c_1 & c_3 \end{vmatrix} + a_3 \begin{vmatrix} b_1 & b_2 \\ c_1 & c_2 \end{vmatrix}$$

$$= \begin{vmatrix} a_1 & a_2 & a_3 \\ b_1 & b_2 & b_3 \\ c_1 & c_2 & c_3 \end{vmatrix}$$

Therefore, the volume V is the absolute value of this determinant. ☐

The scalar expression $\vec{a} \cdot (\vec{b} \times \vec{c})$ is called a **scalar triple product** or **box product**. Its absolute value gives the volume of the parallelepiped, and its sign determines the orientation of the vectors $\vec{a}$, $\vec{b}$, and $\vec{c}$. The scalar triple product is positive if this triple of vectors forms a right-handed system, where the definition of right-handed is the one given in section 1.5 for the standard basis vectors $\vec{i}$, $\vec{j}$, and $\vec{k}$ (even though $\vec{a}$, $\vec{b}$, and $\vec{c}$ are not perpendicular). A change in the order of two of the vectors in a scalar product will result in a change of sign in the answer.

We can now see geometrically that the vectors $\vec{a}$, $\vec{b}$, and $\vec{c}$ are linearly dependent (that is, coplanar) if and only if the volume of the parallelepiped is zero and, hence, if and only if the determinant is zero.

Example 3. Find the volume of the parallelepiped determined by the vectors $\vec{a} = (2, -5, -1)$, $\vec{b} = (4, 0, 1)$, and $\vec{c} = (3, -1, -1)$.

Solution. The scalar triple product is

$$\vec{a} \cdot (\vec{b} \times \vec{c}) = \begin{vmatrix} 2 & -5 & -1 \\ 4 & 0 & 1 \\ 3 & -1 & -1 \end{vmatrix}$$
$$= 2(0 + 1) - (-5)(-4 - 3) - 1(-4 + 0)$$
$$= -29$$

Hence, the volume is 29 cubic units. ☐

Example 4. Show that the vectors $\vec{u} = (3, -2, 7)$, $\vec{v} = (1, 1, -1)$, and $\vec{w} = (4, 1, 2)$ are coplanar.

Solution. They will be coplanar if and only if the determinant, with these vectors as rows, is zero. Now

$$\begin{vmatrix} 3 & -2 & 7 \\ 1 & 1 & -1 \\ 4 & 1 & 2 \end{vmatrix} = 3(3) + 2(6) + 7(-3)$$
$$= 0$$

Hence, the vectors are coplanar.   □

Example 5. Show that the Cartesian equation of the plane through the three non-collinear points $P_1(x_1, y_1, z_1)$, $P_2(x_2, y_2, z_2)$, and $P_3(x_3, y_3, z_3)$ can be written as

$$\begin{vmatrix} x - x_1 & y - y_1 & z - z_1 \\ x_2 - x_1 & y_2 - y_1 & z_2 - z_1 \\ x_3 - x_1 & y_3 - y_1 & z_3 - z_1 \end{vmatrix} = 0$$

Proof. The point $P(x, y, z)$ lies on the plane if and only if the vectors $\overrightarrow{P_1P}$, $\overrightarrow{P_1P_2}$, and $\overrightarrow{P_1P_3}$ are coplanar, that is, if and only if

$$\overrightarrow{P_1P} \cdot (\overrightarrow{P_1P_2} \times \overrightarrow{P_1P_3}) = 0$$

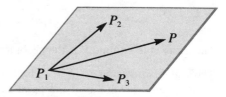

Substituting

$$\overrightarrow{P_1P} = (x - x_1, y - y_1, z - z_1),$$
$$\overrightarrow{P_1P_2} = (x_2 - x_1, y_2 - y_1, z_2 - z_1),$$

and $\overrightarrow{P_1P_3} = (x_3 - x_1, y_3 - y_1, z_3 - z_1)$ in the formula for the scalar triple product, we obtain the determinantal equation of the plane. □

Example 6. Find the equation of the plane determined by the points $P_1(1, 0, -1)$, $P_2(4, -1, 1)$, and $P_3(2, 2, -3)$.

Solution. Since $\overrightarrow{P_1P_2} = (3, -1, 2)$ and $\overrightarrow{P_1P_3} = (1, 2, -2)$, the equation is

$$\begin{vmatrix} x - 1 & y & z + 1 \\ 3 & -1 & 2 \\ 1 & 2 & -2 \end{vmatrix} = 0$$

$$(x - 1)[-(-2) - 2(2)] - y[3(-2) - 2] + (z + 1)[3(2) - (-1)] = 0$$

$$-2(x - 1) + 8y + 7(z + 1) = 0$$

Therefore, the equation of the plane is $2x - 8y - 7z - 9 = 0$.

Check. The points P_1, P_2, and P_3 satisfy this equation.   □

The determinant of a matrix that represents a linear transformation is a measure of the magnification of the transformation.

Let $T:\mathbf{R}^2 \to \mathbf{R}^2$ be the linear transformation taking (x, y) to (u, v), which is defined by

$$T\begin{bmatrix} x \\ y \end{bmatrix} = A\begin{bmatrix} x \\ y \end{bmatrix} = \begin{bmatrix} a_{11} & a_{12} \\ a_{21} & a_{22} \end{bmatrix}\begin{bmatrix} x \\ y \end{bmatrix}$$

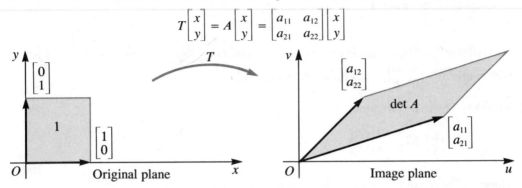

This transformation takes the point $(1, 0)$ to the point (a_{11}, a_{21}) and the point $(0, 1)$ to the point (a_{12}, a_{22}). The square of unit area with sides along the vectors $(1, 0)$ and $(0, 1)$ is transformed under T into a parallelogram with sides along (a_{11}, a_{21}) and (a_{12}, a_{22}). The area of this parallelogram is the absolute value of

$$\det A = \begin{vmatrix} a_{11} & a_{12} \\ a_{21} & a_{22} \end{vmatrix}$$

The sign of the determinant depends on the orientation of its row vectors, $\vec{a}$ and $\vec{b}$. It is positive if $\vec{a}$ and $\vec{b}$ are right-hand-oriented; otherwise it is negative. That is, the determinant is positive if, in going from $\vec{a}$ to $\vec{b}$, you turn in a counterclockwise direction.

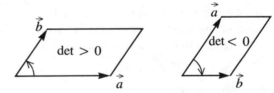

If the determinant is negative, the transformation involves a reflection as well as a possible linear distortion.

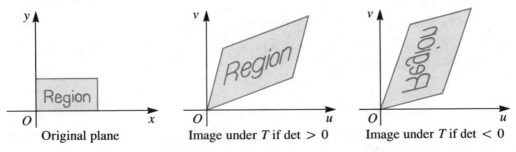

Given any region in the original plane, we can subdivide it into small squares. Each of these small squares of area Δr will transform, under T, into a small parallelogram of area $\Delta r \det A$. By adding up all these sub-regions we are able to justify the following result.

Transformation of Areas

A region of area r in the plane transforms under a linear transformation $T: R^2 \to R^2$ into a region of area $r \det A$.

Example 7. Show that the image of the unit circle, $x^2 + y^2 = 1$, under the transformation with matrix $A = \begin{bmatrix} a & 0 \\ 0 & b \end{bmatrix}$, is an ellipse with area πab.

Solution. The transformation is

$$\begin{bmatrix} u \\ v \end{bmatrix} = \begin{bmatrix} a & 0 \\ 0 & b \end{bmatrix} \begin{bmatrix} x \\ y \end{bmatrix}$$

Hence, $u = ax$ and $v = by$. Substituting these in the equation of the unit circle, $x^2 + y^2 = 1$, we obtain

$$\frac{u^2}{a^2} + \frac{v^2}{b^2} = 1$$

This is the equation of an ellipse with semi-axes a and b.

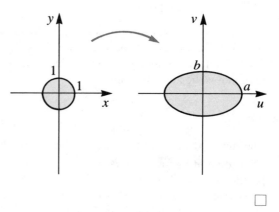

Since $\det A = ab$, areas are magnified by a factor of ab under the transformation. Since the original circle of radius 1 has area π, the ellipse has area πab.

Exercises 5.6

1. Find the area of the parallelogram determined by each pair of vectors.

    a. (4, 5), (5, 4)   **b.** (6, −1), (−4, −2)   **c.** (2, −3), (−4, 6)

2. Find the area of the triangle with vertices (1, 1), (4, 7), and (−1, 6).

3. If $\vec{u} = (2, 1, 1)$, $\vec{v} = (1, 5, -1)$, and $\vec{w} = (4, -3, 1)$, find the volumes of the parallelepipeds determined by the given vectors.

    a. $\vec{u}, \vec{v}, \vec{w}$ **b.** $\vec{u}, 2\vec{v}, 3\vec{w}$ **c.** $\vec{u}, \vec{v}, \vec{u} + \vec{v}$

4. For what values of k are the vectors (2, −1, 3), (−2, 5, −13), and (4, 1, k) coplanar?

5. Find all the values of t such that the vectors (1, 2, −3), (t, −1, 1), and (5, 3, −5) are linearly independent.

6. Find the equation of the plane determined by the given points.

    a. (−1, 1, 2), (4, 3, 2), (3, −1, 0)   **b.** (3, −2, 4), (1, −1, 5), (3, −2, 7)

7. Calculate the determinants of all the matrices in the table on page 174, section 5.3.

8. Sketch and label the image of the unit square, with vertices $O(0, 0)$, $A(1, 0)$, $C(1, 1)$, $B(0, 1)$, under each transformation. Find the determinant associated with each transformation and state which transformation involves reflections.

a. The shear $\quad u = x + 5y$
$$v = \quad\quad y$$

b. The reflection $\quad u = \quad\quad -y$
$$v = -x$$

c. The dilatation $\quad u = \quad 7x$
$$v = \quad\quad 7y$$

Problems 5.6

1. Find the volume of the tetrahedron with vertices $(1, 1, 2)$, $(3, -4, 6)$, $(-7, 0, -1)$, and $(-1, 5, 8)$.

2. Find the area of the pentagon with vertices $(1, 0)$, $(3, 1)$, $(4, 3)$, $(2, 6)$, and $(0, 2)$.

3. Find the volume of the ellipsoid

$$\frac{x^2}{a^2} + \frac{y^2}{b^2} + \frac{z^2}{c^2} = 1$$

by suitably transforming the unit sphere $x^2 + y^2 + z^2 = 1$.

5.7 Inverses of Square Matrices (Optional)

A multiplicative inverse of a real number x is another real number y such that $xy = 1$. Any non-zero real number has such an inverse. The definition of the inverse of a square matrix is similar; however, not all square matrices have inverses.

> ### The Inverse of a Square Matrix
>
> An $n \times n$ matrix A has an inverse B, if B is an $n \times n$ matrix such that $AB = I$ and $BA = I$, where I is the $n \times n$ identity matrix.

If B is an inverse of A, we write $B = A^{-1}$ $\left(\text{but not } \frac{1}{A}\right)$. Notice that A and A^{-1} must both be square matrices of the same size.

It can be proved in general that if A and B are square matrices such that $AB = I$, then $BA = I$; hence, $B = A^{-1}$.

Example 1. Show that $A = \begin{bmatrix} 2 & -1 \\ -3 & 4 \end{bmatrix}$ and $B = \begin{bmatrix} \frac{4}{5} & \frac{1}{5} \\ \frac{3}{5} & \frac{2}{5} \end{bmatrix}$ are inverse matrices.

Solution. We check that $AB = \begin{bmatrix} 2 & -1 \\ -3 & 4 \end{bmatrix} \begin{bmatrix} \frac{4}{5} & \frac{1}{5} \\ \frac{3}{5} & \frac{2}{5} \end{bmatrix} = \begin{bmatrix} 1 & 0 \\ 0 & 1 \end{bmatrix} = I$ and that

$$BA = \begin{bmatrix} \frac{4}{5} & \frac{1}{5} \\ \frac{3}{5} & \frac{2}{5} \end{bmatrix} \begin{bmatrix} 2 & -1 \\ -3 & 4 \end{bmatrix} = \begin{bmatrix} 1 & 0 \\ 0 & 1 \end{bmatrix} = I.$$

$\square$

Theorem. The square matrix A has an **inverse** if and only if

$$\det A \neq 0$$

Proof. We shall prove the result for a 2×2 matrix A, but the proof can be generalized to an $n \times n$ matrix. Let $X = \begin{bmatrix} x \\ y \end{bmatrix}$ and $U = \begin{bmatrix} u \\ v \end{bmatrix}$, and consider the system of equations

$$AX = U \quad \text{or} \quad \begin{aligned} a_{11}x + a_{12}y &= u \\ a_{21}x + a_{22}y &= v \end{aligned}$$

Suppose that A has an inverse A^{-1}. Then multiply $AX = U$ on the left by A^{-1} to obtain $A^{-1}AX = A^{-1}U$. Since $A^{-1}A = I$, the 2×2 identity matrix, and $IX = X$, we obtain $X = A^{-1}U$. Therefore, the system $AX = U$ can be solved for x and y to obtain the unique solution $X = A^{-1}U$. Hence, $\det A \neq 0$.

Conversely, suppose that $\det A \neq 0$, so that by Cramer's Rule the system $AX = U$ has the unique solution, for any u and v, in the form

$$X = BU \quad \text{or} \quad \begin{aligned} x &= b_{11}u + b_{12}v \\ y &= b_{21}u + b_{22}v \end{aligned}$$

for some 2×2 matrix B. Now $U = AX = ABU$, and this matrix equation is valid for any 2×1 matrix U. In particular, if we let $U = \begin{bmatrix} 1 \\ 0 \end{bmatrix}$ and then let $U = \begin{bmatrix} 0 \\ 1 \end{bmatrix}$, we see that the 2×2 matrix AB must have $\begin{bmatrix} 1 \\ 0 \end{bmatrix}$ as its first column and $\begin{bmatrix} 0 \\ 1 \end{bmatrix}$ as its second column, so that $AB = I$. Therefore, B is the inverse of A.

$\square$

This proof gives us a method for finding the inverse of A. If, for any U, we can solve $AX = U$ to obtain the solution $X = BU$, then B will be the inverse of A.

Example 2. Find the inverse of $A = \begin{bmatrix} 3 & 8 \\ -2 & -5 \end{bmatrix}$.

Solution. The matrix equation $AX = U$ is

$$3x + 8y = u$$
$$-2x - 5y = v$$

Solve for x and y, using row operations on the augmented matrix.

$$\left[\begin{array}{cc|c} 3 & 8 & u \\ -2 & -5 & v \end{array}\right] \quad \begin{array}{c} \text{row (1) + row (2)} \\ \sim \end{array} \quad \left[\begin{array}{cc|c} 1 & 3 & u + v \\ -2 & -5 & v \end{array}\right]$$

$$\begin{array}{c} \sim \\ \text{row (2) + 2 × row (1)} \end{array} \quad \left[\begin{array}{cc|c} 1 & 3 & u + v \\ 0 & 1 & 2u + 3v \end{array}\right] \quad \begin{array}{c} \text{row (1) − 3 × row (3)} \\ \sim \end{array} \quad \left[\begin{array}{cc|c} 1 & 0 & -5u - 8v \\ 0 & 1 & 2u + 3v \end{array}\right]$$

Hence, the equivalent system is

$$x = -5u - 8v$$
$$y = 2u + 3v$$

and the inverse matrix is

$$A^{-1} = \begin{bmatrix} -5 & -8 \\ 2 & 3 \end{bmatrix}$$

Check. $\begin{bmatrix} 3 & 8 \\ -2 & -5 \end{bmatrix}\begin{bmatrix} -5 & -8 \\ 2 & 3 \end{bmatrix} = \begin{bmatrix} 1 & 0 \\ 0 & 1 \end{bmatrix} = I$ □

In the above example, we are essentially row-reducing the system

$$\begin{bmatrix} a_{11} & a_{12} \\ a_{21} & a_{22} \end{bmatrix}\begin{bmatrix} x \\ y \end{bmatrix} = \begin{bmatrix} 1 & 0 \\ 0 & 1 \end{bmatrix}\begin{bmatrix} u \\ v \end{bmatrix}$$

to

$$\begin{bmatrix} 1 & 0 \\ 0 & 1 \end{bmatrix}\begin{bmatrix} x \\ y \end{bmatrix} = \begin{bmatrix} b_{11} & b_{12} \\ b_{21} & b_{22} \end{bmatrix}\begin{bmatrix} u \\ v \end{bmatrix}$$

where $B = A^{-1}$. Therefore, this is equivalent to writing an augmented matrix in the form $\left[\begin{array}{cc|cc} a_{11} & a_{12} & 1 & 0 \\ a_{21} & a_{22} & 0 & 1 \end{array}\right] = [A|I]$ and performing Gauss-Jordan elimination until the matrix is of the form $[I|B] = [I|A^{-1}]$, whose left half is the identity matrix. If this is possible, the right half will be the inverse of A. If it is not possible to row reduce the matrix so that the left half is the identity matrix, then A does not have an inverse.

Example 3. Find the inverse of $A = \begin{bmatrix} 2 & 1 & 4 \\ 1 & 1 & 2 \\ -2 & -3 & -2 \end{bmatrix}$.

Solution. Apply Gauss-Jordan elimination to the matrix $[A \mid I]$.

$$\left[\begin{array}{ccc|ccc} 2 & 1 & 4 & 1 & 0 & 0 \\ 1 & 1 & 2 & 0 & 1 & 0 \\ -2 & -3 & -2 & 0 & 0 & 1 \end{array}\right] \quad \begin{array}{c} \text{interchange} \\ \text{rows (1) and (2)} \\ \sim \end{array} \quad \left[\begin{array}{ccc|ccc} 1 & 1 & 2 & 0 & 1 & 0 \\ 2 & 1 & 4 & 1 & 0 & 0 \\ -2 & -3 & -2 & 0 & 0 & 1 \end{array}\right]$$

$$\begin{array}{c} \sim \\ \text{row (2)} - 2 \times \text{row (1)} \\ \text{row (3)} + 2 \times \text{row (1)} \end{array} \left[\begin{array}{ccc|ccc} 1 & 1 & 2 & 0 & 1 & 0 \\ 0 & -1 & 0 & 1 & -2 & 0 \\ 0 & -1 & 2 & 0 & 2 & 1 \end{array}\right] \quad \begin{array}{c} \text{row (1)} + \text{row (2)} \\ \sim \\ \text{row (3)} - \text{row (2)} \end{array} \left[\begin{array}{ccc|ccc} 1 & 0 & 2 & 1 & -1 & 0 \\ 0 & -1 & 0 & 1 & -2 & 0 \\ 0 & 0 & 2 & -1 & 4 & 1 \end{array}\right]$$

$$\begin{array}{c} \sim \\ (-1) \times \text{row (2)} \end{array} \left[\begin{array}{ccc|ccc} 1 & 0 & 2 & 1 & -1 & 0 \\ 0 & 1 & 0 & -1 & 2 & 0 \\ 0 & 0 & 2 & -1 & 4 & 1 \end{array}\right] \quad \begin{array}{c} \text{row (1)} - \text{row (3)} \\ \sim \\ \tfrac{1}{2} \times \text{row (3)} \end{array} \left[\begin{array}{ccc|ccc} 1 & 0 & 0 & 2 & -5 & -1 \\ 0 & 1 & 0 & -1 & 2 & 0 \\ 0 & 0 & 1 & -\tfrac{1}{2} & 2 & \tfrac{1}{2} \end{array}\right]$$

Hence, the inverse is $A^{-1} = \begin{bmatrix} 2 & -5 & -1 \\ -1 & 2 & 0 \\ -\tfrac{1}{2} & 2 & \tfrac{1}{2} \end{bmatrix}$.

Check. $AA^{-1} = \begin{bmatrix} 2 & 1 & 4 \\ 1 & 1 & 2 \\ -2 & -3 & -2 \end{bmatrix}\begin{bmatrix} 2 & -5 & -1 \\ -1 & 2 & 0 \\ -\tfrac{1}{2} & 2 & \tfrac{1}{2} \end{bmatrix} = \begin{bmatrix} 1 & 0 & 0 \\ 0 & 1 & 0 \\ 0 & 0 & 1 \end{bmatrix}$.   □

Example 4. Show that $A = \begin{bmatrix} 0 & 1 & -2 \\ 2 & 1 & 3 \\ 2 & 0 & 5 \end{bmatrix}$ does not have an inverse.

Solution. We shall show that $\det A = 0$.

$$\begin{vmatrix} 0 & 1 & -2 \\ 2 & 1 & 3 \\ 2 & 0 & 5 \end{vmatrix} = 0\begin{vmatrix} 1 & 3 \\ 0 & 5 \end{vmatrix} - 1\begin{vmatrix} 2 & 3 \\ 2 & 5 \end{vmatrix} + (-2)\begin{vmatrix} 2 & 1 \\ 2 & 0 \end{vmatrix}$$
$$= 0 - (10 - 6) - 2(-2)$$
$$= 0$$

Hence, $\det A = 0$, and so A does not have an inverse.   □

If we tried to row reduce $[A \mid I]$ in Example 4, we would find that we could not row-reduce the left half to the identity matrix.

If the coefficient matrix in a system of n linear equations in n variables possesses an inverse, we can use this inverse to solve the system.

Example 5. Solve the system

$$2x + y + 4z = 1$$
$$x + y + 2z = -2$$
$$-2x - 3y - 2z = 3$$

Solution. Write the system as the matrix equation

$$\begin{bmatrix} 2 & 1 & 4 \\ 1 & 1 & 2 \\ -2 & -3 & -2 \end{bmatrix} \begin{bmatrix} x \\ y \\ z \end{bmatrix} = \begin{bmatrix} 1 \\ -2 \\ 3 \end{bmatrix} \quad \text{or} \quad AX = B$$

From Example 3 we know that A has an inverse, and so we can multiply $AX = B$ by A^{-1} on the left to obtain

$$A^{-1}AX = A^{-1}B$$
$$IX = A^{-1}B$$

Hence, $X = A^{-1}B$ is the unique solution. It is

$$\begin{bmatrix} x \\ y \\ z \end{bmatrix} = \begin{bmatrix} 2 & -5 & -1 \\ -1 & 2 & 0 \\ -\frac{1}{2} & 2 & \frac{1}{2} \end{bmatrix} \begin{bmatrix} 1 \\ -2 \\ 3 \end{bmatrix} = \begin{bmatrix} 9 \\ -5 \\ -3 \end{bmatrix}$$

Therefore, $x = 9$, $y = -5$, and $z = -3$. ▫

Exercises 5.7

1. Find the inverses of the following matrices, if they exist.

a. $\begin{bmatrix} 5 & -7 \\ 3 & -4 \end{bmatrix}$ **b.** $\begin{bmatrix} 2 & -4 \\ 3 & 1 \end{bmatrix}$ **c.** $\begin{bmatrix} 2 & -3 \\ 10 & -15 \end{bmatrix}$

d. $\begin{bmatrix} 1 & 0 & 0 \\ 3 & 1 & 0 \\ 2 & 1 & 1 \end{bmatrix}$ **e.** $\begin{bmatrix} 3 & 2 & 1 \\ -1 & 4 & 0 \\ 2 & -1 & 3 \end{bmatrix}$ **f.** $\begin{bmatrix} 1 & 0 & -1 & 1 \\ 0 & 0 & 1 & 0 \\ 1 & -1 & 0 & -1 \\ 0 & 1 & 1 & 0 \end{bmatrix}$

2. Write each system of equations in the form $AX = B$, and calculate the solution using the equation $X = A^{-1}B$.

a. $2x - 3y = 7$ **b.** $2x - 3y = -5$
    $3x - 4y = -2$ $3x - 4y = 1$

3. Find A if $A^{-1} = \begin{bmatrix} 3 & -2 \\ 1 & 6 \end{bmatrix}$.

4. If $A = \begin{bmatrix} 1 & -2 & 1 \\ 2 & -2 & -2 \\ 3 & -6 & 4 \end{bmatrix}$, show that $\det(A^{-1}) = \dfrac{1}{\det A}$.

5. If A and B are 2×2 matrices, prove the product rule for determinants,

$$(\det A)(\det B) = \det(AB)$$

6. Use the previous exercise to prove that $\det(A^{-1}) = \dfrac{1}{\det A}$.

Problems 5.7

1. If $A = \begin{bmatrix} 2 & t & 6 \\ 0 & 2 & t \\ 1 & 0 & 2 \end{bmatrix}$, find all values of t so that A has an inverse.

2. Prove that the inverse of a matrix A is unique. (Hint: Assume that B and C are both inverses of A and prove that $B = C$.)

3. Show that if A and B are 2×2 matrices that have inverses, then AB has an inverse and $(AB)^{-1} = B^{-1}A^{-1}$.

Review Exercises

1. If $A = \begin{bmatrix} 0 & 2 \\ -5 & 1 \end{bmatrix}$, $B = \begin{bmatrix} 3 & -3 \\ 3 & 3 \end{bmatrix}$, $C = \begin{bmatrix} 1 & 4 \\ 2 & 8 \end{bmatrix}$, and $X = \begin{bmatrix} 4 \\ -1 \end{bmatrix}$, compute the following expressions if they are defined.

a. $A + BC$ **b.** $3A - 2B$ **c.** $C + X$ **d.** $X + X$

e. $ABCX$ **f.** $A^2 + B^2$ **g.** $AX + BX$ **h.** $AXBC$

2. Describe, in geometric terms, what each transformation of the plane does. Find the matrix of the transformations that are linear.

a. $T(x, y) = (x + 1, y - 5)$ **b.** $T(x, y) = (7x, 7y)$

c. $T(x, y) = (x + y, x - y)$ **d.** $T(x, y) = (x, 0)$

3. Find the image of the points $(2, 5)$ and $(-3, 1)$ under the linear transformations $\mathbf{R}^2 \rightarrow \mathbf{R}^2$ represented by each matrix.

a. $\begin{bmatrix} 2 & 1 \\ 1 & 2 \end{bmatrix}$ **b.** $\begin{bmatrix} 0 & 0 \\ 0 & 1 \end{bmatrix}$ **c.** $\begin{bmatrix} 4 & -7 \\ 1 & 3 \end{bmatrix}$ **d.** $\begin{bmatrix} 4 & -5 \\ -8 & 10 \end{bmatrix}$

4. Find the linear transformation $T: \mathbf{R}^2 \rightarrow \mathbf{R}^2$ represented by the matrix $\begin{bmatrix} 1 & 0 \\ -3 & 1 \end{bmatrix}$.

Describe the transformation in geometric terms and find the image of the triangle with vertices $(1, 0)$, $(2, 0)$, and $(2, 1)$.

5. Find the image of the circle $x^2 + y^2 = 4$ under the transformation with matrix $\begin{bmatrix} 0 & 3 \\ -3 & 0 \end{bmatrix}$.

6. Sketch the image of the unit square with vertices (0, 0), (0, 1), (1, 1), and (1, 0) under the transformation with the given matrix.

a. $\begin{bmatrix} -3 & 0 \\ 0 & 5 \end{bmatrix}$ b. $\begin{bmatrix} 1 & 2 \\ 2 & 4 \end{bmatrix}$ c. $\begin{bmatrix} 1 & -7 \\ 0 & 1 \end{bmatrix}$ d. $\begin{bmatrix} -\frac{1}{2} & \frac{\sqrt{3}}{2} \\ -\frac{\sqrt{3}}{2} & -\frac{1}{2} \end{bmatrix}$

7. Find the matrix of the linear transformation that consists of a reflection in the x-axis followed by a reflection in the y-axis.

8. Let R be the linear transformation that consists of a shear with matrix $\begin{bmatrix} 1 & b \\ 0 & 1 \end{bmatrix}$ followed by a reflection in the line $x = y$. Find the matrix of $R \circ R \circ R$.

9. Is there a linear transformation $R^2 \rightarrow R^2$ that maps (2, 3) to (1, 2), (0, 1) to (−1, 3), and (1, 0) to (5, 1)? If so, find it.

10. If T is a linear transformation with $T \begin{bmatrix} 1 \\ 1 \end{bmatrix} = \begin{bmatrix} 2 \\ 2 \end{bmatrix}$ and $T \begin{bmatrix} 2 \\ 1 \end{bmatrix} = \begin{bmatrix} -4 \\ 1 \end{bmatrix}$, what is $T \begin{bmatrix} \sqrt{2} + 1 \\ \sqrt{2} - 1 \end{bmatrix}$?

11. Compute $\begin{bmatrix} \frac{1}{\sqrt{2}} & \frac{1}{\sqrt{2}} \\ -\frac{1}{\sqrt{2}} & \frac{1}{\sqrt{2}} \end{bmatrix} \begin{bmatrix} 3 & -1 \\ -1 & 2 \end{bmatrix} \begin{bmatrix} \frac{1}{\sqrt{2}} & -\frac{1}{\sqrt{2}} \\ \frac{1}{\sqrt{2}} & \frac{1}{\sqrt{2}} \end{bmatrix}$.

12. Evaluate the following determinants.

a. $\begin{vmatrix} 10 & 7 \\ -3 & 5 \end{vmatrix}$ b. $\begin{vmatrix} 3 & 2 & -1 \\ 0 & 5 & 1 \\ 4 & -2 & -3 \end{vmatrix}$ c. $\begin{vmatrix} a & 2a & -3a \\ 5 & 1 & -1 \\ -2 & -4 & 6 \end{vmatrix}$

d. $\begin{vmatrix} \frac{\sqrt{3}}{2} & -\frac{1}{2} \\ \frac{1}{2} & \frac{\sqrt{3}}{2} \end{vmatrix}$ e. $\begin{vmatrix} 0 & t & t \\ t & 0 & t \\ t & t & 0 \end{vmatrix}$ f. $\begin{vmatrix} 5 - \sqrt{2} & 5 + \sqrt{2} & 0 \\ \sqrt{2} & 0 & -\sqrt{2} \\ 0 & 5 & 5 \end{vmatrix}$

13. Find all the values of x for which

$$\begin{vmatrix} 1 + x & 1 & 1 \\ 1 & 1 + x & 1 \\ 1 & 1 & 1 + x \end{vmatrix} = -2x$$

14. Find the volume of the parallelepiped with sides along (4, 5, −1), (1, −1, −2), and (2, 0, 1).

15. Show that the vectors (1, 4, 7), (2, 5, 8), and (3, 6, 9) are linearly dependent.

16. Find the equation of the plane containing the points (4, − 1, 0), (− 2, 2, 3), and (5, −1, −1).

17. Use Cramer's Rule to find the value of y in the solution of each system.

a. $3x + 4y = 7$
$\ 5x - \ \ y = 27$

b. $2x + \ \ y - \ \ z = -14$
$\ 3x - 4y - 2z = 7$
$\ -x + 2y - 3z = -43$

18. Write the following system of equations as matrix equations of the form $AX = B$. Find A^{-1} in each case and use it to solve the system.

a. $5x - 6y = -1$
$\ 3x - 4y = 3$

b. $x_1 + 3x_2 - 2x_3 = 3$
$\ 2x_1 + 5x_2 - 2x_3 = 4$
$\ x_1 + 2x_2 + \ \ x_3 = -1$

19. If $A = \begin{bmatrix} 1 & 1 \\ 0 & 1 \end{bmatrix}$ and $B = \begin{bmatrix} 1 & 0 \\ 1 & 1 \end{bmatrix}$, calculate the following matrices and their determinants.

a. A^2B **b.** ABA **c.** $A^{-1}B$ **d.** $BA^{-2}B^{-1}$

The rotation of a Ferris wheel at the Calgary Stampede.

Translations and Rotations

Translations and rotations of either the plane or 3-space are examples of transformations called rigid motions. A rigid motion is a transformation that takes any figure and produces a figure congruent to the original one. For example, if you could pick up the plane, move it, perhaps turn it over, and then replace it, you would have performed a rigid motion of the plane; any triangle in this plane would be transformed into a congruent triangle. A rigid motion is also called an isometry, a Greek term that means distance-preserving.

Rigid Motion

A transformation of the plane is called a **rigid motion** or **isometry** if the distance between the points P and Q is the same as the distance between the image points P' and Q', for all points P and Q in the plane.

Examples of rigid motions are translations, rotations, reflections, and combinations of these transformations. For example, if T is a translation and R is a rotation, then the composite transformation $T \circ R$ is also a rigid motion, consisting of the rotation **followed by** the translation.

A rigid motion that leaves the origin fixed is a linear transformation and hence can be represented by a matrix. The rigid motions that can be represented by matrices are rotations about the origin and reflections about a line through the origin. Since translations move the origin, they are not linear transformations, and therefore a translation cannot be represented by a matrix.

Quadratic equations in two variables represent conic sections, or conics for short. An isometry of a conic, such as an ellipse, parabola, or hyperbola, produces the same type of conic. We shall use translations and rotations to move these figures and to express their equations in standard form.

6.1 Translations

A translation of the plane along the vector $\vec{a}$ moves every point in the plane by an amount $|\vec{a}|$; that is, the point with position vector $\vec{p}$ is moved to the point with position vector $\vec{p} + \vec{a}$. For example, a translation along the vector $(-3\sqrt{2}, 3\sqrt{2})$ moves every point in the plane 6 units in a direction at $135°$ to the x-axis. In terms of coordinates we have the following definition.

> A **translation** $T: \mathbf{R}^2 \to \mathbf{R}^2$ along the vector $\vec{a} = (h, k)$ takes the point $P(x, y)$ to the point $P'(x + h, y + k)$.

This means that $T(x, y) = (u, v)$, where $u = x + h$ and $v = y + k$. We also write the transformation as $(x, y) \to (x + h, y + k)$.

Example 1. Find the image of the triangle ABC, with coordinates $A(-2, 3)$, $B(1, -4)$, and $C(5, 4)$, under the translation along the vector $(6, -5)$. Check that the length AB, the angle at A, and the area of the triangle do not change under this translation.

Solution. The translation along the vector $\vec{a} = (6, -5)$ is the mapping $(x, y) \to (x + 6, y - 5)$. Hence, $A(-2, 3)$ is taken to A', with coordinates $(-2 + 6, 3 - 5) = (4, -2)$, $B(1, -4)$ is taken to $B'(7, -9)$, and $C(5, 4)$ is taken to $C'(11, -1)$.

To check that the length AB is invariant under this translation, we show that AB and $A'B'$ have the same length. Now, $\overrightarrow{AB} = (1, -4) - (-2, 3) = (3, -7)$, and $\overrightarrow{A'B'} = (7, -9) - (4, -2) = (3, -7)$. Hence, AB and $A'B'$ have the same length.

Using the dot product, we obtain

$$\cos(\angle BAC) = \frac{\overrightarrow{AB} \cdot \overrightarrow{AC}}{|\overrightarrow{AB}||\overrightarrow{AC}|}$$

and

$$\cos(\angle B'A'C') = \frac{\overrightarrow{A'B'} \cdot \overrightarrow{A'C'}}{|\overrightarrow{A'B'}||\overrightarrow{A'C'}|}$$

We know that $\overrightarrow{AB} = \overrightarrow{A'B'}$. Now,

$$\overrightarrow{AC} = (5, 4) - (-2, 3) = (7, 1) \text{ and}$$

$$\overrightarrow{A'C'} = (11, -1) - (4, -2) = (7, 1),$$

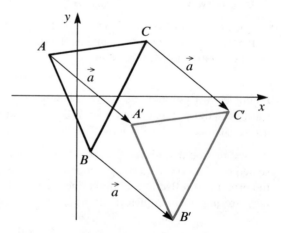

so that $\overrightarrow{AC} = \overrightarrow{A'C'}$. Therefore the angles at A and A' have the same cosine and hence are equal.

Using the cross product, we obtain

$$\text{Area } \triangle ABC - \tfrac{1}{2}|\overrightarrow{AB} \times \overrightarrow{AC}| \quad \text{and}$$

$$\text{Area } \triangle A'B'C' = \tfrac{1}{2}|\overrightarrow{A'B'} \times \overrightarrow{A'C'}|.$$

Since $\overrightarrow{AB} = \overrightarrow{A'B'}$ and $\overrightarrow{AC} = \overrightarrow{A'C'}$, $\triangle ABC$ and $\triangle A'B'C'$ have the same area. □

Example 2. Find the image of the line $Ax + By + C = 0$ under a translation along (h, k).

Solution. The translation takes the point (x, y) into the point $(u, v) = (x + h, y + k)$. Hence, $u = x + h$ and $v = y + k$, and so

$$x = u - h \quad \text{and} \quad y = v - k$$

The point (x, y) lies on the original line $Ax + By + C = 0$ if and only if the point (u, v) satisfies

$$A(u - h) + B(v - k) + C = 0$$
$$Au + Bv - Ah - Bk + C = 0$$

Hence, the image is $\{(u, v) \mid Au + Bv - Ah - Bk + C = 0\}$ or, equivalently,

$\{(x, y) \mid Ax + By - Ah - Bk + C = 0\}$. This is a line with slope $-\frac{A}{B}$. Since the original line has the same slope, the image of a line under a translation is a line parallel to the original line. □

As a general convention, when we transform a figure by a translation or rotation, we shall use the coordinates (x, y) for the points on the original figure and the coordinates (u, v) for those on the transformed figure.

Example 3. Find and sketch the image of the line $y = 2x + 6$ under the translation along the vector $(5, -1)$.

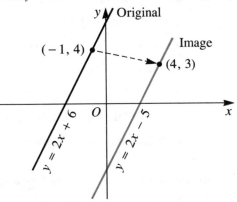

Solution. The translation takes (x, y) to $(u, v) = (x + 5, y - 1)$. Hence,

$$u = x + 5, v = y - 1,$$

and so $x = u - 5, y = v + 1$. Substituting in $y = 2x + 6$, we have

$$v + 1 = 2(u - 5) + 6$$
$$v = 2u - 5$$

Hence, the image of the line $y = 2x + 6$ is the line $y = 2x - 5$.

Alternative Solution. We know that the image is a line parallel to the original line and so has slope 2. One point on the original line is $(-1, 4)$. The image of $(-1, 4)$ under a translation along $(5, -1)$ is $(4, 3)$. Therefore, the image is the line through $(4, 3)$ with slope 2; that is, $y - 3 = 2(x - 4)$ or $y = 2x - 5$. $\square$

Exercises 6.1

1. Determine the image of $(-4, 3)$ under each translation.

    a. along $\vec{a} = (2, -4)$ **b.** $(x, y) \rightarrow (x - 5, y - 2)$

    c. $T(x, y) = (x - 4, y + 5)$ **d.** along $(-3, 5)$

    e. $(x, y) \rightarrow (x + 5, y + 4)$ **f.** along $(4, -3)$

    g. the translation that maps $(2, -1)$ to $(7, 7)$

2. A translation is determined by its effect on a single point. Determine the translation vector for each translation that has the given effect.

    a. $(3, -4) \rightarrow (2, -5)$ **b.** $(8, -3) \rightarrow (8, -3)$

    c. $(0, -7) \rightarrow (-4, 8)$ **d.** $T(-5, 4) = (7, -4)$

    e. $(-1, -3) \rightarrow (5, 2)$ **f.** $T(2, -1) = (-2, 1)$

3. Find the equation of the image of the line ℓ under a translation along $\vec{a}$.

    a. ℓ: $5x - 2y + 3 = 0$, $\vec{a} = (-3, 4)$ **b.** ℓ: $x + 3y - 1 = 0$, $\vec{a} = (6, -2)$

    c. ℓ: $x = 5$, $\vec{a} = (4, -1)$ **d.** ℓ: $2x - 5 = 0$, $\vec{a} = (0, 3)$

4. The coordinates of the vertices of $\triangle PQR$ are $P(2, -5)$, $Q(-3, 4)$, and $R(4, -1)$. A translation along (h, k) takes $\triangle PQR$ to $\triangle P'Q'R'$ and maps $P(2, -5)$ to $P'(0, -1)$. Determine

    a. the translation vector (h, k).

    b. the coordinates of Q' and R'.

    c. the lengths $P'Q'$, $P'R'$, and $Q'R'$.

    d. the angles of $\triangle P'Q'R'$.

    e. the area of $\triangle P'Q'R'$.

    f. the length of the median from Q'.

    g. the coordinates of the centroids of $\triangle P'Q'R'$ and $\triangle PQR$.

5. If $\triangle P'Q'R'$ of Exercise 4 is mapped to $\triangle P''Q''R''$ by a translation along $(-3, -2)$, find the coordinates of P'', Q'', and R'' and find a single translation that will map $\triangle PQR$ to $\triangle P''Q''R''$.

6. A Penrose tiling is an aperiodic tiling of the plane using two types of tiles called "kites" and "darts." Which of the labelled regions in the Penrose tiling are images of each other under a translation?

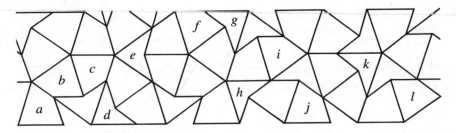

7. In the diagram, determine the translations that take the shaded brick to each of the positions a through d. The bricks are laid parallel to the x-axis and are of size 2×1.

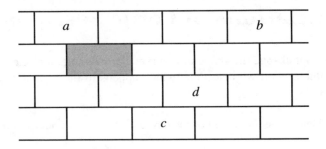

8. Find the equation of the image of the line $2x - 3y + 6 = 0$ after it is translated to pass through the point $(4, -3)$.

9. Find the equation of the line through $(-5, 3)$ that maps into itself after a translation along $(2, 1)$. (That is, the image line and the original line are the same.)

10. If f and g are two translations defined by $f(x, y) = (x - 6, y + 4)$ and $g(x, y) = (x + 3, y - 2)$, determine $f \circ g$ and $g \circ f$.

11. Determine the translation $T \circ S$, where T and S are translations along $\vec{t} = (5, -3)$ and $\vec{s} = (-3, -2)$, respectively.

Problems 6.1

1. If T and S are translations in which $T(a, b) = (m, n)$ and $S(c, d) = (p, q)$, determine the translations.

    a. $T \circ S$ **b.** $S \circ T$

2. If $F : R^2 \rightarrow R^2$ is an isometry, prove that F maps straight lines to straight lines and that F preserves angles.

3. Regular hexagons, with unit sides, tile the plane to form a honeycomb. Select the x-axis as the horizontal.

   a. Find the translations that take the shaded hexagon to each of the positions a through e.

   b. Determine the general translation that will take the shaded hexagon to all other positions.

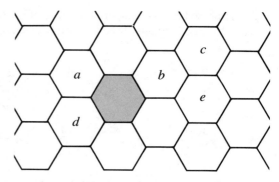

4. Determine the conditions under which the line $\vec{n} \cdot (\vec{r} - \vec{r}_1) = 0$ maps to itself under the translation along $\vec{a}$.

6.2 Translations of Conic Sections

A translation does not change the shape of a curve. For example, a circle will only translate into a circle. In this section we determine what happens to the equations of known conics under translations.

Example 1. Determine the image of the circle $x^2 + y^2 = 6$ under a translation along the vector $(5, -2)$.

Solution. The mapping is $(x, y) \rightarrow (x + 5, y - 2) = (u, v)$.
Hence, $u = x + 5$ and $v = y - 2$. Substituting $x = u - 5$ and $y = v + 2$ into the equation $x^2 + y^2 = 6$, we obtain

$$(u - 5)^2 + (v + 2)^2 = 6$$

Hence, the image is the set

$$\{(u, v) \,|\, (u - 5)^2 + (v + 2)^2 = 6\}$$

or, equivalently,

$$\{(x, y) \,|\, (x - 5)^2 + (y + 2)^2 = 6\}$$

The image is a circle centred at $(5, -2)$ with radius $\sqrt{6}$.

If the equation $(x - 5)^2 + (y + 2)^2 = 6$ is expanded, we obtain

$$x^2 + y^2 - 10x + 4y + 23 = 0$$

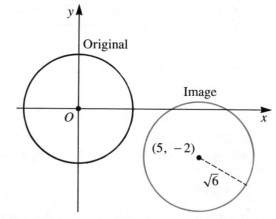

Notice that the translation has introduced the linear terms $-10x$ and $4y$ into the equation. □

In general, the translation along the vector (h, k) maps the circle of radius r centred at (a, b) into the circle of radius r centred at $(a + h, b + k)$.

An ellipse or hyperbola whose centre is at the origin and whose axes are along the coordinate axes has an equation of the form $ax^2 + by^2 = d$. If we apply the translation $(x, y) \rightarrow (x + h, y + k) = (u, v)$, then $x = u - h$, $y = v - k$ and the equation becomes

$$a(u - h)^2 + b(v - k)^2 = d$$

When this is expanded and rearranged, it becomes

$$au^2 + bv^2 - 2ahu - 2bkv + ah^2 + bk^2 - d = 0$$

Hence, the translated curve has an equation of the form

$$ax^2 + by^2 + 2gx + 2fy + c = 0$$

Notice that the quadratic terms ax^2 and by^2 are unchanged; the translation only changes the linear and constant terms.

One of our goals is to simplify a quadratic equation, by eliminating the linear terms, so that we may recognize the type of curve it represents. In the following example the equation can be simplified by translating the curve along the **vector** $(-1, -6)$. In the next section we shall show how such a translation can be determined in any particular case.

Example 2. Show, by translating along $(-1, -6)$, that the curve with equation

$$4x^2 - 9y^2 - 8x + 108y - 284 = 0$$

represents a hyperbola. Find the centre, vertices, and asymptotes of the original hyperbola.

Solution. The transformation is $(x, y) \rightarrow (x - 1, y - 6) = (u, v)$. Substitute $x = u + 1$ and $y = v + 6$ in the equation to obtain

$$4(u + 1)^2 - 9(v + 6)^2 - 8(u + 1) + 108(v + 6) - 284 = 0$$
$$4u^2 + 8u + 4 - 9v^2 - 108v - 324 - 8u - 8 + 108v + 648 - 284 = 0$$

This simplifies to $4u^2 - 9v^2 = -36$ or

$$\frac{u^2}{9} - \frac{v^2}{4} = -1$$

This represents a hyperbola, whose centre is at the origin, $(0, 0)$. Therefore, the original equation must also represent a hyperbola. Since $x = u + 1$ and $y = v + 6$, the centre of the original hyperbola is $(1, 6)$.

The vertices of the translated hyperbola are at $(0, 2)$ and $(0, -2)$. Hence, the original hyperbola has its vertices at $(1, 8)$ and $(1, 4)$.

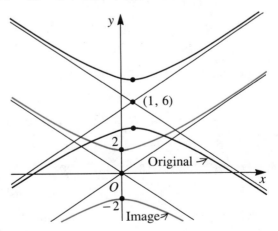

The asymptotes of the image are $2u - 3v = 0$ and $2u + 3v = 0$. We can find the asymptotes of the original curve by setting $u = x - 1$ and $v = y - 6$ to obtain

$$2(x - 1) - 3(y - 6) = 0 \quad \text{and} \quad 2(x - 1) + 3(y - 6) = 0$$

that is,
$$2x - 3y + 16 = 0 \quad \text{and} \quad 2x + 3y - 20 = 0$$

Hence, the asymptotes of the original curve are the lines $2x - 3y + 16 = 0$ and $2x + 3y - 20 = 0$.

Check. A partial check on our calculations can be made by determining the intercepts of the original hyperbola. For the x-intercepts we let $y = 0$, giving the quadratic equation $4x^2 - 8x - 284 = 0$ or $x^2 - 2x - 71 = 0$. Using the quadratic formula and a calculator, we find the x-intercepts to be approximately -7.5 and 9.5. The y-intercepts are found when $x = 0$, giving the quadratic equation $9y^2 - 108y + 284 = 0$. The y-intercepts are approximately 8.1 and 3.9. These values agree with the sketch.   □

Exercises 6.2

1. Determine which of the quadratic equations can be written in the form

$$ax^2 + by^2 + 2gx + 2fy + c = 0$$

   and state the values for a, b, g, f, and c.

   a. $2(x - 3)^2 - 5(y + 1)^2 = 40$ **b.** $3(x + 2)^2 = 5(y - 4)^2$

   c. $\dfrac{x^2}{9} + \dfrac{y^2}{4} = 1$ **d.** $xy = 1$

   e. $y = 4x^2 + 3x - 5$ **f.** $(x + y - 1)(x - 2y + 1) = 0$

2. Determine the equation of the image of each conic under the given translation. Determine the type of curve and the sign of the product of the coefficients of x^2 and y^2. Make a neat sketch of the original and image curves and, where applicable, find the centre, vertices, and asymptotes of both curves.

   a. $x^2 + y^2 = 16;$ $(x, y) \to (x - 3, y + 4)$

   b. $x^2 + 16y^2 = 16;$ $(x, y) \to (x - 5, y + 3)$

   c. $4x^2 - 25y^2 = 100;$ translation along $(3, 1)$

   d. $x^2 - y^2 + 4x + 6y - 21 = 0;$ $(x, y) \to (x + 2, y - 3)$

   e. $25x^2 + 4y^2 - 50x + 24y - 39 = 0;$ $(x, y) \to (x - 1, y + 3)$

   f. $x^2 - 6x - 8y - 31 = 0;$ $(x, y) \to (x - 3, y + 5)$

   g. $9x^2 + 9y^2 - 18x + 36y + 20 = 0;$ $(x, y) \to (x - 1, y + 2)$

   h. $x^2 - y^2 + 4x + 10y - 21 = 0;$ translation along $(2, -5)$

   i. $x^2 + y^2 + 2x + 5 = 0;$ translation along $(1, 0)$

3. Find the equation of the image of the parabola with equation $y^2 = 4px$ under the translation $(x, y) \rightarrow (u, v) = (x + h, y + k)$.

Problems 6.2

1. By examining Exercise 2, state what conclusions you can make with regard to the type of conic represented by the equation

$$ax^2 + by^2 + 2gx + 2fy + c = 0$$

when **(i)** $ab = 0$. **(ii)** $ab > 0$. **(iii)** $ab < 0$.

2. Find the equation and sketch the image of each curve under the given translation.

a. $xy = 1$; $(x, y) \rightarrow (x + 5, y - 2)$

b. $y = x^3$; $(x, y) \rightarrow (x - 1, y + 3)$

c. $y = \sin x$ (x in radians); $(x, y) \rightarrow (x - \dfrac{\pi}{4}, y + 3)$

d. $y = 2^x$; $(x, y) \rightarrow (x + 5, y - 3)$

6.3 Elimination of First Degree Terms in Quadratic Equations

We have seen that the general quadratic equation of the form

$$ax^2 + by^2 + 2gx + 2fy + c = 0$$

transforms under a translation into an equation of a similar form whose second degree terms, ax^2 and by^2, remain unchanged. In this section, we shall show how to simplify such a quadratic equation by translating it so that, if $ab \neq 0$, the first degree terms in x and y vanish. If we succeed in eliminating the first degree terms, the equation will be in the standard form $ax^2 + by^2 = d$, which represents an ellipse if $ab > 0$ and a hyperbola if $ab < 0$. If either $a = 0$ or $b = 0$, we shall not usually be able to eliminate both first degree terms in x and y. However, we can eliminate one of the first degree terms **and** the constant term to obtain an equation of the form $y^2 = 4px$ or $x^2 = 4py$; these are the equations of parabolas in standard form.

The characteristics of a standard conic, such as vertices and any asymptotes, can easily be calculated. By applying the inverse translation, the characteristics of the original conic can be determined.

The following summary shows how a conic's type depends on the coefficients a and b.

The **quadratic equation** $ax^2 + by^2 + 2gx + 2fy + c = 0$ represents

an **ellipse**	if $ab > 0$,
a **circle**	if $a = b$,
a **hyperbola**	if $ab < 0$,
and a **parabola**	if $ab = 0$.

It is possible for degenerate cases to occur; for example, the hyperbola $x^2 - y^2 = d$ degenerates into a pair of intersecting straight lines when $d = 0$. Also the ellipse $2x^2 + 9y^2 = d$ is a point if $d = 0$, and if $d < 0$, it is an "imaginary ellipse" that does not contain any real points. Both a and b cannot be zero; if they were, the equation would not be quadratic.

There are two ways of eliminating the first degree terms from a quadratic equation. We can perform a general translation along the vector (h, k) and determine the values of h and k that make the first degree terms zero, or we can use the technique of "completing the squares" in x and y.

Example 1. Sketch the graph of

$$3x^2 + 2y^2 + 12x - 4y + 8 = 0$$

by changing the equation into a standard form by means of a translation along the vector (h, k).

Solution. Since $ab = (3)(2) = 6 > 0$, the equation represents an ellipse and its standard form will be $3x^2 + 2y^2 = d$. Translate the ellipse, using the transformation $(x, y) \rightarrow (x + h, y + k) = (u, v)$ and substituting $x = u - h$ and $y = v - k$ to obtain

$$3(u - h)^2 + 2(v - k)^2 + 12(u - h) - 4(v - k) + 8 = 0$$
$$3u^2 - 6hu + 3h^2 + 2v^2 - 4kv + 2k^2 + 12u - 12h - 4v + 4k + 8 = 0$$
$$3u^2 + 2v^2 + (-6h + 12)u + (-4k - 4)v + (3h^2 + 2k^2 - 12h + 4k + 8) = 0$$

For the first degree terms to vanish, the coefficients of u and v must be zero; therefore

$$-6h + 12 = 0 \quad \text{and} \quad -4k - 4 = 0$$

That is, $h = 2$ and $k = -1$. The constant term is

$$3h^2 + 2k^2 - 12h + 4k + 8 = 3(2)^2 + 2(-1)^2 - 12(2) + 4(-1) + 8$$
$$= -6$$

Hence, the point (u, v) lies on the image if and only if $3u^2 + 2v^2 - 6 = 0$.

Therefore, the translation

$$(x, y) \rightarrow (x + 2, y - 1)$$

transforms the original ellipse into one with the standard equation $3x^2 + 2y^2 = 6$ or

$$\frac{x^2}{2} + \frac{y^2}{3} = 1$$

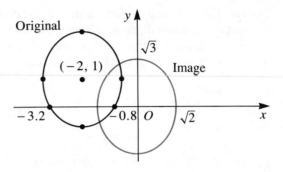

The ellipse has semi-axes of lengths $\sqrt{2}$ and $\sqrt{3}$ and can be mapped to the original ellipse by the inverse translation

$$(x, y) \to (x - 2, y + 1).$$

Hence, the original ellipse has its centre at $(-2, 1)$.

Check. We can determine the intercepts of the original curve. It crosses the x-axis where $y = 0$ and $3x^2 + 12x + 8 = 0$. Hence, the x-intercepts are $x \approx -3.2$ and $x \approx -0.8$. It crosses the y-axis where $x = 0$ and $2y^2 - 4y + 8 = 0$. This quadratic equation in y has no real roots; therefore, the ellipse does not cross the y-axis. This agrees with the sketch. $\square$

Example 2. Sketch the graph of

$$x^2 - 6x - 8y - 23 = 0$$

Solution. Since $ab = (1)(0) = 0$, the curve is a parabola. Translate the curve using the transformation $(x, y) \to (x + h, y + k) = (u, v)$ and by substituting $x = u - h$ and $y = v - k$ we obtain

$$(u - h)^2 - 6(u - h) - 8(v - k) - 23 = 0$$
$$u^2 + (-2h - 6)u - 8v + (h^2 + 6h + 8k - 23) = 0$$

The first degree term in u can be eliminated by setting $-2h - 6 = 0$; that is, $h = -3$. The first degree term in v, $-8v$, cannot be eliminated, but the constant term can be eliminated by setting $h^2 + 6h + 8k - 23 = 0$.

Since $h = -3$, this becomes $8k - 32 = 0$ or $k = 4$. Therefore, if $u = x - 3$ and $v = y + 4$, the equation becomes

$$u^2 = 8v$$

which is the equation of a parabola in standard form with its vertex at $(0, 0)$.

The original equation is a parabola with its vertex at $(3, -4)$.

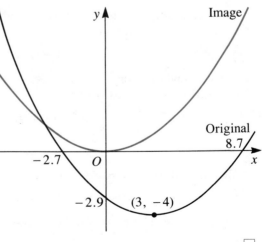

Check. Since the original curve meets the x-axis where $x^2 - 6x - 23 = 0$; that is, $x \approx 8.7$ or -2.7. It meets the y-axis where $x = 0$ and $-8y - 23 = 0$; that is, $y \approx -2.9$.

$\square$

The alternative method of eliminating the first degree terms is to complete the square in x and the square in y. Since the quadratic equation contains no xy term, we can separate the x terms, $ax^2 + 2gx$, and the y terms, $by^2 + 2fy$, and complete the square in each. In Example 3 we show how to simplify a quadratic equation by applying this method to the previous two examples.

Example 3. Find, by completing the squares, the translation that will place the equation in standard form.

a. $3x^2 + 2y^2 + 12x - 4y + 8 = 0$

b. $x^2 - 6x - 8y - 23 = 0$

Solution.
a. Separate the x and y terms in

$$3x^2 + 12x + 2y^2 - 4y + 8 = 0$$

to obtain

$$3(x^2 + 4x) + 2(y^2 - 2y) + 8 = 0$$

Now complete the squares in x and y to obtain

$$3(x^2 + 4x + 4 - 4) + 2(y^2 - 2y + 1 - 1) + 8 = 0$$
$$3(x + 2)^2 + 2(y - 1)^2 - 12 - 2 + 8 = 0$$

Hence, if we substitute $u = x + 2$ and $v = y - 1$ the equation becomes

$$3u^2 + 2v^2 = 6$$

which is a standard form for the equation of an ellipse. The translation required to express the equation in this form is

$$(x, y) \to (u, v) = (x + 2, y - 1)$$

b. In the second equation, $x^2 - 6x - 8y - 23 = 0$, there is no term in y^2; so we can only complete the square in x. Hence,

$$(x^2 - 6x + 9) - 9 - 8y - 23 = 0$$
$$(x - 3)^2 - 8y - 32 = 0$$
$$(x - 3)^2 - 8(y + 4) = 0$$

Therefore, if we set $u = x - 3$ and $v = y + 4$, the equation becomes

$$u^2 = 8v$$

which is the standard form for the equation of a parabola. The required translation is

$$(x, y) \to (u, v) = (x - 3, y + 4) \qquad \square$$

Exercises 6.3

1. Determine the centre and radius of each circle.

   a. $x^2 + y^2 - 2x + 4y - 4 = 0$ **b.** $(x + 3)^2 + (y - 4)^2 = 12$

   c. $4x^2 + 4y^2 - 16x + 32y + 55 = 0$ **d.** $x^2 + y^2 + 4x + 4y = 0$

   e. $9x^2 + 9y^2 + 36y + 31 = 0$ **f.** $x^2 + y^2 - 8x - 6y + 29 = 0$

2. Find the image of each equation after a translation along the vector (h, k). Then find the specific translation that will place the conic in standard position, and give the equation in standard form.

   a. $4x^2 + 9y^2 - 8x + 54y + 49 = 0$ **b.** $y^2 - 8x + 6y + 17 = 0$

   c. $4x^2 - y^2 + 24x - 6y + 31 = 0$ **d.** $4x^2 - y^2 - 8x - 4y + 16 = 0$

3. By completing the squares, determine the translation that will place the conic in standard position and give the equation in standard form.

   a. $4x^2 - y^2 + 16x - 4y + 16 = 0$ **b.** $x^2 - 10x - 8y + 1 = 0$

   c. $x^2 + 9y^2 - 6x - 54y + 81 = 0$ **d.** $5x^2 + 20x + 2y + 22 = 0$

4. Sketch the graph of each equation, labelling the centre and vertices.

   a. $x^2 - 4x - 2y - 6 = 0$

   b. $25x^2 + 4y^2 - 250x + 24y + 561 = 0$

   c. $x^2 + y^2 - 10x + 6y + 34 = 0$

   d. $16x^2 + 16y^2 + 16x - 24y - 3 = 0$

   e. $3y^2 - 4x + 18y + 31 = 0$

   f. $4x^2 + y^2 + 40x - 4y + 100 = 0$

   g. $25x^2 - 4y^2 - 24y - 136 = 0$

(handwritten annotations:)

(d) $16x^2 + 16y^2 + 16x - 24y - 3 = 0$

$16(x^2 + x + \frac{1}{4}) + 16(y^2 - \frac{3}{2}y + \frac{9}{16}) - 3 - 4 - 9 = 0$

$16(x + \frac{1}{2})^2 + 16(y - \frac{3}{4})^2 = 16$

$(x + \frac{1}{2})^2 + (y - \frac{3}{4})^2 = 16$

∴ translation is $(u, v) \Rightarrow (x + \frac{1}{2}, y - \frac{3}{4})$

∴ inverse translation is $x - \frac{1}{2}, y + \frac{3}{4}$ to get original graph.

∴ a circle $u^2 + v^2 = 16$

Problems 6.3

1. Translate each curve to a simpler form and sketch the given curve.

   a. $xy - 5x + y - 11 = 0$ **b.** $x^2 + 2xy + y^2 + 6x + 6y + 5 = 0$

2. Find the equations of the asymptotes of the hyperbola *centre at $(\frac{1}{2}, \frac{3}{4})$*

$$4x^2 - 9y^2 + 24x + 18y + 25 = 0.$$

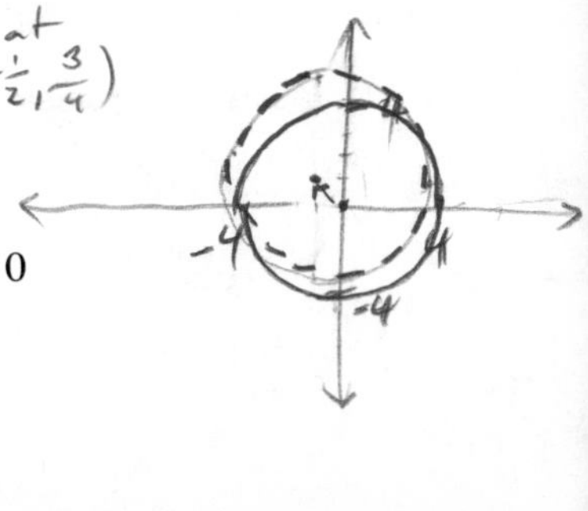

3. Find the centre of the ellipsoid

$$4x^2 + y^2 + 4z^2 - 8x + 6y + 8z + 13 = 0$$

   and sketch the surface in $\mathbf{R}^3$.

(handwritten sketch of a circle in the lower right, with axes marked -4 and -4)

6.4 Rotations

In the previous sections we have seen the effect that translations have on the standard equations
of conics and the techniques used in translating conics to standard position. Not all quadratic
equations can be simplified by translations, but they can be simplified by using both rotations
and translations.

We now introduce rotations of the plane about a fixed point O. These rotations are examples
of rigid motions of the plane. We shall show that a rotation about the origin is a linear
transformation and can be written in terms of a 2×2 matrix.

Fix a point O as the centre of rotation. The
locus of a point P, as it is rotated about O,
is a circle having centre O and radius OP.
The image of P, after a rotation through an
angle θ about the point O, is the point P' on
the locus such that $\angle POP' = \theta$. If $\theta > 0$
the rotation is counterclockwise, and if
$\theta < 0$ the rotation is clockwise. Since P'
lies on the rotation circle, $OP' = OP$.

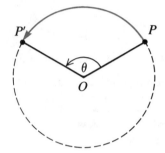

A rotation of the plane through one complete revolution, $360°$ or 2π radians, brings all points
in the plane back to their original positions. A rotation of $180°$ or π radians is equivalent to a
reflection through the centre of rotation O.

Let us look at the rotation of a conic in the
plane. Consider the given ellipse E and
rotate it about the origin. Various positions
of the ellipse are shown as it is rotated. The
dotted circle represents the locus of the
centre of the ellipse. Notice the orientation
of the ellipse as it is rotated. Two of the
ellipses shown have their axes parallel to
the coordinate axes; the equations of these
ellipses are simpler than those of the other
ellipses. Are there any other positions in
which the axes of the ellipse are parallel to
the coordinate axes?

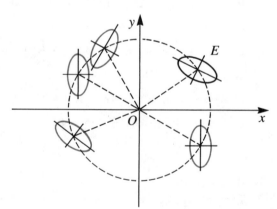

Let us now determine how a rotation about the origin through an angle θ changes the coordinates
of a point.

Let P have coordinates (x, y), where $\angle PON$
$= \alpha$ and $OP = r$. Then $\cos \alpha = \dfrac{x}{r}$ and
$\sin \alpha = \dfrac{y}{r}$, and so

$$x = r \cos \alpha \quad \text{and} \quad y = r \sin \alpha$$

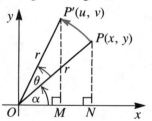

Let the image of P after a rotation through an angle of θ about the origin be the point P' (u, v). Then $OP' = r$ and $\angle P'OM = \alpha + \theta$. Now $\cos(\alpha + \theta) = \dfrac{u}{r}$ and $\sin(\alpha + \theta) = \dfrac{v}{r}$. We wish to find the relation between the coordinates of P' and the coordinates of P. Using the formula for the cosine of a sum of angles, we obtain

$$\begin{aligned}
u &= r\cos(\alpha + \theta) \\
&= r(\cos\alpha\cos\theta - \sin\alpha\sin\theta) \\
&= (r\cos\alpha)\cos\theta - (r\sin\alpha)\sin\theta \\
u &= x\cos\theta - y\sin\theta
\end{aligned}$$

Using the formula for the sine of a sum of angles, we obtain

$$\begin{aligned}
v &= r\sin(\alpha + \theta) \\
&= r(\sin\alpha\cos\theta + \cos\alpha\sin\theta) \\
&= (r\cos\alpha)\sin\theta + (r\sin\alpha)\cos\theta \\
v &= x\sin\theta + y\cos\theta
\end{aligned}$$

The rotation about the origin through the angle θ is represented by the transformation $P(x, y) \to P'(u, v)$, where
$$u = x\cos\theta - y\sin\theta$$
$$v = x\sin\theta + y\cos\theta$$

Example 1. Determine the image of the point $P(5, -4)$ after a rotation of $60°$ about the origin.

Solution. Let the image of $P(x, y)$ be $P'(u, v)$. We know that $(x, y) = (5, -4)$ and $\theta = 60°$; so $\cos\theta = \frac{1}{2}$ and $\sin\theta = \frac{\sqrt{3}}{2}$. Hence, using the above transformation,

$$\begin{aligned}
u &= x\cos\theta - y\sin\theta \\
&= 5\left(\tfrac{1}{2}\right) - (-4)\left(\tfrac{\sqrt{3}}{2}\right) \\
&= \frac{5 + 4\sqrt{3}}{2}
\end{aligned}
\qquad \text{and} \qquad
\begin{aligned}
v &= x\sin\theta + y\cos\theta \\
&= 5\left(\tfrac{\sqrt{3}}{2}\right) + (-4)\left(\tfrac{1}{2}\right) \\
&= \frac{5\sqrt{3} - 4}{2}
\end{aligned}$$

Therefore, the image of $(5, -4)$ after a rotation of $60°$ is $\left(\dfrac{5 + 4\sqrt{3}}{2}, \dfrac{5\sqrt{3} - 4}{2}\right)$.

Check. Using a calculator, we see that the image is approximately $(6.0, 2.3)$. A sketch shows that this answer is plausible.

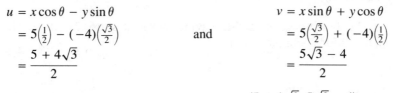

$$r_\theta = \begin{bmatrix} \cos\theta & -\sin\theta \\ \sin\theta & \cos\theta \end{bmatrix} = \begin{bmatrix} u \\ v \end{bmatrix}$$

$$r_T = r_{-\theta} = \begin{bmatrix} \cos\theta & \sin\theta \\ -\sin\theta & \cos\theta \end{bmatrix} = \begin{bmatrix} u \\ v \end{bmatrix}$$

We can write (x, y) and (u, v) as the column vectors $X = \begin{bmatrix} x \\ y \end{bmatrix}$ and $U = \begin{bmatrix} u \\ v \end{bmatrix}$, respectively, and express the rotation equations in terms of matrices.

The rotation about the origin through the angle θ is represented by

$$\begin{bmatrix} u \\ v \end{bmatrix} = \begin{bmatrix} \cos\theta & -\sin\theta \\ \sin\theta & \cos\theta \end{bmatrix} \begin{bmatrix} x \\ y \end{bmatrix} \quad \text{or} \quad U = R_\theta X$$

where $R_\theta = \begin{bmatrix} \cos\theta & -\sin\theta \\ \sin\theta & \cos\theta \end{bmatrix}$ is called the **rotation matrix**.

This shows that every rotation of the plane about the origin is a linear transformation with matrix R_θ. A rotation about any other point does not map the origin to itself and so cannot be a linear transformation.

A rotation through one half a revolution, or $180°$, is represented by the matrix $R_{180°} = \begin{bmatrix} -1 & 0 \\ 0 & -1 \end{bmatrix} = -I$, which takes a point to its image after a reflection through the origin. A rotation through one quarter of a revolution, or $90°$, is represented by $R_{90°} = \begin{bmatrix} 0 & -1 \\ 1 & 0 \end{bmatrix}$.

If you have studied the sections on determinants, you should notice that any rotation matrix must have determinant 1, since

$$\det(R_\theta) = \begin{vmatrix} \cos\theta & -\sin\theta \\ \sin\theta & \cos\theta \end{vmatrix} = \cos^2\theta + \sin^2\theta = 1$$

This provides a partial check for a rotation matrix because if $\det(A) \neq 1$, the matrix A cannot be a rotation matrix.

Example 2. Find the image of $\triangle ABC$, having coordinates $A(6, 2)$, $B(-2, 4)$, $C(4, -2)$, after a rotation of $-150°$ about the origin.

Solution. Since

$$\cos(-150°) = -\cos(30°) = -\frac{\sqrt{3}}{2}$$

$$\text{and } \sin(-150°) = -\sin(30°) = -\frac{1}{2}$$

the matrix for this rotation is

$$R_{-150°} = \begin{bmatrix} -\frac{\sqrt{3}}{2} & \frac{1}{2} \\ -\frac{1}{2} & -\frac{\sqrt{3}}{2} \end{bmatrix}$$

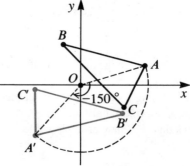

The image of $A(6, 2)$ is $\begin{bmatrix} -\frac{\sqrt{3}}{2} & \frac{1}{2} \\ -\frac{1}{2} & -\frac{\sqrt{3}}{2} \end{bmatrix} \begin{bmatrix} 6 \\ 2 \end{bmatrix} = \begin{bmatrix} -3\sqrt{3} + 1 \\ -3 - \sqrt{3} \end{bmatrix}$.

The image of $B(-2, 4)$ is $\begin{bmatrix} -\frac{\sqrt{3}}{2} & \frac{1}{2} \\ -\frac{1}{2} & -\frac{\sqrt{3}}{2} \end{bmatrix} \begin{bmatrix} -2 \\ 4 \end{bmatrix} = \begin{bmatrix} \sqrt{3} + 2 \\ 1 - 2\sqrt{3} \end{bmatrix}$.

The image of $C(4, -2)$ is $\begin{bmatrix} -\frac{\sqrt{3}}{2} & \frac{1}{2} \\ -\frac{1}{2} & -\frac{\sqrt{3}}{2} \end{bmatrix} \begin{bmatrix} 4 \\ -2 \end{bmatrix} = \begin{bmatrix} -2\sqrt{3} - 1 \\ -2 + \sqrt{3} \end{bmatrix}$.

Hence, the image of A is $A'(-3\sqrt{3} + 1, -3 - \sqrt{3})$, the image of B is $B'(\sqrt{3} + 2, 1 - 2\sqrt{3})$, and the image of C is $C'(-2\sqrt{3} - 1, -2 + \sqrt{3})$. □

Example 3. Determine the matrix for a rotation of $45°$ followed by a reflection in the x-axis. Is this composite transformation equivalent to a single rotation about the origin?

Solution. The matrix for a reflection in the x-axis is $M_x = \begin{bmatrix} 1 & 0 \\ 0 & -1 \end{bmatrix}$, and the matrix for a rotation of $45°$ is $R_{45°} = \begin{bmatrix} \frac{1}{\sqrt{2}} & -\frac{1}{\sqrt{2}} \\ \frac{1}{\sqrt{2}} & \frac{1}{\sqrt{2}} \end{bmatrix}$. The matrix for the rotation followed by the reflection is

$$M_x R_{45°} = \begin{bmatrix} 1 & 0 \\ 0 & -1 \end{bmatrix} \begin{bmatrix} \frac{1}{\sqrt{2}} & -\frac{1}{\sqrt{2}} \\ \frac{1}{\sqrt{2}} & \frac{1}{\sqrt{2}} \end{bmatrix}$$

$$= \begin{bmatrix} \frac{1}{\sqrt{2}} & -\frac{1}{\sqrt{2}} \\ -\frac{1}{\sqrt{2}} & -\frac{1}{\sqrt{2}} \end{bmatrix}$$

Since $\det(M_x R_{45°}) = -1 \neq 1$, the final matrix does not represent a rotation matrix. Hence, a rotation of $45°$ followed by a reflection in the x-axis is not equivalent to a single rotation. □

Exercises 6.4

1. Determine which pairs of points could be images of each other after a rotation about the origin. FIND DISTANCES.

a. $(1, 7), (5, 5)$ b. $(-4, 1), (4, -1)$

c. $(9, 0), (0, -9)$ d. $(5, -6), (3, 7)$

e. $\left(-\frac{\sqrt{3}}{2}, \frac{1}{2}\right), \left(\frac{1}{\sqrt{2}}, -\frac{1}{\sqrt{2}}\right)$ f. $(2\sqrt{6}, -2), (2\sqrt{3}, 2\sqrt{3})$

2. Determine the image of the point P after a rotation of θ about the origin.

a. $P(3, -2), \theta = 60°$ b. $P(6, 2), \theta = -30°$

c. $P(-5, -4), \theta = -135°$ d. $P(-3, 7), \theta = 180°$

e. $P(-2, 0), \theta = 150°$ f. $P(4, 4), \theta = 120°$

$R_\theta = \begin{bmatrix} \cos\theta & -\sin\theta \\ \sin\theta & \cos\theta \end{bmatrix}$

3. a. Verify that the points $(-4, 2)$ and $(-\sqrt{10}, -\sqrt{10})$ are the same distance from the origin.

b. Determine the matrix of the rotation about the origin that takes the point $(-4, 2)$ to $(-\sqrt{10}, -\sqrt{10})$.

c. Determine the angle of the rotation in part b.

4. Make a neat sketch of $\triangle ABC$ and then sketch its images under rotations of $90°$, $-90°$, $180°$, and $330°$ about the origin.

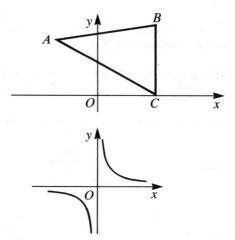

5. Sketch the images of the hyperbola under rotations of $45°$, $135°$, and $300°$ about the origin.

6. The triangle PQR has coordinates $P(-3, 4)$, $Q(2, 1)$, and $R(0, 5)$. Determine the coordinates of its image under a rotation of $240°$ about the origin.

7. Let R_θ be the 2×2 matrix for a rotation of the plane about the origin through an angle θ. Find each matrix.

a. $R_{30°} R_{60°}$ **b.** $R_{60°} R_{45°}$ **c.** $R_{60°} R_{-45°}$

8. Determine the matrix for each transformation.

a. a rotation of $30°$ about the origin followed by a reflection in the y-axis

b. a reflection in the y-axis followed by a rotation of $30°$ about the origin

c. a rotation of $120°$ about the origin followed by a reflection in the origin

d. a reflection in the line $y = x$ followed by a rotation of $135°$

e. the transformation $(x, y) \rightarrow (2x + y, y)$ followed by a rotation of $45°$ about the origin

9. a. Without doing any calculations, write down a single matrix for $R_\theta R_\phi$ and for $R_\theta R_{-\theta}$.

b. Verify your results by matrix multiplication.

Problems 6.4

1. A line ℓ passes through the points $P(5, 0)$ and $Q(-4, 3)$. Determine the equation of the image of ℓ after a rotation of $90°$ about the origin.

2. A line that makes an angle ϕ with the positive x-axis has slope $\tan \phi$. Prove that the matrix that represents a reflection in the line $y = x \tan \phi$ is

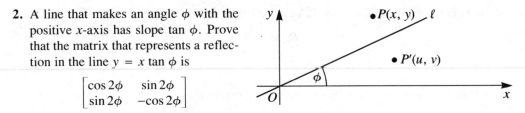

$$\begin{bmatrix} \cos 2\phi & \sin 2\phi \\ \sin 2\phi & -\cos 2\phi \end{bmatrix}$$

3. **a.** Show that the matrix that represents a rotation of 3-space, through an angle θ, about the z-axis is

$$\begin{bmatrix} \cos\theta & -\sin\theta & 0 \\ \sin\theta & \cos\theta & 0 \\ 0 & 0 & 1 \end{bmatrix}$$

b. What is the matrix that represents a rotation of 3-space, through an angle θ, about the y-axis?

4. Find the formula for the rotation, $(x, y) \to (u, v)$, about the point (a, b) through an angle θ. (This is not a linear transformation and, hence, cannot be represented by a matrix.)

6.5 Rotations of Conic Sections

A rotation through an angle θ about the origin is a linear transformation $(x, y) \to (u, v)$. The quantities u and v can be expressed in terms of x and y as

$$u = x\cos\theta - y\sin\theta$$
$$v = x\sin\theta + y\cos\theta$$

This rotation can be written in matrix form as

$$\begin{bmatrix} u \\ v \end{bmatrix} = \begin{bmatrix} \cos\theta & -\sin\theta \\ \sin\theta & \cos\theta \end{bmatrix} \begin{bmatrix} x \\ y \end{bmatrix} \quad \text{or} \quad U = R_\theta X$$

where $U = \begin{bmatrix} u \\ v \end{bmatrix}$, $X = \begin{bmatrix} x \\ y \end{bmatrix}$, and R_θ is the matrix of a rotation through the angle θ about the origin.

To determine the equation of the image of a curve, such as the hyperbola $4x^2 - y^2 = 16$, after a rotation about the origin, we have to substitute for x and y in the equation. We therefore have to express x and y in terms of u and v. One way to do this is to solve the above system of linear equations for x and y in terms of u and v. Alternatively, we can achieve this by noticing that a rotation through θ followed by a rotation through $-\theta$ brings all points back to their initial position; hence $R_{-\theta}R_\theta = I$, the 2×2 identity matrix. That is, the inverse matrix of R_θ is $R_{-\theta}$, where

$$R_{-\theta} = \begin{bmatrix} \cos(-\theta) & -\sin(-\theta) \\ \sin(-\theta) & \cos(-\theta) \end{bmatrix} = \begin{bmatrix} \cos\theta & \sin\theta \\ -\sin\theta & \cos\theta \end{bmatrix}$$

Multiply the matrix equation $U = R_\theta X$ on the left by $R_{-\theta}$ to obtain

$$R_{-\theta}U = R_{-\theta}R_\theta X$$
$$= IX$$
$$= X$$

This matrix equation now expresses x and y in terms of u and v.

The rotation about the origin through an angle θ, $U = R_\theta X$, has the **inverse transformation**

$$X = R_{-\theta}U \quad \text{or} \quad \begin{aligned} x &= u\cos\theta + v\sin\theta \\ y &= -u\sin\theta + v\cos\theta \end{aligned}$$

Example 1. Determine the equation of the image of the line $2x + y - 3 = 0$ after a rotation through $45°$ about the origin.

Solution. A rotation of $45°$ about the origin yields the transformation $U = R_{45°}X$ or $X = R_{-45°}U$. That is,

$$x = u\cos 45° + v\sin 45° = \frac{1}{\sqrt{2}}u + \frac{1}{\sqrt{2}}v$$

$$y = -u\sin 45° + v\cos 45° = -\frac{1}{\sqrt{2}}u + \frac{1}{\sqrt{2}}v$$

Substitute for x and y in the equation of the line $2x + y - 3 = 0$ to obtain

$$2\left(\frac{u}{\sqrt{2}} + \frac{v}{\sqrt{2}}\right) + \left(-\frac{u}{\sqrt{2}} + \frac{v}{\sqrt{2}}\right) - 3 = 0$$
$$2u + 2v - u + v - 3\sqrt{2} = 0$$
$$u + 3v - 3\sqrt{2} = 0$$

Hence, the image is the line
$x + 3y - 3\sqrt{2} = 0$, which crosses the axes
at $(3\sqrt{2}, 0)$ and $(0, \sqrt{2})$.

Check. Since the image line is obtained from the original line by a rotation about the origin, the distance from the origin to each of the lines should be the same. Using the formula in section 4.6, the distance from the origin to the original line is $\frac{|-3|}{\sqrt{2^2 + 1^2}} = \frac{3}{\sqrt{5}}$, and the distance from the origin to the image line is $\frac{|-3\sqrt{2}|}{\sqrt{1^2 + 3^2}} = \frac{3\sqrt{2}}{\sqrt{10}} = \frac{3}{\sqrt{5}}$.   □

Example 2. Determine the equation of the image of the hyperbola

$$4x^2 - y^2 = 16$$

after a rotation of $60°$ about the origin.

Solution. The rotation is given by $X = R_{-60°}U$ or

$$x = u \cos 60° + v \sin 60° = \tfrac{1}{2}u + \tfrac{\sqrt{3}}{2}v$$

$$y = -u \sin 60° + v \cos 60° = -\tfrac{\sqrt{3}}{2}u + \tfrac{1}{2}v$$

Substituting into the equation $4x^2 - y^2 = 16$, we obtain

$$4\left(\frac{u + \sqrt{3}v}{2}\right)^2 - \left(\frac{-\sqrt{3}u + v}{2}\right)^2 = 16$$
$$4u^2 + 8\sqrt{3}uv + 12v^2 - 3u^2 + 2\sqrt{3}uv - v^2 = 64$$
$$u^2 + 10\sqrt{3}uv + 11v^2 = 64$$

Hence, the equation of the image hyperbola is

$$x^2 + 10\sqrt{3}xy + 11y^2 = 64.$$

The axes of the original hyperbola are along the coordinate axes. The axes of the rotated hyperbola will be along lines through the origin making angles of 60° and 150° with the x-axis. The vertices of the original hyperbola are $(2, 0)$ and $(-2, 0)$. Since the transformation is $U = R_{60°}X$, one vertex of the image hyperbola is

$$\begin{bmatrix} u \\ v \end{bmatrix} = \begin{bmatrix} \tfrac{1}{2} & -\tfrac{\sqrt{3}}{2} \\ \tfrac{\sqrt{3}}{2} & \tfrac{1}{2} \end{bmatrix} \begin{bmatrix} 2 \\ 0 \end{bmatrix}$$

that is, $(1, \sqrt{3})$. The other vertex is $(-1, -\sqrt{3})$.

Notice that this rotation has made the equation more complicated; it has introduced an extra term involving xy. In the next section we shall show how to reverse this procedure to eliminate an xy term and so reduce a complicated quadratic equation to one in standard form.

Besides writing rotations in terms of matrices, it is also possible to write quadratic equations of the form $ax^2 + 2hxy + by^2 = k$ in terms of matrices. The determination of the image equation can then be calculated by matrix multiplication.

Before we do this, we must first establish the definition and some properties of the transpose of a matrix. We will be primarily concerned with matrices of size 2×2, 2×1, and 1×2, though the definitions and properties can be generalized to larger matrices.

The **transpose** of an $m \times n$ matrix A is the $n \times m$ matrix A^t in which the ith **row** of A becomes the ith **column** of A^t. For example, if $A = \begin{bmatrix} a & b \\ c & d \end{bmatrix}$ then $A^t = \begin{bmatrix} a & c \\ b & d \end{bmatrix}$. The transpose of $X = \begin{bmatrix} x \\ y \end{bmatrix}$ is $X^t = [x \quad y]$.

The transpose of $B = \begin{bmatrix} 4 & 3 \\ -2 & -1 \end{bmatrix}$ is $B^t = \begin{bmatrix} 4 & -2 \\ 3 & -1 \end{bmatrix}$. The transpose of $C = \begin{bmatrix} 7 \\ -5 \end{bmatrix}$ is

$C^t = [7 \quad -5]$.

A square matrix A is called **symmetric** if $A = A^t$. A 2×2 symmetric matrix is of the form
$A = \begin{bmatrix} a & h \\ h & b \end{bmatrix}$.

Note that the elements of a symmetric matrix are symmetric with respect to the leading diagonal from the top left to the bottom right of the matrix. For a 2×2 matrix this means that the element in the first row and second column must be the same as the element in the second row and first column.

If $B = \begin{bmatrix} 2 & 4 \\ -1 & 0 \end{bmatrix}$, $B^t = \begin{bmatrix} 2 & -1 \\ 4 & 0 \end{bmatrix}$. Since $B \neq B^t$, B is not a symmetric matrix.

Transpose of a Product

If A and B are two matrices whose product, AB, is defined, then

$$(AB)^t = B^t A^t$$

That is, the transpose of a product of matrices is the product of the transposes in reverse order.

Proof. We shall prove the result for a 2×2 matrix A and a 2×1 matrix B, though it is true for any pair of matrices whose product is defined.

Let $A = \begin{bmatrix} p & q \\ r & s \end{bmatrix}$ and $B = \begin{bmatrix} u \\ v \end{bmatrix}$. Then

$$AB = \begin{bmatrix} p & q \\ r & s \end{bmatrix} \begin{bmatrix} u \\ v \end{bmatrix}$$
$$= \begin{bmatrix} pu + qv \\ ru + sv \end{bmatrix}$$
$$(AB)^t = [pu + qv \quad ru + sv]$$
$$B^t A^t = [u \quad v] \begin{bmatrix} p & r \\ q & s \end{bmatrix}$$
$$= [pu + qv \quad ru + sv]$$

Therefore, $(AB)^t = B^t A^t$.   □

The transpose of a product of more than two matrices is the product of the transposes in reverse order, as long as the products are defined. Hence, for three matrices, $(ABC)^t = C^t B^t A^t$. Another fact about transposes that you should try to prove is that $(A^t)^t = A$.

> The **quadratic equation** $ax^2 + 2hxy + by^2 = k$ can be written in **matrix form** as
>
> $$X^tAX = K$$
>
> where $A = \begin{bmatrix} a & h \\ h & b \end{bmatrix}$, $X = \begin{bmatrix} x \\ y \end{bmatrix}$, and K is the 1×1 matrix $[k]$.

Proof. The left side of the matrix product is

$$X^tAX = [x \quad y]\begin{bmatrix} a & h \\ h & b \end{bmatrix}\begin{bmatrix} x \\ y \end{bmatrix}$$

$$= [ax + hy \quad hx + by]\begin{bmatrix} x \\ y \end{bmatrix}$$

$$= [ax^2 + hxy + hxy + by^2]$$

$$= [ax^2 + 2hxy + by^2]$$

$$= [k]$$

$$= K \qquad \square$$

The matrix on the right side is a 1×1 matrix $[k]$, which we shall often write just as the real number k. Note that A is a symmetric matrix whose diagonal elements are the coefficients of x^2 and y^2 and whose off-diagonal elements are **half** the coefficient of xy. For example, $5x^2 - \sqrt{3}xy + 4y^2 = 1$ can be written in matrix form as

$$[x \quad y]\begin{bmatrix} 5 & -\frac{\sqrt{3}}{2} \\ -\frac{\sqrt{3}}{2} & 4 \end{bmatrix}\begin{bmatrix} x \\ y \end{bmatrix} = 1$$

The reason for writing a quadratic equation in matrix form is that it transforms very nicely under rotations. Under the rotation $U = R_\theta X$ or $X = RU$, where $R = R_{-\theta}$, the matrix equation $X^tAX = K$ transforms to

$$(RU)^tA(RU) = K$$

By a property of transposes, $(RU)^t = U^tR^t$, so the matrix equation becomes

$$U^tR^tARU = K$$

which can be written as

$$U^tBU = K$$

where B is the 2×2 matrix R^tAR. Now, by the properties of transposes,

$$B^t = (R^tAR)^t$$

$$= R^tA^t(R^t)^t$$

$$= R^tAR$$

$$= B$$

Hence, B is a symmetric matrix.

> **The rotation about the origin** through an angle θ transforms the matrix equation $X'AX = K$ to $U'BU = K$, where
>
> $$B = R'AR \quad \text{and} \quad R = R_{-\theta}$$

Therefore, we only need to determine $B = R'AR$ in order to obtain the matrix form of a transformed equation.

Example 3. Use matrices to determine the equation of the image of the hyperbola $4x^2 - y^2 = 16$ after a rotation of $60°$ about the origin.

Solution. The rotation in matrix form is $X = RU$ where

$$R = R_{-60°} = \begin{bmatrix} \cos 60° & \sin 60° \\ -\sin 60° & \cos 60° \end{bmatrix} = \begin{bmatrix} \frac{1}{2} & \frac{\sqrt{3}}{2} \\ -\frac{\sqrt{3}}{2} & \frac{1}{2} \end{bmatrix}$$

Hence, $R = \frac{1}{2}\begin{bmatrix} 1 & \sqrt{3} \\ -\sqrt{3} & 1 \end{bmatrix}$ and $R' = \frac{1}{2}\begin{bmatrix} 1 & -\sqrt{3} \\ \sqrt{3} & 1 \end{bmatrix}$. The matrix form of the hyperbola $4x^2 - y^2 = 16$ is $X'AX = 16$, where $A = \begin{bmatrix} 4 & 0 \\ 0 & -1 \end{bmatrix}$. The matrix form of the image hyperbola will be $U'BU = 16$, where

$$\begin{aligned} B &= R'AR \\ &= \left(\frac{1}{2}\begin{bmatrix} 1 & -\sqrt{3} \\ \sqrt{3} & 1 \end{bmatrix}\right)\begin{bmatrix} 4 & 0 \\ 0 & -1 \end{bmatrix}\left(\frac{1}{2}\begin{bmatrix} 1 & \sqrt{3} \\ -\sqrt{3} & 1 \end{bmatrix}\right) \\ &= \frac{1}{4}\begin{bmatrix} 4 & \sqrt{3} \\ 4\sqrt{3} & -1 \end{bmatrix}\begin{bmatrix} 1 & \sqrt{3} \\ -\sqrt{3} & 1 \end{bmatrix} \\ &= \frac{1}{4}\begin{bmatrix} 1 & 5\sqrt{3} \\ 5\sqrt{3} & 11 \end{bmatrix} \end{aligned}$$

Therefore, the matrix form of the image hyperbola is

$$[u \quad v]\frac{1}{4}\begin{bmatrix} 1 & 5\sqrt{3} \\ 5\sqrt{3} & 11 \end{bmatrix}\begin{bmatrix} u \\ v \end{bmatrix} = 16$$

$$[u + 5\sqrt{3}v \quad 5\sqrt{3}u + 11v]\begin{bmatrix} u \\ v \end{bmatrix} = 64$$

$$u^2 + 10\sqrt{3}uv + 11v^2 = 64$$

Therefore, the equation of the image hyperbola is $x^2 + 10\sqrt{3}xy + 11y^2 = 64$.

Check. This example is the same as Example 2. □

One might have the impression that the method of Example 2 is easier than that of Example 3. However, Example 3 provides a more systematic approach and, as the equations become more complex, this matrix technique provides the only feasible method.

Example 4. Find the equation of the curve $x^2 - xy + y^2 = 2$ after a rotation of $45°$ about the origin. Name and sketch the curve and its image.

Solution. The matrix form of the curve is $X^t A X = 2$ and the transformation is $X = RU$, where

$$R = R_{-45°} = \begin{bmatrix} \cos 45° & \sin 45° \\ -\sin 45° & \cos 45° \end{bmatrix} = \begin{bmatrix} \frac{1}{\sqrt{2}} & \frac{1}{\sqrt{2}} \\ -\frac{1}{\sqrt{2}} & \frac{1}{\sqrt{2}} \end{bmatrix} = \frac{1}{\sqrt{2}}\begin{bmatrix} 1 & 1 \\ -1 & 1 \end{bmatrix}$$

$$R^t = \frac{1}{\sqrt{2}}\begin{bmatrix} 1 & -1 \\ 1 & 1 \end{bmatrix}, \quad \text{and} \quad A = \begin{bmatrix} 1 & -\frac{1}{2} \\ -\frac{1}{2} & 1 \end{bmatrix}$$

The image curve is $U^t B U = 2$, where

$$B = R^t A R$$

$$= \frac{1}{\sqrt{2}}\begin{bmatrix} 1 & -1 \\ 1 & 1 \end{bmatrix}\begin{bmatrix} 1 & -\frac{1}{2} \\ -\frac{1}{2} & 1 \end{bmatrix}\frac{1}{\sqrt{2}}\begin{bmatrix} 1 & 1 \\ -1 & 1 \end{bmatrix}$$

$$= \left(\frac{1}{\sqrt{2}}\right)^2\begin{bmatrix} \frac{3}{2} & -\frac{3}{2} \\ \frac{1}{2} & \frac{1}{2} \end{bmatrix}\begin{bmatrix} 1 & 1 \\ -1 & 1 \end{bmatrix}$$

$$= \frac{1}{2}\begin{bmatrix} 3 & 0 \\ 0 & 1 \end{bmatrix}$$

Hence, the image curve is

$$[u \quad v]\frac{1}{2}\begin{bmatrix} 3 & 0 \\ 0 & 1 \end{bmatrix}\begin{bmatrix} u \\ v \end{bmatrix} = 2$$

$$3u^2 + v^2 = 4$$

This is the ellipse $3x^2 + y^2 = 4$, with vertices at $(0, 2)$ and $(0, -2)$. Hence, the original curve must also be an ellipse.

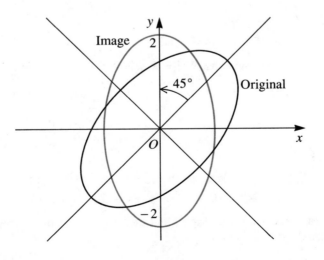

Exercises 6.5

1. Let $A = \begin{bmatrix} 2 & 7 \\ -1 & 3 \end{bmatrix}$, $B = \begin{bmatrix} 5 & 0 \\ 2 & -1 \end{bmatrix}$, $C = \begin{bmatrix} 3 \\ -2 \end{bmatrix}$, and $D = [-4, \; 5]$.

Calculate each quantity.

a. A^t	**b.** B^t	**c.** C^t	**d.** D^t
e. $(AB)^t$	**f.** B^tA^t	**g.** DAC	**h.** C^tBC
i. DC	**j.** C^tD^t	**k.** AA^t	**l.** A^tA
m. DAB	**n.** $B^tA^tD^t$	**o.** D^tC^t	**p.** B^tAB

2. Write the quadratic equations in matrix form.

a. $3x^2 + 5y^2 = 16$ **b.** $3x^2 - 4xy + 5y^2 = 1$

c. $x^2 + xy - 2y^2 = 0$ **d.** $xy = 8$

3. Determine the quadratic expression $X^tAX = ax^2 + 2hxy + by^2$ for each matrix A.

a. $\begin{bmatrix} 5 & \sqrt{3} \\ \sqrt{3} & 5 \end{bmatrix}$ **b.** $\begin{bmatrix} -3 & -\frac{1}{2} \\ -\frac{1}{2} & 1 \end{bmatrix}$ **c.** $\begin{bmatrix} 1 & 2 \\ 2 & 0 \end{bmatrix}$

4. For each curve, determine an equation of its image under a rotation of θ about the origin. Sketch both the original and image curves.

a. $5x + 3y = 15$, $\theta = 150°$

b. $4x^2 + 16y^2 = 9$, $\theta = 45°$

c. $x^2 - 4y^2 = 16$, $\theta = 30°$

d. $xy = 4$, $\theta = -45°$

e. $x^2 = 16y$, $\theta = 60°$

f. $x^2 + 3xy + y^2 = 10$, $\theta = 45°$

5. If R_θ is a rotation matrix, show that $R_\theta^{-1} = R_{-\theta} = R_\theta^t$. (That is, the inverse of R_θ is $R_\theta^{-1} = R_\theta^t$.)

$R_\theta^{-1} = R_{-\theta} = R_\theta^t$ important function !!

Problems 6.5

1. Translate the conic

$$3x^2 + 10xy + 3y^2 + 8x + 24y - 12 = 0$$

so that its centre moves to the origin, and then rotate the curve through 45° about the origin. Sketch the original curve.

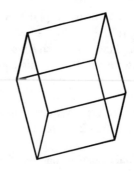

2. Write a computer program to display a rotating cube on the screen. Let α be a fixed angle, say $5°$ or 0.1 radians. The program should be written so that pressing one key causes the cube to rotate by α about the y-axis, another key rotates the cube by $-\alpha$ about the y-axis, a third key rotates it by α about the z-axis and a fourth key rotates it by $-\alpha$ about the z-axis.

Store the coordinates of four vertices of a cube in 3-space as A, B, C, and D. Initially let

$$A = \begin{bmatrix} 1 \\ 1 \\ 1 \end{bmatrix}, B = \begin{bmatrix} -1 \\ 1 \\ 1 \end{bmatrix}, C = \begin{bmatrix} 1 \\ -1 \\ 1 \end{bmatrix}, \text{ and } D = \begin{bmatrix} 1 \\ 1 \\ -1 \end{bmatrix}, \text{ so that the other vertices are } -A, \ -B,$$

$-C$ and $-D$. Rotate the cube by means of the 3×3 rotation matrix R that depends on the key pressed. (These matrices are given in Problem 3 of section 6.4.) Project the cube onto the screen by means of a linear transformation $\boldsymbol{R}^3 \rightarrow \boldsymbol{R}^2$ using a matrix such as

$$P = \begin{bmatrix} -0.52 & 1 & 0 \\ -0.34 & 0 & 1 \end{bmatrix}.$$

Here is a possible outline of the program:

PROGRAM ROTATE
    Initialize A, B, C, D with the standard cube
    Repeat
        Calculate PA, PB, PC, PD
        Clear previous screen
        Plot $\pm PA$, $\pm PB$, $\pm PC$, $\pm PD$ and join appropriate vertices
        Read keyboard
        Find the rotation matrix R corresponding to key pressed
        Calculate RA, RB, RC, RD and replace A by RA, etc.
    until stop.

6.6 Elimination of the xy term in Quadratic Equations

The general quadratic equation in two variables

$$ax^2 + 2hxy + by^2 + 2gx + 2fy + c = 0 \tag{1}$$

represents a curve in the plane that is a conic or a degenerate conic or has no graph. The quadratic part, $ax^2 + 2hxy + by^2$, is referred to as a **quadratic form**. In the previous sections we considered the case when h was zero. We shall now show that it is possible to find a rotation about the origin that transforms equation 1 into equation 2,

$$a'u^2 + b'v^2 + 2g'u + 2f'v + c = 0 \tag{2}$$

which has no uv term. We shall show in section 6.7 how a further translation can be performed to express equation 2 in standard form.

If the original equation has the form $ax^2 + 2hxy + by^2 + c = 0$, then the rotation that eliminates the xy term will transform the equation directly into standard form and the conic's properties such as vertices, lengths of semi-axes and asymptotes can be determined.

Equation 1 can be written in matrix form. We have seen that the quadratic form, $ax^2 + 2hxy + by^2$, can be expressed as X^tAX, where $X = \begin{bmatrix} x \\ y \end{bmatrix}$ and $A = \begin{bmatrix} a & h \\ h & b \end{bmatrix}$. The linear terms $2gx + 2fy$ can be expressed as $2GX$, where G is the 1×2 matrix $[g \quad f]$. Thus the matrix form of equation 1 is

$$X^tAX + 2GX + C = 0$$

where C is the 1×1 matrix $[c]$.

We shall normally use matrix notation for a conic and for a rotation. For a quadratic form in two variables the rotation could equally well be done without matrices. However, the matrix approach makes it easier to generalize to quadratics in three variables that represent surfaces, such as ellipsoids and hyperboloids in 3-space, and to quadratics in n variables.

If we rotate the curve using the matrix R_θ, then $U = R_\theta X$ and $X = RU$, where

$$R = R_{-\theta} = \begin{bmatrix} \cos\theta & \sin\theta \\ -\sin\theta & \cos\theta \end{bmatrix}$$

Under this rotation the matrix equation $X^tAX + 2GX + C = 0$ becomes

$$(RU)^tA(RU) + 2G(RU) + C = 0$$
$$U^tR^tARU + 2GRU + C = 0$$

This is of the form

$$U^tBU + 2HU + C = 0$$

where $B = R^tAR$ is a 2×2 matrix and $H = GR$ is a 1×2 matrix. The second degree terms are contained in U^tBU, the first degree terms are in $2HU$, and the constant term C is unchanged.

Now we try to choose the rotation angle θ so as to eliminate the xy term. This is the same as making B a diagonal matrix. We have

$$B = R'AR$$

$$= \begin{bmatrix} \cos\theta & -\sin\theta \\ \sin\theta & \cos\theta \end{bmatrix} \begin{bmatrix} a & h \\ h & b \end{bmatrix} \begin{bmatrix} \cos\theta & \sin\theta \\ -\sin\theta & \cos\theta \end{bmatrix}$$

$$= \begin{bmatrix} a\cos\theta - h\sin\theta & h\cos\theta - b\sin\theta \\ a\sin\theta + h\cos\theta & h\sin\theta + b\cos\theta \end{bmatrix} \begin{bmatrix} \cos\theta & \sin\theta \\ -\sin\theta & \cos\theta \end{bmatrix} \tag{3}$$

$$= \begin{bmatrix} a' & h' \\ h' & b' \end{bmatrix} \tag{4}$$

Our aim is to choose θ so as to make h' equal to zero. Now by multiplying the matrices in (3) we obtain

$$h' = a\cos\theta\sin\theta - h\sin^2\theta + h\cos^2\theta - b\sin\theta\cos\theta$$
$$= (a - b)(\sin\theta\cos\theta) + h(\cos^2\theta - \sin^2\theta)$$

Setting $h' = 0$ and using the formulas for the sine and cosine of 2θ, we have

$$(a - b)(\sin\theta\cos\theta) + h(\cos^2\theta - \sin^2\theta) = 0$$
$$\tfrac{1}{2}(a - b)\sin 2\theta + h\cos 2\theta = 0$$
$$(b - a)\sin 2\theta = 2h\cos 2\theta$$

If $a = b$ but $h \neq 0$, then $\cos 2\theta = 0$. In this case one solution is $\theta = 45°$. If $a \neq b$, we can divide by $b - a$ to obtain the following theorem.

Elimination of the xy-term

The xy term can be eliminated from the equation

$$ax^2 + 2hxy + by^2 + 2gx + 2fy + c = 0$$

by a rotation through an angle θ, where

$$\tan 2\theta = \frac{2h}{b - a}, \quad \text{when} \quad a \neq b$$

or $\theta = 45°$, when $a = b$.

Notice that the angle of rotation depends only on the coefficents of x^2, xy, and y^2 and not on g, f, or c. Hence, to determine the rotation, we need only consider the terms of second degree, that is the quadratic form $ax^2 + 2hxy + by^2$.

Also notice that if θ is one value satisfying the equation $\tan 2\theta = \dfrac{2h}{b - a}$, then $\theta + 90°$ also satisfies it, since

$$\tan 2(\theta + 90°) = \tan(2\theta + 180°) = \tan 2\theta$$

Hence, if a rotation through θ eliminates the xy term, then so will rotations through $\theta + 90°$, $\theta + 180°$, and $\theta + 270°$. This agrees with the fact that the semi-axes of a conic are perpendicular.

Example 1. Determine a rotation matrix R so that the transformation $X = RU$ will eliminate the xy term in the equation.

a. $x^2 + xy + y^2 = 5$

b. $31x^2 + 10\sqrt{3}xy + 21y^2 = 144$

c. $4x^2 - 24xy + 11y^2 + 72x - 116y + 204 = 0$

Solution.

a. Since $a = b = 1$, the angle of rotation can be taken to be $45°$ and the rotation matrix is

$$R_{-45°} = \begin{bmatrix} \cos 45° & \sin 45° \\ -\sin 45° & \cos 45° \end{bmatrix} = \begin{bmatrix} \frac{1}{\sqrt{2}} & \frac{1}{\sqrt{2}} \\ -\frac{1}{\sqrt{2}} & \frac{1}{\sqrt{2}} \end{bmatrix}$$

b. The required angle of rotation is θ where

$$\tan 2\theta = \frac{10\sqrt{3}}{21 - 31}$$
$$= -\sqrt{3}$$

Since $\tan 2\theta$ is negative, 2θ lies in the second or fourth quadrant. Let 2θ lie in the second quadrant so that $2\theta = 120°$. Hence, $\theta = 60°$. The required rotation matrix is therefore

$$R_{-60°} = \begin{bmatrix} \cos 60° & \sin 60° \\ -\sin 60° & \cos 60° \end{bmatrix} = \begin{bmatrix} \frac{1}{2} & \frac{\sqrt{3}}{2} \\ -\frac{\sqrt{3}}{2} & \frac{1}{2} \end{bmatrix}$$

If we take 2θ in the fourth quadrant, we obtain $2\theta = 300°$ and $\theta = 150°$. This yields another possible rotation that will eliminate the xy term. If the conic were an ellipse, a rotation of $60°$ might place the major axis parallel to the x-axis. A further rotation of $90°$, that is a rotation of $150°$, would then place the major axis parallel to the y-axis.

c. The required angle of rotation is θ where

$$\tan 2\theta = \frac{-24}{11 - 4}$$
$$= \frac{-24}{7}$$

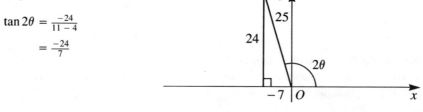

Even though this is not the tangent of a standard angle, we can find the rotation matrix without determining θ, by finding the exact values of $\sin \theta$ and $\cos \theta$. Since $\tan 2\theta$ is negative, we may take the angle in the second quadrant. In the diagram the right-angled triangle has a hypotenuse of $\sqrt{7^2 + 24^2} = 25$. Hence, $\cos 2\theta = -\frac{7}{25}$. We can find $\sin \theta$ and $\cos \theta$ from the cosine double angle formula. Since

$$\cos 2\theta = 1 - 2\sin^2\theta$$

we have
$$\sin^2\theta = \frac{1 - \cos 2\theta}{2}$$

$$= \frac{1 + \frac{7}{25}}{2}$$

$$= \frac{25 + 7}{2(25)}$$

$$= \frac{16}{25}$$

Hence, $\sin\theta = \pm\frac{4}{5}$. Since 2θ was in the second quadrant, we may take θ to be in the first quadrant so that $\sin\theta = \frac{4}{5}$. Since

$$\cos^2\theta = 1 - \sin^2\theta$$

$$= 1 - \frac{16}{25}$$

$$= \frac{9}{25}$$

and since θ lies in the first quadrant, $\cos\theta = \frac{3}{5}$. Therefore, the rotation matrix is

$$R = R_{-\theta} = \begin{bmatrix} \frac{3}{5} & \frac{4}{5} \\ -\frac{4}{5} & \frac{3}{5} \end{bmatrix} = \frac{1}{5}\begin{bmatrix} 3 & 4 \\ -4 & 3 \end{bmatrix}$$

Check.

$$R^t A R = \left(\frac{1}{5}\right)^2 \begin{bmatrix} 3 & -4 \\ 4 & 3 \end{bmatrix}\begin{bmatrix} 4 & -12 \\ -12 & 11 \end{bmatrix}\begin{bmatrix} 3 & 4 \\ -4 & 3 \end{bmatrix}$$

$$= \frac{1}{25}\begin{bmatrix} 60 & -80 \\ -20 & -15 \end{bmatrix}\begin{bmatrix} 3 & 4 \\ -4 & 3 \end{bmatrix}$$

$$= \frac{1}{25}\begin{bmatrix} 500 & 0 \\ 0 & -125 \end{bmatrix}$$

Since the off-diagonal terms are zero, the xy term will be zero in the transformed equation.

□

Example 2. Determine the rotation required to eliminate the xy term of the equation

$$2x^2 + 4\sqrt{3}xy - 2y^2 = 36$$

Find the equation of the rotated curve and sketch both curves.

Solution. A rotation through θ that will eliminate the xy term is obtained using

$$\tan 2\theta = \frac{2h}{b - a}$$

$$= \frac{4\sqrt{3}}{(-2) - 2}$$

$$= -\sqrt{3}$$

The angle 2θ can be chosen in the second quadrant so that $2\theta = 120°$ and $\theta = 60°$. Hence, a rotation through $60°$ will eliminate the xy term.

The corresponding rotation matrix is $R = R_{-60°} = \begin{bmatrix} \frac{1}{2} & \frac{\sqrt{3}}{2} \\ -\frac{\sqrt{3}}{2} & \frac{1}{2} \end{bmatrix}$. The original equation is

$X^t A X = 36$, where $A = \begin{bmatrix} 2 & 2\sqrt{3} \\ 2\sqrt{3} & -2 \end{bmatrix}$, and this transforms to $U^t B U = 36$, where

$$B = R^t A R$$

$$= \left(\tfrac{1}{2}\right)^2 \begin{bmatrix} 1 & -\sqrt{3} \\ \sqrt{3} & 1 \end{bmatrix} \begin{bmatrix} 2 & 2\sqrt{3} \\ 2\sqrt{3} & -2 \end{bmatrix} \begin{bmatrix} 1 & \sqrt{3} \\ -\sqrt{3} & 1 \end{bmatrix}$$

$$= \tfrac{1}{4} \begin{bmatrix} -4 & 4\sqrt{3} \\ 4\sqrt{3} & 4 \end{bmatrix} \begin{bmatrix} 1 & \sqrt{3} \\ -\sqrt{3} & 1 \end{bmatrix}$$

$$= \begin{bmatrix} -4 & 0 \\ 0 & 4 \end{bmatrix}$$

Therefore, the transformed equation $U^t B U = 36$ is $-4u^2 + 4v^2 = 36$ or $u^2 - v^2 = -9$. Thus, any point (x, y) lies on the rotated curve if and only if

$$\frac{x^2}{9} - \frac{y^2}{9} = -1$$

This is a hyperbola in standard form with its axes along the coordinate axes and its vertices at $(0, 3)$ and $(0, -3)$. The asymptotes are the lines $y = \pm x$.

The original hyperbola must have its axes along lines through the origin making angles of $-60°$ and $30°$ with the x-axis. If we use the transformation $X = RU$, the vertex $(0, 3)$ transforms to

$$X = \begin{bmatrix} \frac{1}{2} & \frac{\sqrt{3}}{2} \\ -\frac{\sqrt{3}}{2} & \frac{1}{2} \end{bmatrix} \begin{bmatrix} 0 \\ 3 \end{bmatrix} = \begin{bmatrix} \frac{3\sqrt{3}}{2} \\ \frac{3}{2} \end{bmatrix}$$

Hence, the vertices of the original hyperbola are $\left(\frac{3\sqrt{3}}{2}, \frac{3}{2}\right)$ and $\left(-\frac{3\sqrt{3}}{2}, -\frac{3}{2}\right)$.

Check. We can check the sketch by noticing that the original hyperbola has x-intercepts at $x = \pm\sqrt{18} \approx \pm4.24$ and does not meet the y-axis since the y-intercepts are roots of $-2y^2 = 36$.

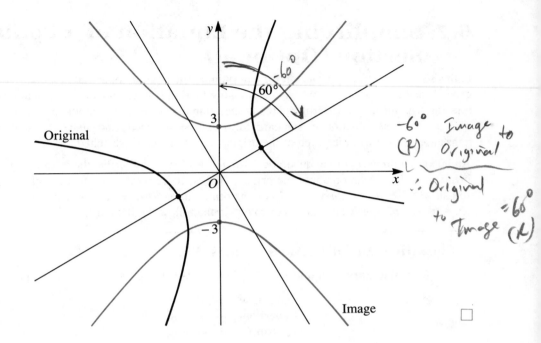

Original

Image

Handwritten annotations:
$-60°$ Image to (R) Original

∴ Original to Image $= 60°$ (R)

Exercises 6.6

1. Determine a rotation matrix R so that the transformation $X = RU$ will eliminate the xy term.

   a. $3x^2 + 2\sqrt{3}xy + 5y^2 = 36$ **b.** $x^2 - 4xy + y^2 = 16$

   c. $x^2 + 2\sqrt{3}xy - y^2 = 4$ **d.** $x^2 - 2\sqrt{3}xy - y^2 = 0$

   e. $2x^2 + \sqrt{3}xy + y^2 = 1$ **f.** $5x^2 + 4xy + 5y^2 = 0$

   g. $xy + 4 = 0$ **h.** $31x^2 + 10\sqrt{3}xy + 21y^2 = 144$

   i. $7x^2 - 4xy + 4y^2 = 240$ **j.** $4x^2 + 24xy - 3y^2 - 468 = 0$

2. Apply the rotation determined in each part of Exercise 1 to obtain the image equation in standard form. Sketch the original and image curves.

Problems 6.6

1. Sketch and name each curve.

   a. $y = \dfrac{x - 2}{x + 3}$

   b. $3x^2 + 2\sqrt{3}xy + y^2 + 4x - 4\sqrt{3}y + 16 = 0$

2. Write a computer program to find the angle required to rotate a given curve with equation $ax^2 + 2hxy + by^2 = c$ into standard position, and then display the transformed equation.

6.7 Simplifying the Equation of a Conic Section (Optional)

In this section we prove a criterion for determining the type of conic that is represented by a general quadratic equation. We also show how to simplify any quadratic equation by first rotating to eliminate the xy term and then translating to express the equation in standard form. The graph of the equation in standard form can be sketched, and since the rotation and translation are known, the graph of the original equation can be sketched.

An important property of the quadratic form $ax^2 + 2hxy + by^2$ is that the quantity $ab - h^2$ is invariant under a rotation about the origin. That is, if we rotate a curve through an angle θ so that $X^tAX = ax^2 + 2hxy + by^2$ is transformed into $U^tBU = a'u^2 + 2h'uv + b'v^2$, then $ab - h^2 = a'b' - h'^2$. This allows us to obtain the following theorem.

Classification of Conic Sections

The **general quadratic equation** $ax^2 + 2hxy + by^2 + 2gx + 2fy + c = 0$ represents

$$
\begin{aligned}
&\text{an \textbf{ellipse}} &&\text{if} && ab - h^2 > 0, \\
&\text{a \textbf{hyperbola}} &&\text{if} && ab - h^2 < 0, \\
&\text{a \textbf{parabola}} &&\text{if} && ab - h^2 = 0.
\end{aligned}
$$

The above cases include the possibility that the conic may be degenerate or that it has no graph.

Proof. Rotate the curve about the origin through an angle θ to eliminate the xy term in its equation. That is, use the transformation $X = RU$, where $R = R_{-\theta}$, to change

$$X^tAX = ax^2 + 2hxy + by^2 \text{ into } U^tBU = a'u^2 + b'v^2, \text{ where } B = R^tAR = \begin{bmatrix} a' & 0 \\ 0 & b' \end{bmatrix}. \quad B = R^t A R$$

If you have not covered the sections on determinants, you can verify directly, using equation 3 of section 6.6, that $a'b' = ab - h^2$.

If you have covered determinants, recall from Exercise 5 of section 5.7 that the determinant of a product is equal to the product of the determinants and also that the determinant of a rotation matrix is 1. Then

$$
\begin{aligned}
\det B &= \det(R^tAR) \\
&= \det R^t \det A \det R \\
&= \det R \det A \det R \\
&= \det A
\end{aligned}
$$

Hence, $\begin{vmatrix} a' & h' \\ h' & b' \end{vmatrix} = \begin{vmatrix} a & h \\ h & b \end{vmatrix}$ and so $a'b' - h'^2 = ab - h^2$.

It follows from section 6.3 that the type of the transformed conic is determined by the sign of $a'b'$, since $h' = 0$. If $a'b' > 0$, the conic is an ellipse, if $a'b' < 0$ it is a hyperbola, and if $a'b' = 0$ it is a parabola. $\qquad\square$

Example 1. Identify the curve

$$4x^2 - 4xy + y^2 - 8\sqrt{5}x - 16\sqrt{5}y = 0$$

and determine the transformation that will eliminate the xy term. Find the equation of the image curve and sketch both curves.

Solution. Since the expression $ab - h^2 = 4(1) - (-2)^2 = 0$, the curve is a parabola. A rotation through θ will eliminate the xy term if

$$\tan 2\theta = \frac{2h}{b - a}$$

$$= \frac{-4}{1 - 4}$$

$$= \frac{4}{3}$$

Since $\tan 2\theta$ is positive, take 2θ in the first quadrant so that θ is in the first quadrant and $\sin \theta$ and $\cos \theta$ are both positive. From the diagram, note that $\cos 2\theta = \frac{3}{5}$. From the formula $\cos 2\theta = 1 - 2 \sin^2 \theta$, it follows that $2 \sin^2 \theta = 1 - \cos 2\theta$, and therefore

$$\sin \theta = + \sqrt{\frac{1 - \cos 2\theta}{2}}$$

$$= \sqrt{\frac{1 - \frac{3}{5}}{2}}$$

$$= \frac{1}{\sqrt{5}}$$

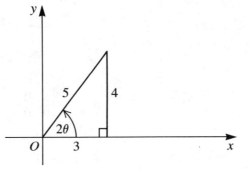

and

$$\cos \theta = + \sqrt{1 - \sin^2 \theta}$$

$$= \sqrt{1 - \frac{1}{5}}$$

$$= \frac{2}{\sqrt{5}}$$

Hence, the rotation matrix is

$$R = R_{-\theta} = \begin{bmatrix} \cos \theta & \sin \theta \\ -\sin \theta & \cos \theta \end{bmatrix} = \begin{bmatrix} \frac{2}{\sqrt{5}} & \frac{1}{\sqrt{5}} \\ -\frac{1}{\sqrt{5}} & \frac{2}{\sqrt{5}} \end{bmatrix} = \frac{1}{\sqrt{5}} \begin{bmatrix} 2 & 1 \\ -1 & 2 \end{bmatrix}$$

and the transformation $X = RU$ is

$$\begin{bmatrix} x \\ y \end{bmatrix} = \frac{1}{\sqrt{5}} \begin{bmatrix} 2 & 1 \\ -1 & 2 \end{bmatrix} \begin{bmatrix} u \\ v \end{bmatrix} \quad \text{or} \quad \begin{aligned} x &= \frac{2u + v}{\sqrt{5}} \\ y &= \frac{-u + 2v}{\sqrt{5}} \end{aligned}$$

The matrix form of the original curve is

$$X^t A X + 2GX = 0, \quad \text{where} \quad A = \begin{bmatrix} 4 & -2 \\ -2 & 1 \end{bmatrix} \quad \text{and} \quad 2G = [-8\sqrt{5} \quad -16\sqrt{5}]$$

This transforms under $X = RU$ to

$$(RU)^t A(RU) + 2G(RU) = 0$$
$$U^t R^t ARU + 2GRU = 0$$
$$U^t BU + 2HU = 0$$

where $B = R^t AR$ and $H = GR$. Now,

$$B = R^t AR$$

$$= \frac{1}{\sqrt{5}} \begin{bmatrix} 2 & -1 \\ 1 & 2 \end{bmatrix} \begin{bmatrix} 4 & -2 \\ -2 & 1 \end{bmatrix} \frac{1}{\sqrt{5}} \begin{bmatrix} 2 & 1 \\ -1 & 2 \end{bmatrix}$$

$$= \frac{1}{5} \begin{bmatrix} 10 & -5 \\ 0 & 0 \end{bmatrix} \begin{bmatrix} 2 & 1 \\ -1 & 2 \end{bmatrix}$$

$$= \begin{bmatrix} 5 & 0 \\ 0 & 0 \end{bmatrix}$$

$$2H = 2GR$$

$$= [-8\sqrt{5} \quad -16\sqrt{5}] \frac{1}{\sqrt{5}} \begin{bmatrix} 2 & 1 \\ -1 & 2 \end{bmatrix}$$

$$= [-8 \quad -16] \begin{bmatrix} 2 & 1 \\ -1 & 2 \end{bmatrix}$$

$$= [0 \quad -40]$$

Hence, the transformed equation is

$$U^t \begin{bmatrix} 5 & 0 \\ 0 & 0 \end{bmatrix} U + [0 \quad -40] U = 0$$

$$[u \quad v] \begin{bmatrix} 5 & 0 \\ 0 & 0 \end{bmatrix} \begin{bmatrix} u \\ v \end{bmatrix} + [0 \quad -40] \begin{bmatrix} u \\ v \end{bmatrix} = 0$$

$$5u^2 - 40v = 0$$

$$u^2 = 8v$$

Thus, any point (x, y) lies on the rotated curve if $x^2 = 8y$. This is a parabola whose vertex is at the origin and whose axis is the y-axis. The angle of rotation is $\theta = \frac{1}{2}\left((\tan^{-1} \frac{4}{3}\right) \approx 27°$.

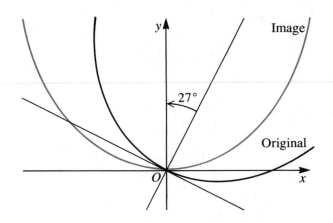

Check. The sketch of the original parabola can be checked by using the intercepts. The x-intercepts are x at 0 and $2\sqrt{5}$, and the y-intercepts are 0 and $16\sqrt{5}$. □

Example 2. Determine the type of the curve
$$2x^2 - 5xy + 2y^2 + 2x + 2y - 4 = 0$$

Find a rotation that will eliminate the xy term, and find the translation necessary to place the equation in standard form. Sketch the original curve.

Solution. The expression $ab - h^2 = 2(2) - \left(-\frac{5}{2}\right)^2 = -\frac{9}{4} < 0$, and so the curve is a hyperbola.
Since $a = b$, a rotation through $45°$ will eliminate the xy term. The rotation matrix is

$$R = R_{-45°} = \frac{1}{\sqrt{2}}\begin{bmatrix} 1 & 1 \\ -1 & 1 \end{bmatrix}$$

and the transformation $X = RU$ transforms the original curve

$$X^tAX + 2GX - 4 = 0, \quad \text{where } A = \begin{bmatrix} 2 & -\frac{5}{2} \\ -\frac{5}{2} & 2 \end{bmatrix} \text{and } 2G = [2 \quad 2]$$

to the curve $U^tBU + 2HU - 4 = 0$. The matrices B and $2H$ are

$$B = R^tAR$$

$$= \frac{1}{\sqrt{2}}\begin{bmatrix} 1 & -1 \\ 1 & 1 \end{bmatrix}\begin{bmatrix} 2 & -\frac{5}{2} \\ -\frac{5}{2} & 2 \end{bmatrix}\frac{1}{\sqrt{2}}\begin{bmatrix} 1 & 1 \\ -1 & 1 \end{bmatrix}$$

$$= \frac{1}{2}\begin{bmatrix} \frac{9}{2} & -\frac{9}{2} \\ -\frac{1}{2} & -\frac{1}{2} \end{bmatrix}\begin{bmatrix} 1 & 1 \\ -1 & 1 \end{bmatrix}$$

$$= \frac{1}{2}\begin{bmatrix} 9 & 0 \\ 0 & -1 \end{bmatrix}$$

and
$$2H = 2GR$$

$$= [2 \quad 2]\tfrac{1}{\sqrt{2}}\begin{bmatrix} 1 & 1 \\ -1 & 1 \end{bmatrix}$$

$$= \tfrac{1}{\sqrt{2}}[0 \quad 4]$$

Hence, the transformed equation is

$$[u \quad v]\tfrac{1}{2}\begin{bmatrix} 9 & 0 \\ 0 & -1 \end{bmatrix}\begin{bmatrix} u \\ v \end{bmatrix} + \tfrac{1}{\sqrt{2}}[0 \quad 4]\begin{bmatrix} u \\ v \end{bmatrix} - 4 = 0$$

$$9u^2 - v^2 + 4\sqrt{2}v - 8 = 0$$

Complete the square in v to obtain

$$9u^2 - (v - 2\sqrt{2})^2 = 0$$

The translation $(u, v) \to (s, t) = (u, v - 2\sqrt{2})$ transforms this equation into the standard form

$$9s^2 - t^2 = 0$$

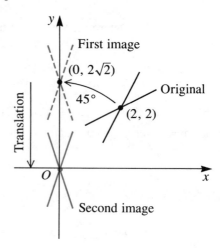

This is the equation of a degenerate hyperbola, namely a pair of straight lines through the origin with slopes ± 3.

The two lines represented by the equation $9s^2 - t^2 = 0$ are $3s = t$ and $3s = -t$, and they intersect at $(0, 0)$. The two lines represented by the equation

$$9u^2 - (v - 2\sqrt{2})^2 = 0$$

are $3u = v - 2\sqrt{2}$ and $3u = -v + 2\sqrt{2}$, and they intersect at $(0, 2\sqrt{2})$. The transformation $U = R_{45°}X$ is

$$u = \frac{x - y}{\sqrt{2}}$$

$$v = \frac{x + y}{\sqrt{2}}$$

Under this transformation, the line $3u = v - 2\sqrt{2}$ becomes

$$3\left(\frac{x - y}{\sqrt{2}}\right) = \frac{x + y}{\sqrt{2}} - 2\sqrt{2}$$

$$x - 2y + 2 = 0$$

Similarly, the other line transforms into

$$2x - y - 2 = 0$$

Hence, the original equation represents the two straight lines $x - 2y + 2 = 0$ and $2x - y - 2 = 0$ that intersect in the point $(2, 2)$.

Check. Since the curve represents two lines, the left side of the original equation can be decomposed into two linear factors:

$$2x^2 - 5xy + 2y^2 + 2x + 2y - 4 = (x - 2y + 2)(2x - y - 2)$$ $\square$

Exercises 6.7

1. Determine a rotation matrix R so that the transformation $X = RU$ will eliminate the xy term.

   a. $11x^2 - 6xy + 3y^2 = 18$ **b.** $4x^2 + 12xy + 9y^2 = 52$

   c. $4x^2 - 20xy + 25y^2 = 0$ **d.** $6x^2 + 24xy - y^2 = 30$

   e. $x^2 - 2xy + y^2 - 12\sqrt{2}x + 4\sqrt{2}y = 0$ **f.** $xy - 4x - 2y = 0$

   g. $16x^2 - 24xy + 9y^2 + 250y - 575 = 0$

2. Use the expression $ab - h^2$ to identify the type of the curve represented by each equation in Exercise 1.

3. Apply the rotation determined in each part of Exercise 1 and if necessary, a translation, to obtain the image equation in standard form. Sketch each curve and check that the type agrees with your answer to Exercise 2.

Problems 6.7

1. Find the vertices and the equations of the asymptotes of the hyperbola
$$5x^2 + 40xy + 35y^2 + 24\sqrt{5}x + 78\sqrt{5}y + 315 = 0$$

2. Determine the equation and type of the conic passing through the five given points.

   a. $(2, 0)$, $(-2, 0)$, $(0, 2)$, $(0, -2)$, $(8, -2)$

   b. $(0, 0)$, $(10, 0)$, $(0, -2)$, $(1, 3)$, $(1, -3)$

Review Exercises

1. Determine the image of the point $(3, -2)$ under the transformation represented by each expression.

   a. $(x, y) \rightarrow (x + 2, y - 4)$ b. Translation along $\vec{a} = (-2, 4)$

   c. $\begin{bmatrix} 3 & 2 \\ -2 & 1 \end{bmatrix}$ d. $\begin{bmatrix} \frac{\sqrt{3}}{2} & 1 \\ -1 & \frac{\sqrt{3}}{2} \end{bmatrix}$

2. Determine the image of the point (x, y) under the translation for which the image of $(-3, 5)$ is the given point.

   a. $(-4, 3)$ b. $(2, -1)$ c. $(0, 0)$ d. $(4, 5)$

3. The point $(-2, 3)$ lies on the line ℓ_1, and the point $(3, 5)$ lies on the line ℓ_2. A translation $T(x, y) = (x + 3, y - 2)$ maps ℓ_1 to ℓ_2. Find the equations of ℓ_1 and ℓ_2.

4. Find the equation of the image of each conic under the mapping $(x, y) \rightarrow (x + 2, y + 5)$.

   a. $x^2 + y^2 = 4$ b. $x^2 = -8y$

   c. $\dfrac{x^2}{4} + \dfrac{y^2}{25} = 1$ d. $xy = -12$

5. Determine the translation that eliminates the linear terms in each equation.

   a. $3x^2 + y^2 - 6x + 2y - 5 = 0$

   b. $4x^2 - 5y^2 + 16x + 10y = 0$

   c. $2xy - x + 2y - 6 = 0$

   d. $4x^2 - 12xy + 9y^2 + 8x - 12y + 4 = 0$

6. Sketch the graph of each equation, labelling the centre and vertices.

   a. $25x^2 + 4y^2 - 100x + 24y + 36 = 0$

   b. $x^2 + y^2 - 4x + 6y - 12 = 0$

   c. $y^2 + 4x - 4y - 4 = 0$

   d. $2x^2 + y^2 + 12x - 2y + 19 = 0$

   e. $x^2 - 4y^2 - 6x - 40y - 87 = 0$

7. Determine the matrix $A = \begin{bmatrix} a & h \\ h & b \end{bmatrix}$ so that each quadratic form $ax^2 + 2hxy + by^2$ can be written in the form $X^t AX$.

   a. $3x^2 - 2xy + 5y^2$ b. $x^2 + 4xy$

   c. $x^2 + 2\sqrt{3}xy + y^2$ d. xy

8. Write the quadratic form $ax^2 + 2hxy + by^2$ determined by each matrix.

a. $\begin{bmatrix} 3 & 1 \\ 1 & 2 \end{bmatrix}$
 b. $\begin{bmatrix} 4 & -3 \\ -3 & 0 \end{bmatrix}$
 c. $\begin{bmatrix} 2 & \frac{3\sqrt{3}}{2} \\ \frac{3\sqrt{3}}{2} & -1 \end{bmatrix}$

9. Consider each equation.

a. $5x^2 - 2\sqrt{3}xy + 3y^2 = 36$

b. $x^2 + 3xy + y^2 - 10 = 0$

c. $5x^2 + 4xy + 8y^2 - 9 = 0$

d. $3x^2 + 2\sqrt{3}xy + y^2 = 3$

e. $41x^2 - 84xy + 76y^2 = 169$

f. $5x^2 - 6xy + 5y^2 = 0$

(i) Determine a rotation matrix R so that the transformation $X = RU$ will eliminate the xy term.

(ii) Use the expression $ab - h^2$ to identify the type of each conic.

(iii) Apply an appropriate transformation to express each conic in standard form.

(iv) Sketch each curve, labelling the centre and vertices.

10. By a suitable rotation and translation, reduce each equation to the standard form of a conic. Sketch each curve and determine its vertices.

a. $x^2 - 4xy + y^2 + 4\sqrt{2}x - 2\sqrt{2}y + 11 = 0$

b. $13x^2 + 6\sqrt{3}xy + 7y^2 - (16\sqrt{3} + 8)x - (16 - 8\sqrt{3})y - 32 = 0$

c. $2x^2 - 72xy + 23y^2 + 20x - 110y - 175 = 0$

d. $4x^2 - 4xy + y^2 - 8\sqrt{5}x - 16\sqrt{5}y = 0$

11. Determine the value of c so that the graph of $xy - 2x + 3y + c = 0$ represents two straight lines.

(b) $y^2 - 8x + 6y + 17 = 0$

$(v-k)^2 - 8(u-h) + 6(v-k) + 17 = 0$

$v^2 - 2vk + k^2 - 8u + 8h + 6v - 6k + 17 = 0$

$v^2 + (-2k + 6)v + (-8)u + (k^2 + 8h - 6k + 17) = 0$

$2k = 6$ $k^2 + 8h - 6k + 17 = 0$

$k = 3$ $9 + 8h - 18 + 17 = 0$

                    $8 + 8h = 0$

$v^2 - 8u = 0$ $8h = -8$

$x^2 = 8y$ $h = -1$

$T(x,y) = (x - 1, y + 3)$

Mathematical induction is analogous to the theory of falling dominoes.

Mathematical Induction

CHAPTER **7**

The word **induction** has a variety of meanings. Physicists and engineers refer to "electromagnetic induction," whereby magnetic fields are created by electric currents. In the natural sciences "empirical induction" is the process of drawing general conclusions on the basis of repeated observations. After we throw a ball into the air 1000 times and watch it fall down, "inductive reasoning" leads us to conclude that the ball will fall down again the next time we throw it up.

Mathematical induction has a special meaning of its own. It is a method of proving statements that is especially well suited to situations involving a sequence of cases. In this chapter we shall discuss this method and use it to prove some interesting results.

7.1 The Scope of Induction

Imagine a never-ending sequence of dominoes, all standing on end. Suppose that each domino is close enough to its neighbour that if the kth domino falls to the right, it will cause the next domino, labelled $k + 1$, to fall. This in turn will knock over the domino labelled $k + 2$, and so on. In order to ensure that *all* the dominoes will eventually fall, we merely tip over the first domino.

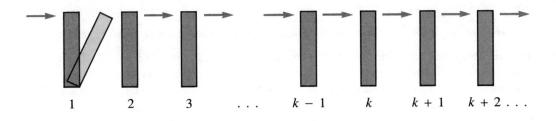

$$1 \qquad 2 \qquad 3 \qquad \ldots \qquad k - 1 \qquad k \qquad k + 1 \qquad k + 2 \ldots$$

The Principle of Mathematical Induction resembles the situation with the dominoes. Instead of a sequence of dominoes, we are given a sequence of mathematical statements or propositions:

$$P_1, P_2, P_3, P_4, \ldots, P_{k-1}, P_k, P_{k+1}, \ldots$$

The dominoes had to be tipped over in succession. The statements have to be proved in succession.

In this section we give examples of such sequences of mathematical statements, **without worrying about their proofs for the moment**.

Example 1. This example is about summation formulas. The first statement P_1, states that $1 = \frac{1(1+1)}{2}$. The second statement, P_2, is that $1 + 2 = \frac{2(2+1)}{2}$. The third, P_3, is that $1 + 2 + 3 = \frac{3(3+1)}{2}$. For any positive integer n, the nth statement, P_n, states that

$$1 + 2 + 3 + \ldots + n = \frac{n(n+1)}{2}.$$

$\square$

This summation formula has been known since antiquity. It is said that Gauss discovered it on his own when he was 10 years old. Notice that this nth statement gives the general case and describes **all** the statements $P_1, P_2, P_3, \ldots$ simultaneously.

Before attempting to verify a statement by mathematical induction, one often needs to make an *educated guess* as to what that statement might be. This can be quite challenging and is often done by examining a number of cases. For example, after noticing that $1 + 2 = 2^2 - 1$, $1 + 2 + 2^2 = 2^3 - 1$, $1 + 2 + 2^2 + 2^3 = 2^4 - 1$, we might guess that generally $1 + 2 + \ldots + 2^n = 2^{n+1} - 1$.

Example 2. This example comes from number theory. For any positive integer n, let P_n be the claim that 7 is a factor of $n^7 - n$; that is, $\frac{n^7 - n}{7}$ is an integer. For instance, P_1 states that 7 is a factor of $1^7 - 1$. Next, P_2 states that 7 is a factor of $2^7 - 2$; that is, $\frac{126}{7}$ is an integer. After that, P_3 states that 7 divides $3^7 - 3 = 2184$ exactly, and so on. $\square$

The French mathematician, Pierre-Simon de Fermat (1601–1665), extended the above example. He proved that $\frac{n^p - n}{p}$ is an integer whenever p is a prime number and n is any positive integer. Three hundred and fifty years later, this theorem of Fermat's forms the basis for a modern scheme of computer encryption. This is a way of communicating electronically using a secret code that is quite secure. The theorem is used in conjunction with enormous primes containing over 100 digits.

Exercises 7.1

1. For each mathematical statement P_n, write out the first statement, P_1, and the third statement, P_3.

   a. $1^2 + 2^2 + \ldots + n^2 = \dfrac{n(n + 1)(2n + 1)}{6}$

   b. $\dfrac{1}{2} + \dfrac{1}{6} + \ldots + \dfrac{1}{n(n + 1)} = \dfrac{n}{n + 1}$

   c. Every set of n objects has 2^n subsets (including the empty subset and the whole set).

   d. For each positive integer n, $2n^3 + 3n^2 + n$ is divisible by 6.

   e. For each positive integer n, $2^{\frac{1}{n}} \le 1 + \dfrac{1}{n}$.

   f. Any set of n lines in the plane divides the plane into at most $\dfrac{n^2 + n + 2}{2}$ regions.

2. Guess the general nth statement for each sequence of statements.

   a. 5 is a factor of $1^5 - 1$, 5 is a factor of $2^5 - 2$, 5 is a factor of $3^5 - 3$, 5 is a factor of $4^5 - 4$, . . .

   b. Given two points, there is one line segment joining them. Given three points, there are three line segments joining any two of them. Given four points, there are six line segments joining any two of them. . . .

   c. $\frac{d}{dx}x = 1$, $\frac{d}{dx}x^2 = 2x$, $\frac{d}{dx}x^3 = 3x^2$, . . .

3. State the $(k + 1)$st term in each sum in which the kth term has been shown.

   a. $0 + 3 + 8 + \ldots + (k^2 - 1) + \ldots$

   b. $1 - 3 + 5 - \ldots + (-1)^{k-1}(2k - 1) + \ldots$

   c. $-85 - 70 - 27 + 44 + \ldots + (2k + 3)(7k - 24) + \ldots$

4. By examining the first few cases, try to guess the formula for each sum or product.

   a. $1 + 3 + 5 + \ldots + (2n - 1)$

   b. $1 + 2 + 4 + \ldots + 2^{n-1}$

   c. $2 + 4 + 6 + \ldots + 2n$

   d. $\left(1 - \frac{1}{4}\right)\left(1 - \frac{1}{9}\right)\left(1 - \frac{1}{16}\right) \cdots \left(1 - \dfrac{1}{(n + 1)^2}\right)$

Problems 7.1

1. Consider the sequence of squares in the diagram. Each square is formed by joining the midpoints of the next larger square. Let L be the length of the side of the largest square. If this is the first square in the nested sequence of squares, write down the length of the side and the area of the nth square in the sequence.

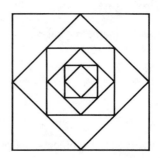

2. The objects in the figure below are the first three approximations to the Koch snowflake discovered by H. von Koch in 1904.

Each approximation is obtained from the previous one by deleting the middle third of every segment and replacing it with two sides of an equilateral triangle. If the side of the initial triangle is of length l, find the length of a segment and the perimeter of the nth approximation. What happens to the perimeter and to the area inside as n increases indefinitely? This snowflake is one of the oldest examples of a newly discovered mathematical object called a fractal. See *The Fractal Geometry of Nature* by B. B. Mandelbrot (Freeman, San Francisco, 1983) for many other examples in mathematics and science.

7.2 The Principle of Mathematical Induction

The following general situation lends itself to the method of induction. Suppose that we are given a sequence of mathematical statements or propositions

$$P_1, P_2, P_3, \ldots, P_{n-1}, P_n, P_{n+1}, \ldots$$

such as those encountered in the previous section. We may suspect that all of them are true. How are we to convince ourselves and others that they are indeed true?

Suppose we succeed in verifying that P_1 is true. Then suppose we verify that the truth of each statement P_k forces the next statement P_{k+1} to be true. Then there is no hope of ever finding a false statement, and each P_n must be true. This idea is formalized in the following principle.

The Principle of Mathematical Induction

Every statement in a sequence of statements $P_1, P_2, P_3, \ldots, P_n, \ldots$ is true if these steps are followed.

1. Verify that the first statement P_1 is true.

2. Assume that the kth statement P_k is true, and use this to show that the next statement P_{k+1} is true.

If we succeed in checking these steps, then step 1 shows that P_1 is true, step 2 then forces P_2 to be true, which forces P_3 to be true, etc. It is like the dominoes. Knock down the first and make sure that each domino will knock down the next. In due course each domino will fall.

The best way to appreciate this method is by doing a variety of examples.

Example 1. Prove that $1 + 2 + 3 + \ldots + n = \dfrac{n(n + 1)}{2}$, for all positive integers n.

Solution. We shall use mathematical induction.

Step 1: The first statement, P_1, states that $1 = \frac{1(1 + 1)}{2}$. This is clearly true.

Step 2: Assume that the kth statement, P_k, is true; that is, assume that

$$1 + 2 + 3 + \ldots + k = \frac{k(k + 1)}{2}.$$

Now, using this assumption, prove that P_{k+1} is true; that is, prove that

$$1 + 2 + 3 + \ldots + (k + 1) = \frac{(k + 1)(k + 2)}{2}$$

We have

$$1 + 2 + 3 + \ldots + (k + 1) = (1 + 2 + 3 + \ldots + k) + (k + 1)$$
$$= \frac{k(k + 1)}{2} + (k + 1) \quad \text{from the assumption}$$
$$= \frac{k(k + 1) + 2(k + 1)}{2}$$
$$= \frac{(k + 1)(k + 2)}{2}$$

So indeed, the $(k + 1)$st statement does follow from the kth statement.

Therefore, by the Principle of Mathematical Induction, the summation formula is true for all positive integers n. $\square$

Example 2. Prove that for all positive integers n,

$$(1)(3) + (2)(4) + (3)(5) + \ldots + n(n + 2) = \frac{n(n + 1)(2n + 7)}{6}$$

Solution. Again we shall use mathematical induction.

Step 1: When $n = 1$, the result is $(1)(3) = \frac{(1)(2)(9)}{6}$, which is true.

Step 2: Assume that the result is true for $n = k$. That is, assume that

$$(1)(3) + (2)(4) + (3)(5) + \ldots + k(k + 2) = \frac{k(k + 1)(2k + 7)}{6}$$

We now have to prove that

$$(1)(3) + (2)(4) + \ldots + (k + 1)(k + 3) = \frac{(k + 1)(k + 2)[2(k + 1) + 7]}{6}$$

$$= \frac{(k + 1)(k + 2)(2k + 9)}{6}$$

We have

$$(1)(3) + (2)(4) + \ldots + (k + 1)(k + 3) = (1)(3) + \ldots + k(k + 2) + (k + 1)(k + 3)$$

$$= \frac{k(k + 1)(2k + 7)}{6} + (k + 1)(k + 3)$$

$$= \frac{(k + 1)}{6}[k(2k + 7) + 6(k + 3)]$$

Notice that we take out the common factor $(k + 1)$ from the expression and that we do not multiply out the whole expression unless we are forced to. Hence,

$$(1)(3) + (2)(4) + \ldots + (k + 1)(k + 3) = \frac{(k + 1)}{6}[2k^2 + 13k + 18]$$

$$= \frac{(k + 1)(k + 2)(2k + 9)}{6}$$

Hence, the result is true for $n = k + 1$ whenever it is true for $n = k$.

Therefore, by the Principle of Mathematical Induction, the result is true for all positive integers n.   ▢

Example 3. Prove that $\dfrac{n^3 - n}{3}$ is an integer for every positive integer n.

Solution. We shall use induction.

Step 1: For $n = 1$, $\dfrac{1^3 - 1}{3} = 0$, which is indeed an integer. Therefore, the result is true for $n = 1$.

Step 2: Assume that $\dfrac{k^3 - k}{3}$ is an integer, and try to prove that $\dfrac{(k + 1)^3 - (k + 1)}{3}$ is also an integer.

Expanding, we have $(k + 1)^3 = k^3 + 3k^2 + 3k + 1$ so

$$\frac{(k + 1)^3 - (k + 1)}{3} = \frac{k^3 + 3k^2 + 2k}{3}$$

$$= \frac{k^3 - k + 3k^2 + 3k}{3}$$

$$= \frac{k^3 - k}{3} + (k^2 + k)$$

By our assumption, $\dfrac{k^3 - k}{3}$ is an integer, and $k^2 + k$ is clearly an integer; therefore,

$\dfrac{(k + 1)^3 - (k + 1)}{3}$ must also be an integer.

Hence, the Principle of Mathematical Induction shows that $\dfrac{n^3 - n}{3}$ is an integer for all positive integers n. $\qquad\square$

Exercises 7.2

1. Use mathematical induction to verify the formulas for all positive integers n.

a. $1^2 + 2^2 + 3^2 + \ldots + n^2 = \dfrac{n(n + 1)(2n + 1)}{6}$

b. $1^3 + 2^3 + 3^3 + \ldots + n^3 = \left[\dfrac{n(n + 1)}{2}\right]^2$

c. $1^2 + 3^2 + 5^2 + \ldots + (2n - 1)^2 = \dfrac{n(2n - 1)(2n + 1)}{3}$

d. $1 + 3 + 5 + \ldots + (2n - 1) = n^2$

e. $(1)(2) + (2)(3) + (3)(4) + \ldots + n(n + 1) = \dfrac{n(n + 1)(n + 2)}{3}$

f. $\dfrac{1}{(1)(3)} + \dfrac{1}{(2)(4)} + \dfrac{1}{(3)(5)} + \ldots + \dfrac{1}{n(n + 2)} = \dfrac{n(3n + 5)}{4(n + 1)(n + 2)}$

2. a. Use mathematical induction to prove the formula for the sum of n terms of the **arithmetic series** with initial term a and common difference d:

$$a + (a + d) + (a + 2d) + \ldots + [a + (n - 1)d] = na + \frac{n(n - 1)}{2}d$$

b. Give another proof using the result of Example 1.

3. a. Use mathematical induction to prove the formula for the sum of n terms of a **geometric series** with initial term a and common ratio r:

$$a + ar + ar^2 + \ldots + ar^{n-1} = \frac{a(1 - r^n)}{1 - r}, \quad \text{for } r \neq 1$$

b. If S denotes the sum of the geometric series in part a, give another proof that does not use induction. $\left(\text{Hint: } S = \dfrac{S - rS}{1 - r}.\right)$

4. Use mathematical induction to prove that each statement is true for all positive integers n.

a. $n(n + 5)$ is divisible by 2.

b. The sum of the cubes of three successive integers is divisible by 9.

c. 3 divides $n^3 + 3n^2 + 2n$.

5. Either prove that the following numbers are integers for all positive values of n or give a counter-example.

a. $\dfrac{n^5 - n}{5}$

b. $\dfrac{n^6 - n}{6}$

c. $\dfrac{n^7 - n}{7}$

Problems 7.2

1. Guess a formula for the summations and prove that your guess is correct.

a. $1 - 3 + 5 - 7 + 9 - 11 + \ldots + (-1)^{n-1}(2n - 1)$

b. $1^2 - 3^2 + 5^2 - 7^2 + \ldots + (-1)^{n-1}(2n - 1)^2$

2. Find the sum of the first $3n$ terms of the series

$$1 + \tfrac{1}{2} - \tfrac{1}{4} + \tfrac{1}{8} + \tfrac{1}{16} - \tfrac{1}{32} + \tfrac{1}{64} + \tfrac{1}{128} - \tfrac{1}{256} + \ldots$$

As n increases indefinitely, what value does this sum approach?

3. Prove that $2n^3 + 3n^2 + n$ is divisible by 6 for every positive integer n.

7.3 Summation Notation

In the previous sections it was often necessary to find the sum of n numbers, $x_1, \ldots, x_n$. It can become quite tedious to write out this sum as

$$x_1 + x_2 + x_3 + \ldots + x_{n-1} + x_n$$

A shorter way of denoting such sums is to use **sigma** or **summation notation**:

$$\sum_{i=1}^{n} x_i$$

This compact notation is read as "the sum as i ranges from 1 to n of the numbers x_i." The symbol Σ is the Greek capital letter sigma; it corresponds to the Latin letter S, which is the first letter in the word sum. In the above example, the variable "i," called the index of summation, could be replaced by any other variable; for that reason it is sometimes called a "dummy" variable or a "dummy" index.

For example, the geometric series with initial term a and common ratio r can be written as

$$\sum_{k=0}^{n-1} ar^k = a + ar + ar^2 + \ldots + ar^{n-1}$$

The following box contains the simplest properties of the summation notation. They can be proved by expanding each side.

Properties of the Summation Notation

1. $\displaystyle\sum_{i=1}^{n}(a_i + b_i) = \sum_{i=1}^{n} a_i + \sum_{i=1}^{n} b_i$

2. $\displaystyle\sum_{i=1}^{n} ka_i = k\sum_{i=1}^{n} a_i$

3. $\displaystyle\sum_{i=1}^{n} k = \underbrace{k + k + \ldots + k}_{n \text{ terms}} = nk$

We now present more examples on the use of induction to verify summation formulas.

Example 1. Prove that, for any positive integer n,

$$\sum_{j=1}^{n}(2j - 1) = n^2$$

Solution. We shall use induction.
Step 1: When $n = 1$, the equation becomes $1 = 1^2$, which is clearly true.

Step 2: Assume that the equation holds when $n = k$; that is, assume that $\sum_{j=1}^{k}(2j - 1) = k^2$.

Now verify that the equation holds for $n = k + 1$. By isolating the last term, we have

$$\sum_{j=1}^{k+1}(2j - 1) = \sum_{j=1}^{k}(2j - 1) + [2(k + 1) - 1]$$
$$= k^2 + (2k + 1)$$
$$= (k + 1)^2$$

Thus, the $(k + 1)$st equation holds whenever the kth equation holds. Since the first equation is true, the Principle of Mathematical Induction tells us that $\sum_{j=1}^{n}(2j - 1) = n^2$ for all positive integers n. $\qquad\square$

Example 2. Prove that, for any integer n,

$$\sum_{i=1}^{n}(4i^3 - 12i) = n(n + 1)(n + 3)(n - 2)$$

Use this result to evaluate $\sum_{i=6}^{27}(4i^3 - 12i)$.

Proof. We shall prove the summation formula by induction.
Step 1: When $n = 1$, the left side is -8 and the right side is $1(2)(4)(-1)$, which is also -8.

Step 2: Suppose that the result is true for $n = k$ and prove the result for $n = k + 1$; that is, prove that

$$\sum_{i=1}^{k+1}(4i^3 - 12i) = (k + 1)[(k + 1) + 1][(k + 1) + 3][(k + 1) - 2]$$
$$= (k + 1)(k + 2)(k + 4)(k - 1)$$

We have

$$\sum_{i=1}^{k+1}(4i^3 - 12i) = \sum_{i=1}^{k}(4i^3 - 12i) + [4(k+1)^3 - 12(k+1)]$$

$$= k(k+1)(k+3)(k-2) + (k+1)[4(k+1)^2 - 12]$$
$$= k(k+1)(k+3)(k-2) + (k+1)(4k^2 + 8k - 8)$$
$$= (k+1)(k^3 + k^2 - 6k + 4k^2 + 8k - 8)$$
$$= (k+1)(k^3 + 5k^2 + 2k - 8)$$
$$= (k+1)(k^2 + 6k + 8)(k-1) \quad \text{(by the Factor Theorem)}$$
$$= (k+1)(k+2)(k+4)(k-1)$$

Hence, the result is also true for $n = k + 1$ whenever it is true for $n = k$. Since the result is true for $n = 1$, it follows from the Principle of Mathematical Induction that the result is true for all positive integers n.

Now we can write

$$\sum_{i=6}^{27}(4i^3 - 12i) = \sum_{i=1}^{27}(4i^3 - 12i) - \sum_{i=1}^{5}(4i^3 - 12i)$$

$$= (27)(28)(30)(25) - (5)(6)(8)(3)$$
$$= 566\,280 \qquad \square$$

Exercises 7.3

1. Convert the sums from sigma notation to expanded form.

a. $\displaystyle\sum_{i=0}^{n}\sqrt{i}$ 　　　　 **b.** $\displaystyle\sum_{k=2}^{4}k^k$ 　　　　 **c.** $\displaystyle\sum_{i=2}^{4}\frac{(-1)^{i+1}}{(i+1)(i+3)}$

2. Express the sums in sigma notation.

a. $1 + 3 + 5 + \ldots + (2n - 1)$ 　　　　 **b.** $\dfrac{1}{2(3)} + \dfrac{1}{3(4)} + \ldots + \dfrac{1}{(n+1)(n+2)}$

c. $4 + 4 + \ldots + 4$ (taken 16 times) 　　　　 **d.** $\dfrac{1}{2} + \dfrac{3}{4} + \dfrac{5}{6} + \ldots + \dfrac{99}{100}$

3. Prove properties 1 and 2 of the summation notation.

4. Compute the sums.

   a. $\displaystyle\sum_{i=0}^{10}\frac{1}{2^i}$ **b.** $\displaystyle\sum_{j=1}^{20}\frac{1}{j}$ (use a calculator)

   c. $\displaystyle\sum_{k=0}^{12}\sin(k\pi)$ **d.** $\displaystyle\sum_{k=0}^{1000}(3+5k)$ (do not use a calculator)

5. By expanding each side, verify that

$$\sum_{i=0}^{n}x^i y^{n-i}=\sum_{k=0}^{n}x^{n-k}y^k$$

6. Use mathematical induction to verify the formulas.

   a. $\displaystyle\sum_{k=1}^{n}(2k+5)=n(n+6)$ **b.** $\displaystyle\sum_{p=1}^{n}(6p^2-1)=n^2(2n+3)$

   c. $\displaystyle\sum_{j=1}^{n}(j-1)j=\frac{(n-1)n(n+1)}{3}$ **d.** $\displaystyle\sum_{j=1}^{n}j^4=\frac{n(n+1)(6n^3+9n^2+n-1)}{30}$

   e. $\displaystyle\sum_{k=1}^{n}(2k-1)^2=\frac{1}{3}n(4n^2-1)$ **f.** $\displaystyle\sum_{r=0}^{n-1}[2^r+2(-1)^r]=2^n-(-1)^n$

do during your spare.

7. Use the results of Exercise 6 to evaluate each sum.

   a. $\displaystyle\sum_{k=5}^{20}(2k+5)$ **b.** $10^4+11^4+12^4+\ldots+49^4+50^4$

8. Is the following statement true? If so, give convincing reasons; if not, give a counter-example.

$$\sum_{k=1}^{n}x_k y_k=\left(\sum_{k=1}^{n}x_k\right)\left(\sum_{k=1}^{n}y_k\right)$$

9. Write the formulas for the sums of the general arithmetic and geometric series, using sigma notation.

10. a. Guess a formula for

$$\sum_{j=1}^{n} \frac{1}{j(j+1)}$$

and use mathematical induction to prove that your guess is correct.

b. Give a different verification of your formula for $\sum_{j=1}^{n} \frac{1}{j(j+1)}$, using the fact that

$$\frac{1}{j(j+1)} = \frac{1}{j} - \frac{1}{j+1}$$

The series, $\sum_{j=1}^{n} \left(\frac{1}{j} - \frac{1}{j+1} \right)$ is an example of a telescoping series. Why do you think this term is used?

Problems 7.3

1. If n is any positive integer, prove each statement.

a. $\sum_{j=1}^{n} \frac{j}{2^j} = 2 - \left(\frac{n+2}{2^n} \right)$

b. $\sum_{j=1}^{n} \frac{1}{(4j-3)(4j+1)} = \frac{n}{4n+1}$

2. For any real number x, such that $x \neq 1$, prove that

$$\sum_{r=1}^{n} rx^r = \frac{x - (n+1)x^{n+1} + nx^{n+2}}{(1-x)^2}$$

a. by using mathematical induction.

b. by using calculus and differentiating (with respect to x) the formula for the sum of the geometric series $\sum_{r=0}^{n} x^r$.

3. Conjecture a formula for $\sum_{t=1}^{n} \dfrac{1}{4t^2 - 1}$ and prove that your conjecture is correct.

4. Use induction to show that

$$\sum_{j=1}^{2m} (-1)^{j+1} \frac{1}{j} = \sum_{j=1}^{m} \frac{1}{m+j}$$

5. Write a computer program to calculate the sum $\sum_{j=1}^{n} f(j)$, for a fixed function $f(j)$. Apply your program to various sums in the exercises and compare the results of the computer calculations with the results you previously obtained.

7.4 Further Induction Problems

We have already seen that mathematical induction is helpful in the verification of summation formulas. However, the method is also useful in many other situations. We illustrate a variety of such examples in this section.

In step 1 of an induction proof, the first statement that we have proved has always been P_1. However, it is possible to start the induction with any particular value of n, say n_0, if we wish to prove the result for $n \geq n_0$. Imagine that we knock down the fifth domino in our never-ending sequence of dominoes; then the nth domino will fall for $n \geq 5$.

In step 2 of an induction proof, the assumption that the kth statement holds is called the **induction hypothesis**. In proving a result by induction, it is wise to write out this induction hypothesis explicitly, and also the next statement to be proved. This helps to determine the direction of the proof, because the induction hypothesis **must** be used in the proof of the next statement.

Example 1. Prove that $3^n > 20n$, for each integer $n \geq 4$.

Solution. For $n = 1, 2,$ and 3, it is not true that $3^n > 20n$. We therefore start the induction with $n = 4$.

Step 1: When $n = 4$, $3^n = 81$ and $20n = 80$, and so $3^n > 20n$.

Step 2: Assume as induction hypothesis that $3^k > 20k$, for each integer $k \geq 4$. We have to prove that $3^{k+1} > 20(k + 1)$. We have

$$3^{k+1} = 3(3^k)$$
$$3^{k+1} > 3(20k) \quad \text{(by the induction hypothesis)}$$
$$3^{k+1} > 20k + 40k$$
$$3^{k+1} > 20k + 20 \quad \left(\text{since } k \geq 4 > \tfrac{1}{2}\right)$$
$$3^{k+1} > 20(k + 1)$$

and the result is true for $n = k + 1$. Therefore, by mathematical induction, $3^n > 20n$ for all $n \geq 4$. $\square$

The product of the first n integers is often used in mathematics; it is given the special notation

$$n! = n(n - 1)(n - 2) \ldots (3)(2)(1)$$

and is called **n factorial**.

For example, $3! = (3)(2)(1) = 6$, and $6! = (6)(5)(4)(3)(2)(1) = 720$. You will quite likely find a button on your calculator labelled $x!$. The function n factorial grows extremely quickly as n gets larger; anything larger than $14!$ will contain more digits than your calculator can display, and so only the first few significant digits will be shown in scientific notation. Anything larger than $69!$ will probably overflow the storage capacity of your calculator because $70! > 10^{100}$.

Example 2. Prove that $n! \geq 2^{n-1}$ for all positive integers n.

Solution. We shall prove the result by induction.

Step 1: For $n = 1$, $1! = 1$ and $2^{n-1} = 1$; since $1 \geq 1$, the result holds.

Step 2: As induction hypothesis suppose that $k! \geq 2^{k-1}$. We need to prove that $(k + 1)! \geq 2^k$.

If $k \geq 1$, then $k + 1 \geq 2$ and it follows from the induction hypothesis that

$$(k + 1)! = (k!)(k + 1)$$
$$(k + 1)! \geq (2^{k-1})(2)$$
$$(k + 1)! \geq 2^k$$

Hence, the result follows from the Principle of Mathematical Induction. $\square$

Example 3. Prove that n straight lines subdivide the plane into at most $\dfrac{n^2 + n + 2}{2}$ regions.

Solution. We shall prove the result by induction on n. One line cuts the plane into exactly two regions. When $n = 1$, $\dfrac{n^2 + n + 2}{2} = 2$, and so the result holds.

When we add a second line, it could intersect, be parallel to, or be coincident with, the first line. Therefore, when $n = 2$, there could be four, three, or two regions. This agrees with the result for $n = 2$, which states that there are **at most** four regions. When $n = 3$, we get at most $7 = \frac{3^2 + 3 + 2}{2}$ regions.

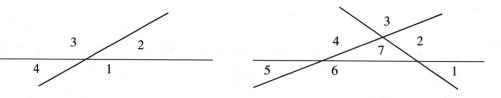

As an induction hypothesis, suppose that k lines will divide the plane into at most $\dfrac{k^2 + k + 2}{2}$ regions. Consider $(k + 1)$ lines, $L_1, L_2, \ldots, L_k, L_{k+1}$, in the plane, and try to prove that they give rise to at most $\dfrac{(k + 1)^2 + (k + 1) + 2}{2}$ regions.

By the induction hypothesis, the first k lines, $L_1, L_2, \ldots, L_k$, divide the plane into at most $\dfrac{k^2 + k + 2}{2}$ regions. When the line L_{k+1} is drawn, it will create more regions by splitting some regions into two. How many old regions can it pass through?

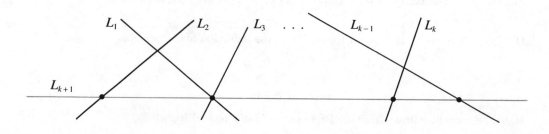

The line L_{k+1} will intersect the first k lines in **at most** k points. (It may be fewer, if L_{k+1} is parallel to one of the previous lines, or if L_{k+1} passes through a point of intersection of the old lines.) Now k distinct points on L_{k+1} divide the line L_{k+1} into $k + 1$ segments, each lying in a different region. A segment that lies in a region cuts that region into two, thereby creating one extra region. Therefore, the maximum number of extra regions formed by L_{k+1} is $k + 1$. Hence, the total number of regions is at most

$$\frac{k^2 + k + 2}{2} + k + 1 = \frac{k^2 + 3k + 4}{2}$$
$$= \frac{(k + 1)^2 + (k + 1) + 2}{2}$$

By mathematical induction, the result is true for all positive integers n. $\square$

Example 4. If A is the 2×2 matrix $\begin{bmatrix} 1 & 2 \\ 2 & 1 \end{bmatrix}$, prove that $A^n = \frac{1}{2}\begin{bmatrix} 3^n + (-1)^n & 3^n - (-1)^n \\ 3^n - (-1)^n & 3^n + (-1)^n \end{bmatrix}$

for all positive integers n.

Solution. We shall prove the result by induction. When $n = 1$, the right side is $\frac{1}{2}\begin{bmatrix} 3 - 1 & 3 + 1 \\ 3 + 1 & 3 - 1 \end{bmatrix}$, which is the same as A^1.

As the induction hypothesis, suppose that $A^k = \frac{1}{2}\begin{bmatrix} 3^k + (-1)^k & 3^k - (-1)^k \\ 3^k - (-1)^k & 3^k + (-1)^k \end{bmatrix}$. Now try to deduce that $A^{k+1} = \frac{1}{2}\begin{bmatrix} 3^{k+1} + (-1)^{k+1} & 3^{k+1} - (-1)^{k+1} \\ 3^{k+1} - (-1)^{k+1} & 3^{k+1} + (-1)^{k+1} \end{bmatrix}$. We have

$$A^{k+1} = A^k A$$
$$= \frac{1}{2}\begin{bmatrix} 3^k + (-1)^k & 3^k - (-1)^k \\ 3^k - (-1)^k & 3^k + (-1)^k \end{bmatrix}\begin{bmatrix} 1 & 2 \\ 2 & 1 \end{bmatrix} \quad \text{(by the hypothesis)}$$
$$= \frac{1}{2}\begin{bmatrix} 3^k + (-1)^k + 2(3^k) - 2(-1)^k & 2(3^k) + 2(-1)^k + 3^k - (-1)^k \\ 3^k - (-1)^k + 2(3^k) + 2(-1)^k & 2(3^k) - 2(-1)^k + 3^k + (-1)^k \end{bmatrix}$$
$$= \frac{1}{2}\begin{bmatrix} 3^{k+1} - (-1)^k & 3^{k+1} + (-1)^k \\ 3^{k+1} + (-1)^k & 3^{k+1} - (-1)^k \end{bmatrix}$$
$$= \frac{1}{2}\begin{bmatrix} 3^{k+1} + (-1)^{k+1} & 3^{k+1} - (-1)^{k+1} \\ 3^{k+1} - (-1)^{k+1} & 3^{k+1} + (-1)^{k+1} \end{bmatrix} \quad (\text{since } (-1)^k = -(-1)^{k+1})$$

The result for $n = k + 1$ has been proved with the help of the induction hypothesis, and so, by mathematical induction, the result is true for all positive integers n. $\square$

Example 5. Prove that $x + y$ is a factor of $x^{2n+1} + y^{2n+1}$, for any integers x and y, and any non-negative integer n.

Solution. We shall prove the result by induction on n, starting with $n = 0$. For $n = 0$, $x^{2n+1} + y^{2n+1} = x + y$, which is clearly divisible by $x + y$.

As the induction hypothesis, suppose that $x + y$ is a factor of $x^{2k+1} + y^{2k+1}$. We have to prove that $x + y$ is a factor of $x^{2(k+1)+1} + y^{2(k+1)+1}$, that is, that $x + y$ is a factor of $x^{2k+3} + y^{2k+3}$.

We have to use the induction hypothesis, and so we have to introduce the expression $x^{2k+1} + y^{2k+1}$ into our calculations. We can arrange this by expressing $x^{2k+3} + y^{2k+3}$ as follows:

$$\begin{aligned}
x^{2k+3} + y^{2k+3} &= x^2(x^{2k+1}) + y^{2k+3} \\
&= x^2(x^{2k+1} + y^{2k+1}) - x^2 y^{2k+1} + y^{2k+3} \\
&= x^2(x^{2k+1} + y^{2k+1}) - y^{2k+1}(x^2 - y^2)
\end{aligned}$$

By the induction hypothesis, $x + y$ is a factor of $x^{2k+1} + y^{2k+1}$. Since $x^2 - y^2 = (x + y)(x - y)$, it follows that $x + y$ is a factor of $x^2 - y^2$. Therefore, $x + y$ divides the right side of the above equation, and hence, $x + y$ divides the left side, $x^{2k+3} + y^{2k+3}$.

The result for $k + 1$ has now been proved with the help of the induction hypothesis, and so, by the Principle of Mathematical Induction, the result is true for all positive integers n. ☐

The reader may feel that, in Example 5, some "magic" trick was used when $x^2 y^{2k+1}$ was added and subtracted. The purpose of such a trick was to create a situation in which the induction hypothesis could be used.

Induction is ideally suited to dealing with recursive sequences. A **recursive sequence** is a sequence of numbers

$$x_1, x_2, \ldots, x_{n-2}, x_{n-1}, x_n, \ldots$$

where the nth term, x_n, is defined in terms of the preceding terms x_{n-1}, x_{n-2}, etc. For example, what happens if one enters 500 in a calculator and repeatedly presses the square root key? One will generate a sequence of numbers $x_1, x_2, \ldots$, where

$$x_1 = 500, \quad x_{n+1} = \sqrt{x_n}, \quad \text{for } n \geq 1$$

Try this on your calculator. What seems to happen?

Another example is the famous Fibonacci sequence, which is defined by the rule

$$x_1 = 1, \quad x_2 = 1, \quad x_{n+2} = x_{n+1} + x_n, \quad \text{for } n \geq 1$$

The first few terms of the sequence are 1, 1, 2, 3, 5, 8, 13, 21, 34, 55, 89, . . .

Leonardo of Pisa ($c1170$-1250), who is now known as Fibonacci, wrote an early book on arithmetic and algebra. In it he extolled the virtue of doing arithmetic in the Arabic decimal system, instead of the awkward Roman numeral system that was still being used. One problem in his book concerned the breeding of rabbits. Assume that each male-female pair of rabbits bears a single male-female pair of offspring two months after birth, and each month thereafter.

If we start with one newborn pair and assume that none die, the total number of pairs of rabbits at the end of each month will form the elements of the above sequence.

The Fibonacci sequence occurs in many diverse situations in nature and mathematics. It appears in the arrangement of scales on a pine cone or the seeds in a sunflower. It has so many wonderful mathematical properties that there is a whole journal, called the *Fibonacci Quarterly*, devoted to them; a few of these properties are described in Problem 3.

Example 6. Let $x_1, x_2, \ldots$ be the recursive sequence of positive numbers defined by the rule $x_1 = 1$, $x_{n+1} = \sqrt{5 + x_n}$, for $n \geq 1$. Prove that the terms of the sequence increase but are always less than 3.

Solution. We are asked to show that $x_{n+1} > x_n$ and that $x_n < 3$, for all $n \geq 1$. We shall prove these results separately by induction starting with $x_{n+1} > x_n$.

Step 1: The first statement is $x_2 > x_1$. Since $x_1 = 1$ and $x_2 = \sqrt{6}$, this statement is true.

Step 2: Assume that the kth statement, $x_{k+1} > x_k$, holds. We need to prove that $x_{k+2} > x_{k+1}$.

By the induction hypothesis, $x_{k+1} > x_k$. Therefore, $5 + x_{k+1} > 5 + x_k$ and, since the numbers are positive, $\sqrt{5 + x_{k+1}} > \sqrt{5 + x_k}$. By the recursive definition, $\sqrt{5 + x_{k+1}} = x_{k+2}$ and $\sqrt{5 + x_k} = x_{k+1}$; hence, $x_{k+2} > x_{k+1}$. Therefore, by mathematical induction, $x_{n+1} > x_n$ for all $n \geq 1$.

We shall now prove $x_n < 3$ for all n.

Step 1: When $n = 1$, $x_1 = 1 < 3$.

Step 2: Suppose that $x_k < 3$. We must prove that $x_{k+1} < 3$.

Since $x_k < 3$, it follows that $5 + x_k < 8$. Hence,

$$x_{k+1} = \sqrt{5 + x_k}$$
$$x_{k+1} < \sqrt{8} < 3$$

Therefore, by mathematical induction, $x_n < 3$ for all $n \geq 1$. □

An increasing sequence that never goes beyond 3 must converge to some number; that is, its terms must get closer and closer to some number, called the limit of the sequence. Using your calculator, compute the terms of the sequence in Example 6 until the outputs stabilize. Why would you expect the limit, x, of the sequence to satisfy the equation $x = \sqrt{5 + x}$? Find the solution of this equation and compare it with your stabilized output.

Exercises 7.4

1. Prove that each statement holds for all positive integers n.

   a. $(1 + x)^n \geq 1 + nx$, for $x \geq 0$ **b.** 6 is a factor of $n^3 - n$

   c. 7 is a factor of $23^{3n} - 1$ **d.** $2n + 4 \leq (n + 2)!$

   e. 4 divides $3^n - 2n - 1$

2. Prove directly by induction that $\dfrac{n^4}{4} < \displaystyle\sum_{k=1}^{n} k^3$.

3. Show that $x - y$ divides $x^n - y^n$, for each positive integer n.

4. Prove that $5^n > 40n$, for $n \geq 3$.

5. Which of the results are true for all integers $n \geq 1$? Either prove the result or give a counter-example.

   a. $\displaystyle\sum_{k=1}^{n} k! = 3^{n-1}$ **b.** $\displaystyle\sum_{k=-2}^{n} k = \dfrac{(n+3)(n-2)}{2}$

   c. $n! \leq n^4$ **d.** 7 is a factor of $5^n + n + 1$

   e. $\displaystyle\sum_{k=1}^{n} 2k = n^2 + n + 2$ **f.** $\displaystyle\sum_{k=1}^{n} (2k - 1) = 3n^2 - 6n + 4$

6. Prove that n distinct circles intersect each other in at most $n(n - 1)$ points.

7. If $A = \begin{bmatrix} 1 & 2 \\ 0 & 3 \end{bmatrix}$, guess a formula for A^n and justify your guess.

8. A sequence is defined recursively by $x_{n+1} = \sqrt{13 + x_n}$, for $n \geq 1$.

   a. If $x_1 = 4$, prove that the sequence is increasing.

   b. If $x_1 = 5$, prove that the sequence is decreasing.

9. If a sequence is defined recursively by $x_1 = 3$, $x_2 = 5$, and $x_{n+2} = 3x_{n+1} - 2x_n$, for $n \geq 1$, prove that $x_n = 2^n + 1$. (As the induction hypothesis, assume that $x_k = 2^k + 1$ and $x_{k-1} = 2^{k-1} + 1$.)

10. What is wrong with the following proof that all horses are the same colour? We shall prove by induction that "in any set of n horses, all the horses are the same colour."

    When $n = 1$, the statement is clearly true. Suppose that, in any set of k horses, all horses are the same colour. Take a set of $k + 1$ horses $H_1, H_2, \ldots, H_k, H_{k+1}$; we have to show they are all the same colour. By the induction hypothesis, the first k horses $H_1, H_2, \ldots, H_k$ are all one colour, and also the last k horses $H_2, H_3, \ldots, H_{k+1}$ are all one colour. Hence, all the horses are the same colour as H_2, and the result is proved.

Problems 7.4

1. a. Prove that $\left(1 - \frac{1}{4}\right)\left(1 - \frac{1}{9}\right)\left(1 - \frac{1}{16}\right)\cdots\left(1 - \frac{1}{n^2}\right) = \frac{n+1}{2n}$, for $n \geq 2$.

b. Guess what number the infinite product $\left(1 - \frac{1}{4}\right)\left(1 - \frac{1}{9}\right)\left(1 - \frac{1}{16}\right)\cdots$ represents.

c. Guess a formula for the n-fold product

$$\left(1 + \frac{1}{1}\right)\left(1 + \frac{1}{2}\right)\left(1 + \frac{1}{3}\right)\cdots\left(1 + \frac{1}{n}\right)$$

and prove that your conjecture is correct.

2. How many interior diagonals does a convex polygon with n sides have? Justify your answer.

3. The Fibonacci sequence is defined by the rule $x_1 = 1$, $x_2 = 1$, $x_{n+1} = x_n + x_{n-1}$, for $n \geq 2$. Prove that

a. $x_{n+1} < \left(\frac{7}{4}\right)^n$

b. $x_1^2 + x_2^2 + \ldots + x_n^2 = x_n x_{n+1}$

c. $x_n = \frac{\alpha^n - \beta^n}{\sqrt{5}}$, where $\alpha = \frac{1 + \sqrt{5}}{2}$ and $\beta = \frac{1 - \sqrt{5}}{2}$.

The number $\alpha = \frac{1 + \sqrt{5}}{2}$ is known as the "golden ratio." A "golden rectangle" is one whose sides are in the ratio $\alpha : 1$ and that has the property that when a square is cut out of it, the remaining rectangle has similar proportions; that is, $\frac{\alpha}{1} = \frac{1}{\alpha - 1}$. The golden rectangle is considered the rectangle whose shape is the most aesthetically pleasing and is the most aesthetically pleasing and has been used in art and architecture for centuries. The Greek Parthenon has proportions almost exactly in the golden ratio.

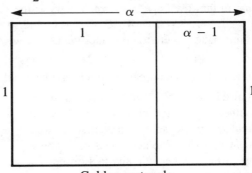

Golden rectangle

4. Write a computer program to evaluate and display the values of the sequence $x_n = ax_{n-1} + bx_{n-2}$, for $n \geq 3$, with initial values $x_1 = c$ and $x_2 = d$. Your program should allow you to stop and print the sequence.

7.5 The Binomial Theorem

The formula $(a + b)^2 = a^2 + 2ab + b^2$ is well-known. The expression "$a + b$," involving two terms, is called a binomial. By repeated multiplication, you could easily expand some low powers of this binomial, such as $(a + b)^3$ and $(a + b)^4$. However, the Binomial Theorem will provide a formula for expanding $(a + b)^n$, for any positive integer n. Let us write down the first few powers of $(a + b)$.

$$(a + b)^0 = 1$$
$$(a + b)^1 = 1a^1 + 1b^1$$
$$(a + b)^2 = 1a^2 + 2a^1b^1 + 1b^2$$
$$(a + b)^3 = 1a^3 + 3a^2b^1 + 3a^1b^2 + 1b^3$$
$$(a + b)^4 = 1a^4 + 4a^3b^1 + 6a^2b^2 + 4a^1b^3 + 1b^4$$
$$(a + b)^5 = 1a^5 + 5a^4b^1 + 10a^3b^2 + 10a^2b^3 + 5a^1b^4 + 1b^5$$
$$(a + b)^6 = 1a^6 + 6a^5b^1 + 15a^4b^2 + 20a^3b^3 + 15a^2b^4 + 6a^1b^5 + 1b^6$$

The integers appearing before each of the a^ib^j's (such as the 10 in front of a^3b^2) are called the **binomial coefficients**. We could expand $(a + b)^n$ if we knew a formula for the general binomial coefficient. Remove the a^ib^j's from the above expansions and take a close look at these coefficients.

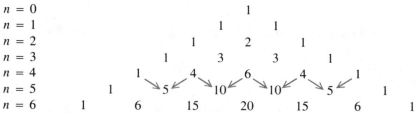

$n = 0$					1				
$n = 1$				1		1			
$n = 2$			1		2		1		
$n = 3$		1		3		3		1	
$n = 4$	1		4		6		4		1
$n = 5$	1		5		10		10		5		1
$n = 6$	1	6		15		20		15		6	1

This array is called **Pascal's Triangle**. The coefficients follow a definite pattern. Notice that in the row for $n = 5$, each entry is the sum of the two numbers immediately above it: $1 = 0 + 1$, $5 = 1 + 4$, $10 = 4 + 6$, and so on. This pattern prevails throughout the array. If this pattern were to continue, the next row would be

1	7	21	35	35	21	7	1

Indeed, this general pattern holds and we shall prove it shortly.

Blaise Pascal (1623-1662), the great French mathematician and philosopher, wrote his treatise on the above triangular arrangement in 1654. The array had been known by earlier mathematicians in Europe, and by Chinese mathematicians as early as 1100. However, Pascal's work brought together many different aspects of these numbers: the binomial coefficients, their recursive definition, their combinatorial properties, and their connection with probability.

The commonly accepted notation for the **binomial coefficient** of $a^{n-r}b^r$ in the expansion of $(a + b)^n$ is $\binom{n}{r}$. This symbol stands for a single integer and should not be confused with a column vector in 2-space.

For example, by looking at Pascal's triangle, we see that $\binom{3}{2} = 3$, $\binom{5}{0} = 1$, $\binom{5}{2} = 10$, $\binom{7}{4} = 35$. The coefficients of $a^n b^0$ and $a^0 b^n$ are both 1, and so $\binom{n}{0} = 1$ and $\binom{n}{n} = 1$ for all positive integers n.

Observe that in the expansion

$$(a + b)^n = \underbrace{(a + b)(a + b)(a + b) \ldots (a + b)}_{n \text{ factors}}$$

a contribution to the term $a^{n-r}b^r$ occurs whenever we choose b from r of the n factors and a from the remaining $n - r$ factors. Thus, the integer $\binom{n}{r}$ is the number of ways of choosing r of the b's from the n factors. That is, $\binom{n}{r}$ is the number of ways of choosing r objects from a set of n objects. Therefore, the symbol $\binom{n}{r}$ is called "*n* choose *r*."

In the "*n* choose *r*" notation, Pascal's triangle has the following appearance.

$$\binom{0}{0}$$
$$\binom{1}{0} \quad \binom{1}{1}$$
$$\binom{2}{0} \quad \binom{2}{1} \quad \binom{2}{2}$$
$$\binom{3}{0} \quad \binom{3}{1} \quad \binom{3}{2} \quad \binom{3}{3}$$

When this notation is used, the general binomial expansion is

$$(a + b)^n = \binom{n}{0}a^n + \binom{n}{1}a^{n-1}b^1 + \ldots + \binom{n}{r}a^{n-r}b^r + \ldots + \binom{n}{n-1}a^1b^{n-1} + \binom{n}{n}b^n$$

We can now state and prove our conjectured pattern in Pascal's triangle.

The Law of Pascal's Triangle

For $n \geq 1$ and $1 \leq r \leq n$, the elements in one row of Pascal's triangle can be computed from the previous row by using the formula

$$\binom{n + 1}{r} = \binom{n}{r - 1} + \binom{n}{r}$$

Proof. The binomial coefficient $\binom{n+1}{r}$ occurs in the expansion of $(a + b)^{n+1}$, whereas the coefficients $\binom{n}{r-1}$ and $\binom{n}{r}$ occur in the expansion of $(a + b)^n$. Using the relation $(a + b)^{n+1} = (a + b)(a + b)^n$, and expanding $(a + b)^{n+1}$ and $(a + b)^n$, we obtain

$$\binom{n+1}{0}a^{n+1} + \ldots + \binom{n+1}{r}a^{n+1-r}b^r + \ldots + \binom{n+1}{n+1}b^{n+1} =$$
$$(a + b)\left[\binom{n}{0}a^n + \ldots + \binom{n}{r-1}a^{n-r+1}b^{r-1} + \binom{n}{r}a^{n-r}b^r + \ldots + \binom{n}{n}b^n\right]$$

On the left side, the coefficient of $a^{n+1-r}b^r$ is $\binom{n+1}{r}$. On the right side, the terms $b\binom{n}{r-1}a^{n-r+1}b^{r-1}$ and $a\binom{n}{r}a^{n-r}b^r$ are the only ones to contribute to $a^{n+1-r}b^r$. Hence,

$$\binom{n+1}{r} = \binom{n}{r-1} + \binom{n}{r}.$$

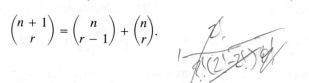

This gives a recursive method for computing the binomial coefficients. An explicit and more convenient formula for the binomial coefficients was found by Newton in 1665 and can be proved by induction.

Binomial Coefficient Formula

If n is a positive integer and $1 \le r \le n$, then

$$\binom{n}{r} = \frac{n(n-1)(n-2)\ldots(n-r+1)}{r!}$$

If the numerator and denominator are multiplied by $(n - r)!$, the formula for the general binomial coefficient can also be written as

$$\binom{n}{r} = \frac{n!}{(n-r)!r!}$$

We define the symbol 0! to be 1, so that the above formula is correct even for $r = 0$ and $r = n$.

Using this formula, let us calculate a few binomial coefficients.

$$\binom{4}{2} = \frac{(4)(3)}{(2)(1)} = 6, \quad \binom{8}{3} = \frac{(8)(7)(6)}{(3)(2)(1)} = 56, \quad \binom{8}{4} = \frac{(8)(7)(6)(5)}{(4)(3)(2)(1)} = 70$$

Proof. When $r = n$, the result is always true since $\binom{n}{n} = \dfrac{n!}{n!} = 1$. We shall prove the result by induction on n for the remaining values of r from 1 to $n - 1$. When $n = 1$, the result is true since $\binom{1}{1} = \dfrac{1}{1!} = 1$.

Assume the kth statement as the induction hypothesis; namely, assume that

$$\binom{k}{r} = \frac{k(k-1)\ldots(k-r+1)}{r!}, \quad \text{for all } r \text{ from 1 to } k - 1$$

Using the induction hypothesis, we have to prove the statement

$$\binom{k+1}{r} = \frac{(k+1)k(k-1)\ldots(k-r+2)}{r!}, \quad \text{for all } r \text{ from 1 to } k$$

By the Law of Pascal's Triangle, $\binom{k+1}{1} = \binom{k}{0} + \binom{k}{1} = 1 + k$, so that the next statement is true for $r = 1$. If $2 \leq r \leq k$, by the Law of Pascal's Triangle,

$$\binom{k+1}{r} = \binom{k}{r-1} + \binom{k}{r}$$

$$= \frac{k(k-1)\ldots(k-r+2)}{(r-1)!} + \frac{k(k-1)\ldots(k-r+1)}{r!}$$

$$= \frac{k(k-1)\ldots(k-r+2)[r + (k-r+1)]}{r!}$$

$$= \frac{(k+1)k(k-1)\ldots(k-r+2)}{r!}$$

Hence, by the Principle of Mathematical Induction, the result is true for all positive n. □

When we summarize the above results, we obtain the Binomial Theorem.

The Binomial Theorem

If n is a positive integer, then

$$(a + b)^n = \sum_{r=0}^{n} \binom{n}{r} a^{n-r} b^r$$

where $\binom{n}{r} = \dfrac{n(n-1)\ldots(n-r+1)}{r!}$.

If we expand the right side of the Binomial Theorem, we obtain

$$(a + b)^n = a^n + na^{n-1}b + \frac{n(n-1)}{(2)(1)} a^{n-2}b^2 + \ldots + \binom{n}{r} a^{n-r}b^r + \ldots + nab^{n-1} + b^n$$

The **general term** of this expansion is the $(n + 1)$st term $\binom{n}{r} a^{n-r}b^r$.

Example 1. Expand $\left(2x + \dfrac{3}{x}\right)^6$ by the Binomial Theorem.

Solution. **We have**

$$\left(2x + \frac{3}{x}\right)^6 = \sum_{r=0}^{6} \binom{6}{r}(2x)^{6-r}\left(\frac{3}{x}\right)^r$$

$$= (2x)^6 + 6(2x)^5\left(\frac{3}{x}\right) + \frac{(6)(5)}{2!}(2x)^4\left(\frac{3}{x}\right)^2 + \frac{(6)(5)(4)}{3!}(2x)^3\left(\frac{3}{x}\right)^3 + \frac{(6)(5)}{2!}(2x)^2\left(\frac{3}{x}\right)^4$$

$$+ 6(2x)\left(\frac{3}{x}\right)^5 + \left(\frac{3}{x}\right)^6$$

$$= 64x^6 + 576x^4 + 2160x^2 + 4320 + 4860x^{-2} + 2916x^{-4} + 729x^{-6} \qquad \square$$

Example 2. Find the coefficients of x^9 and x^{10} in the expansion of $(1 + 5x^3)^8$.

Solution. **The general term in this expansion is** $\binom{8}{r}(5x^3)^r = \binom{8}{r}5^r x^{3r}$.

Set $3r = 9$, giving $r = 3$, and so the coefficient of x^9 is

$$\binom{8}{3}5^3 = \frac{(8)(7)(6)}{(3)(2)(1)}5^3$$

$$= 56(5^3)$$

$$= 7000$$

The coefficient of x^{10} must be zero because the exponent of x in the general term is $3r$, which can never equal 10 since r must be an integer. $\qquad \square$

In addition to being useful in algebraic computations, the Binomial Theorem has significance in the theory of probability. For example, if a coin is tossed 100 times, the probability that "heads" will occur r times is

$$P(r\,\text{heads}) = \binom{100}{r}\left(\frac{1}{2}\right)^{100}$$

Can you show that

$$P(0\ \text{heads}) + P(1\ \text{head}) + \ldots + P(100\ \text{heads}) = 1?$$

Exercises 7.5

1. Find the coefficient of x^k, for the specified value of k, in each binomial expansion.

a. $(5 + x)^6$, $k = 3$

b. $\left(x + \dfrac{1}{x}\right)^{10}$, $k = -2$

c. $\left(x^3 + \dfrac{2}{x^2}\right)^5$, $k = 5$

d. $\left(x^2 - \dfrac{2}{x^2}\right)^3$, $k = 0$

e. $(2x - 3x^2)^{13}$, $k = 17$

f. $(2x^2 - x^{-3})^7$, $k = -6$

2. Prove that $\dbinom{n}{r} = \dbinom{n}{n-r}$. This demonstrates the symmetry in Pascal's triangle.

3. a. Expand $(1 - 1)^n$ by the Binomial Theorem and obtain a formula for

$\dbinom{n}{0} - \dbinom{n}{1} + \dbinom{n}{2} - \ldots + (-1)^n \dbinom{n}{n}$. Verify your formula for $n = 6$.

b. Expand $(1 + 1)^n$ by the Binomial Theorem and obtain a formula for

$\dbinom{n}{0} + \dbinom{n}{1} + \ldots + \dbinom{n}{n}$.

4. Expand by the Binomial Theorem.

a. $(2a + b)^6$

b. $(a - 1)^5$

c. $\left(x - \dfrac{1}{x}\right)^8$

d. $(4x^2 - 3y^3)^4$

5. Write $(1 - \sqrt{2})^6$ in the form $a + b\sqrt{2}$, where a and b are integers.

6. a. Expand $\left(2 + \dfrac{1}{100}\right)^5$ by the Binomial Theorem and then find the value of $(2.01)^5$ correct to three decimal places.

b. Use the Binomial Theorem to find the value of $(1.99)^5$ correct to three decimal places.

c. Use the Binomial Theorem to find the value of $(1.02)^{10}$ correct to three decimal places. (Check your answers with a calculator.)

7. What are the coefficients of x^{14} and x^{15} in the expansion of $(2 - x^2)^5(3 + x^4)^3$?

8. What is the coefficient of x^8 in the expansion of $(x + 2)^{10}\left(5 - \dfrac{1}{x}\right)^6$?

Problems 7.5

1. a. Expand $(1 + x)^n + (1 - x)^n$ and collect like powers of x. Then substitute $x = 1$ and obtain a formula for the sum of the even-numbered binomial coefficients

$$\binom{n}{0} + \binom{n}{2} + \binom{n}{4} + \cdots$$

b. Repeat the procedure for $(1 + x)^n - (1 - x)^n$ to obtain a formula for

$$\binom{n}{1} + \binom{n}{3} + \binom{n}{5} + \cdots$$

2. By taking the derivative of the binomial expansion of $(1 + x)^n$, prove that

$$n(1 + x)^{n-1} = \sum_{r=1}^{n} r\binom{n}{r} x^{r-1}$$

Substitute $x = -1$ to obtain an identity for the binomial coefficients, and substitute $x = 1$ to obtain another identity.

3. Write a computer program to calculate the binomial coefficient $\binom{n}{r}$. Try to avoid an overflow.

4. If A and B are 2×2 matrices, does the Binomial Theorem hold for $(A + B)^n$?

Review Exercises

1. Prove each statement for all positive integers n.

a. $(0)(1) + (1)(3) + (2)(5) + (3)(7) + \ldots + (n - 1)(2n - 1) = \dfrac{n(n - 1)(4n + 1)}{6}$

b. $1(1!) + 2(2!) + 3(3!) + \ldots + n(n!) = (n + 1)! - 1$

c. $n^3 + 5n$ is divisible by 3   **d.** $5^n - 1$ is divisible by 4

e. $\displaystyle\sum_{r=1}^{n} (4r - 3) = n(2n - 1)$ **f.** $\displaystyle\sum_{k=1}^{n} \binom{k + 2}{3} = \binom{n + 3}{4}$

2. Which of the following are true for all positive integers n? Either prove the result or give a counter-example.

a. $\sum_{r=1}^{n} (3r^2 + r) = n(n + 1)^2$

b. $\sum_{r=1}^{n} (r^2 - 2) = \dfrac{(n - 1)(2n^2 + 5n - 6)}{6}$

c. $\sum_{r=1}^{n} r2^r = 2 + (n - 1)2^{n+1}$

d. $\sum_{p=1}^{n} (p^3 - 1) = \dfrac{(n - 1)n(n + 1)(n + 4)}{4}$

e. $(n^3 + 1)(n^3 - 1)$ is divisible by 7.

f. $n^2 + n + 1$ is never divisible by 2.

g. $\sum_{k=1}^{n} \binom{n}{k} 2^k = 3^n - 1$

h. $\binom{2n + 4}{6}$ is divisible by $\binom{n + 2}{3}$.

i. $\left(1 + \dfrac{1}{n}\right)^n \geq 2$

3. Evaluate.

a. $\sum_{k=1}^{40} k(3k - 1)$

b. $\sum_{r=20}^{50} r^3$

4. **a.** Prove that $\left(\dfrac{5}{3}\right)^n > 4$, for $n \geq 3$.

b. Prove that $5^n > 4(3^n)$, for $n \geq 3$.

5. A sequence is defined recursively by $x_1 = 1$, and $x_{n+1} = \sqrt{1 + 2x_n}$, for $n \geq 1$. Prove that $x_n < 4$ and that $x_{n+1} > x_n$, for all $n \geq 1$.

6. Determine and prove formulas for each sum.

a. $\sum_{k=1}^{n} (2k - 3)$

b. $\sum_{i=1}^{n} i(i - 1)$

c. $\sum_{k=1}^{n} (k^2 + 2^k)$

d. $\sum_{j=5}^{n} j^2$

7. Find the coefficient of x^k, for the specified value of k, in each expansion.

a. $(1 + 3x)^{10}$, $k = 5$

b. $(3 - \sqrt{2}x^2)^9$, $k = 8$

c. $(ax + bx^{-1})^6$, $k = 0$

d. $\left(\dfrac{2}{3x} - 3x^2\right)^8$, $k = 2$

8. Prove that $n\binom{n - 1}{r} = (r + 1)\binom{n}{r + 1}$.

9. Expand $(3 - x)^6$ by the Binomial Theorem and find the value of $(2.98)^6$ correct to two decimal places.

10. Each side of a triangle is subdivided into n equal parts by $(n - 1)$ points, and lines parallel to the sides are drawn joining these points. The lines subdivide the original triangle into a number of small congruent triangular regions. Calculate the number of regions.

11. Let A be a 2×2 matrix and let I be the 2×2 identity matrix. Prove that

$$(I - A) \sum_{k=0}^{n-1} A^k = I - A^n$$

for all positive integers n.

The centre slice from the seashell, Nautilus pompilius. Spiral shapes can be conveniently represented using polar coordinates.

Complex Numbers

CHAPTER **8**

The complex number system is an extension of the real number system that allows us to solve any quadratic equation. For example, there are no real solutions to the equation $x^2 = -1$, but there are solutions in the complex numbers; they will be square roots of -1. Complex numbers have many applications in diverse areas, such as alternating current circuits, aerodynamic design, and quantum mechanics, as well as most branches of mathematics.

Square roots of negative numbers were tentatively introduced in the sixteenth century to solve quadratic equations that did not have any real roots. But, since they had no concrete interpretation at that time, they were usually ignored. Most mathematicians were still uneasy about accepting negative numbers. Descartes, in his book *La Géométrie*, published in 1637, coined the term ''imaginary'' for these roots of negative numbers. Euler, in 1777, was the first person to use the symbol ''i'' for a square root of -1. In 1799, Gauss proved the important theorem that every polynomial equation, with real or complex coefficients, has a complex solution. It was only in the nineteenth century that these complex numbers began to be accepted and used regularly. However, the term ''imaginary'' still persists today.

8.1 The Construction of Complex Numbers

The complex number system will be defined as an extension of the real number system, just as the real number system is an extension of the rational number system. For example, the quadratic equation $x^2 = 2$ has no rational solutions, and so a larger system, called the real number system, is introduced, in which this equation does have a solution. The symbol "$\sqrt{2}$" is defined as the positive real number whose square is 2.

However, the real number system is not sufficient to solve all quadratic equations. The equation

$$x^2 = -1$$

has no real solution, because the square of any real number can never be negative. We therefore introduce the symbol "i" to stand for a new kind of number whose square is -1; that is,

$$i^2 = -1$$

We would like to add and multiply this symbol i with any real number to form numbers like $3 + i, 2i, (-\sqrt{3})i$, and $-7 + 5i$. Therefore, we construct all the complex numbers as follows.

A **complex number** is an expression of the form $a + bi$, where a and b are real numbers. The set of all complex numbers is

$$\{a + bi \mid a, b \in \mathbf{R}\}$$

If $z = a + bi$ is such a complex number, then $a + bi$ is said to be the **standard form** for z. The real number a is called the **real part** of z and is denoted by $\text{Re}(z)$. The real number b is called the **imaginary part** of z and is denoted by $\text{Im}(z)$.

For example, $z = 3 + 4i$ is a complex number whose real part is 3 and whose imaginary part is 4. If the imaginary part of a complex number is zero, we equate that complex number with its real part, so that $-6 + 0i$ would be equated with the real number -6. Hence, every real number is also a complex number. A complex number whose real part is zero, such as $0 + 5i$, is called **purely imaginary** and is usually denoted by just $5i$.

Engineers often use the symbol j instead of i, because they tend to use i as a symbol for current.

We define the operations on complex numbers so that the addition and multiplication of complex numbers are commutative, associative, and distributive. Hence, two complex numbers can be added and subtracted by using the usual laws of algebra and by treating the symbol i as an algebraic unknown. Furthermore, the complex number $a + ib$ is the same as $a + bi$, and we shall write a complex number like $2 + (-3)i$ simply as $2 - 3i$.

Addition and Subtraction of Complex Numbers

$$(a + bi) + (c + di) = (a + c) + (b + d)i$$
$$(a + bi) - (c + di) = (a - c) + (b - d)i$$

If we multiply two complex numbers, using the usual laws of algebra, we obtain a quantity i^2 in the product. Since the fundamental property of i is that $i^2 = -1$, we obtain the following multiplication rule:

$$(a + bi)(c + di) = ac + (ad + bc)i + bdi^2$$
$$= ac + (ad + bc)i - bd$$
$$= (ac - bd) + (ad + bc)i$$

Multiplication of Complex Numbers

$$(a + bi)(c + di) = (ac - bd) + (ad + bc)i$$

Example 1. If $z = 4 + 7i$ and $w = -3 + i$, find $z + w$, $z - w$, and zw.

Solution.

$$z + w = (4 + 7i) + (-3 + i)$$
$$= (4 - 3) + (7 + 1)i$$
$$= 1 + 8i$$
$$z - w = (4 + 7i) - (-3 + i)$$
$$= (4 + 3) + (7 - 1)i$$
$$= 7 + 6i$$

$$zw = (4 + 7i)(-3 + i)$$
$$= 4(-3) + 4i + 7i(-3) + 7i^2$$
$$= -12 + 4i - 21i + 7(-1)$$
$$= -19 - 17i$$

Hence, $z + w = 1 + 8i$, $z - w = 7 + 6i$, and $zw = -19 - 17i$. $\square$

Example 2. Find the standard form and the real and imaginary parts of $(2 + 3i)^2$.

Solution.

$$(2 + 3i)^2 = 4 + 12i + 9i^2$$
$$= 4 + 12i + 9(-1)$$
$$= -5 + 12i$$

Hence, the real part is -5, the imaginary part is 12, and the standard form is $-5 + 12i$. $\square$

If the complex number $a + bi$ is zero, then both the real and imaginary parts must be zero; that is, $a = b = 0$. (If this were not so, we would obtain $i = -\frac{a}{b}$, which is impossible since i is not a real number.) If two complex numbers are equal, say

$$a + bi = c + di$$

then

$$(a - c) + (b - d)i = 0$$

and it follows that $a = c$ and $b = d$. Hence, if two complex numbers are equal, we may equate their real parts and equate their imaginary parts.

Equality of Complex Numbers

If a, b, c, and d are real numbers, then

$$a + bi = c + di \quad \text{if and only if } a = c \text{ and } b = d$$

Example 3. Find all the solutions of the equation $z^2 = -4$.

Solution. Let $z = a + bi$, where $a, b \in \mathbf{R}$, so that

$$\begin{aligned}
z^2 &= (a + bi)^2 \\
&= a^2 + 2abi - b^2 \\
&= (a^2 - b^2) + 2abi
\end{aligned}$$

Now if $z^2 = -4$,

$$(a^2 - b^2) + 2abi = -4 + 0i$$

This is an equality between two complex numbers, and so, equating the real parts of each side, we obtain

$$(a^2 - b^2) = -4$$

and, equating the imaginary parts of each side, we obtain

$$2ab = 0$$

This second equation implies that either $a = 0$ or $b = 0$. If $a = 0$, the first equation gives us $-b^2 = -4$, and so $b = \pm 2$. If $b = 0$, the first equation gives us $a^2 = -4$, which has no solution for real a.

Hence, the only solutions are $a = 0$ and $b = \pm 2$. Therefore, $z = 2i$ and $z = -2i$ are all the solutions to the equation $z^2 = -4$. $\qquad\qquad\square$

Note that -4 has two complex square roots, namely $\pm 2i$. In general, every number, real or complex, has two complex square roots that are negatives of each other. If a is real and positive, the symbol $\sqrt{a}$ refers to the positive square root of a. However, if a is negative or non-real, the symbol $\sqrt{a}$ is ambiguous, as it is not clear to which square root it refers. This notation can lead to faulty conclusions; for example, $\sqrt{a}\sqrt{b} \neq ab$, if $a = b = -1$. Therefore, we shall not use the notation $\sqrt{z}$ when z is a complex number, except for the form $\pm\sqrt{z}$, when referring to both roots.

Exercises 8.1

1. Find the real and imaginary parts of the complex numbers.

    a. $6 + 11i$ **b.** $-7i$ **c.** 14 **d.** $-1 - 2i$

2. Compute $z + w$ and zw.

a. $z = 2 + 3i$
$w = 1 + i$

b. $z = 2 + i$
$w = 2 - i$

c. $z = 4 + 5i$
$w = i$

d. $z = -1 + 5i$
$w = 7 - 11i$

e. $z = \sqrt{5}$
$w = 2 - 6i$

f. $z = -1 + 3i$
$w = -4 - 2i$

3. Express the complex numbers in standard form.

a. $(1 + i)^2$

b. $(2 + 4i) + (7 - i)$

c. $(-5i)^2$

d. $(-4 + i)(-4 - i)$

e. $(2 - i)^2 + (1 + 2i)^2$

f. $(\pi - \sqrt{3}i)^2$

g. $(\sqrt{7} - \sqrt{3}i)(\sqrt{7} + \sqrt{3}i)$

h. $\left(\frac{1}{2} + \frac{1}{3}i\right)\left(\frac{2}{3} - \frac{1}{2}i\right)$

4. Solve for z.

a. $6i + z = 2 - 3i$

b. $(4 - 3i) + z = 7 + 3i$

5. Find all the complex solutions.

a. $z^2 = -3$

b. $z^2 = i$

c. $z^2 = 7$

6. If $z = a + bi$, when is $(2 - 3i)z$ real?

7. If $z = a + bi$, when is $(-4 + 5i)z$ purely imaginary?

Problems 8.1

1. Write a computer program that multiplies two complex numbers together and displays the result.

2. If $f(z) = z^2 + 2z + 2$ is a complex function of the complex variable z, evaluate each quantity.

a. $f(i)$

b. $f(-1 + i)$

c. $f(-1)$

d. $f(1 + i)$

3. Show that addition and multiplication of complex numbers of the form $a + bi$ are equivalent to addition and multiplication, respectively, of matrices of the form $\begin{bmatrix} a & b \\ -b & a \end{bmatrix}$.

8.2 The Complex Plane

Since each complex number $z = a + bi$ is determined by the two real numbers a and b, we can represent this complex number geometrically as the point in the plane with Cartesian coordinates (a, b). This provides a one-to-one correspondence between the complex numbers and the points in the plane. That is, corresponding to each complex number, there is a unique point in the plane and, conversely, each point in the plane corresponds to a unique complex number.

The plane in this representation is called the **complex plane**. Each real number a is also the complex number $a + 0i$ that corresponds to a point $(a, 0)$ on the x-axis. Therefore, the x-axis is called the **real axis**. A purely imaginary number $z = 0 + bi$ corresponds to a point on the y-axis; therefore, the y-axis is called the **imaginary axis**.

This geometric interpretation of the complex numbers was discovered independently by the Norwegian, Caspar Wessel (1745-1818), the Swiss, Jean-Robert Argand (1768-1822), and Carl F. Gauss. The complex plane is often called the Argand diagram.

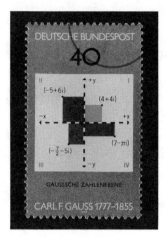

Example 1. Plot the following complex numbers in the complex plane: $4 + 3i$, $-2 + 4i$, 3, $4i$, $-5 - i$, $-2i$.

Solution. These complex numbers are represented by the points $(4, 3)$, $(-2, 4)$, $(3, 0)$, $(0, 4)$, $(-5, -1)$, and $(0, -2)$, respectively.

The complex number

$$z = a + bi$$

can also be represented as a vector from the origin to the point with coordinates (a, b). The complex numbers in Example 1 are represented as vectors in the figure at the right. We shall refer to z geometrically as either the point with coordinates (a, b) or the vector from the origin to that point, depending on which point of view is more convenient.

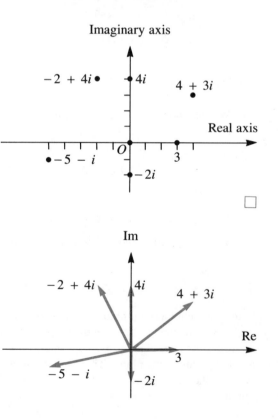

Notice that the addition of the two complex numbers $z_1 = a_1 + b_1i$ and $z_2 = a_2 + b_2i$ corresponds to the addition of their corresponding vectors (a_1, b_1) and (a_2, b_2).

Complex addition: $(a_1 + b_1i) + (a_2 + b_2i) = (a_1 + a_2) + (b_1 + b_2)i$
Vector addition: $(a_1, b_1) + (a_2, b_2) = (a_1 + a_2, b_1 + b_2)$

Similarly, subtraction of complex numbers corresponds to subtraction of vectors.

Addition and subtraction of complex numbers corresponds to addition and subtraction of vectors.

The full geometric description of complex multiplication will be given when we introduce the polar form of a complex number in section 8.6. Notice, in the meantime, that if we multiply $z = a + bi$ by i, we obtain

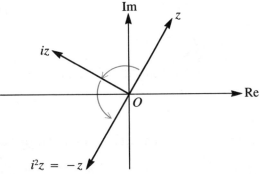

$$iz = i(a + bi)$$
$$= -b + ai$$

The vectors (a, b) and $(-b, a)$ have the same length and are perpendicular, since the dot product $(a, b) \cdot (-b, a) = 0$. Hence, the vector representation of iz is obtained by rotating the vector representation of z through an angle of $\frac{\pi}{2}$ radians (or 90°) in a counterclockwise direction.

The relationship $i^2 = -1$ can be illustrated on this diagram by finding the vector representation of i^2z. Rotate the vector $z = a + bi$ through $\frac{\pi}{2}$ radians and then through another $\frac{\pi}{2}$ radians to end up at $i^2z = -a - bi = -z$. As we would expect, multiplying a complex number z by i^2 or -1 is the same as rotating the corresponding vector through π radians.

If $a + bi$ is any complex number, then $(a + bi)(a - bi) = a^2 + b^2$, which is always a real number. This relationship, which is useful in finding reciprocals of complex numbers and in division, leads to the following definition.

The **complex conjugate** of $z = a + bi$ is $\bar{z} = a - bi$.

Geometrically, the complex conjugate, $\bar{z}$, is the reflection of z in the real axis. If z is real, then z lies on the real axis and its conjugate, $\bar{z}$, is equal to z.

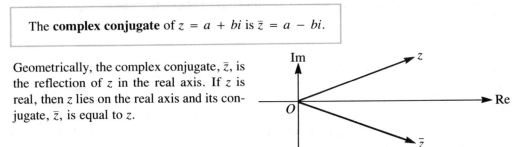

Example 2. If $z_1 = -2 + 3i$ and $z_2 = 0 - 5i$, find $\bar{z}_1$, $\bar{z}_2$, $z_1\bar{z}_1$, and $z_2\bar{z}_2$.

Solution. We have $\bar{z}_1 = -2 - 3i$ and $\bar{z}_2 = 0 + 5i$, and therefore

$$z_1\bar{z}_1 = (-2 + 3i)(-2 - 3i)$$
$$= (-2)^2 + (-3)^2$$
$$= 13$$
$$z_2\bar{z}_2 = (0 - 5i)(0 + 5i)$$
$$= 25$$

□

Properties of the Complex Conjugate

If $z = a + bi$, and z_1 and z_2 are complex numbers, then

- $z\bar{z} = a^2 + b^2$, which is always real and non-negative
- $\bar{\bar{z}} = z$
- $\overline{z_1 + z_2} = \bar{z}_1 + \bar{z}_2$
- $\overline{z_1 z_2} = \bar{z}_1 \bar{z}_2$
- $z = \bar{z}$ if and only if z is a real number

Proof of $\overline{z_1 z_2} = \bar{z}_1 \bar{z}_2$.
Let $z_1 = a_1 + b_1 i$ and let $z_2 = a_2 + b_2 i$, so that

$$\overline{z_1 z_2} = \overline{(a_1 + b_1 i)(a_2 + b_2 i)}$$
$$= \overline{(a_1 a_2 - b_1 b_2) + (a_1 b_2 + a_2 b_1)i}$$
$$= (a_1 a_2 - b_1 b_2) - (a_1 b_2 + a_2 b_1)i$$
$$= (a_1 - b_1 i)(a_2 - b_2 i)$$
$$= \bar{z}_1 \bar{z}_2$$

The proofs of the other properties are left as an exercise.

□

Since the number $z\bar{z} = a^2 + b^2$ is real and non-negative, it has a non-negative real square root $\sqrt{a^2 + b^2}$. This number $\sqrt{a^2 + b^2}$ is the distance from the origin to the point (a, b) and equals the length of the vector (a, b). It is called the **modulus** or **absolute value** of z and is denoted by $|z|$.

The **modulus** or **absolute value** of $a + bi$ is $|a + bi| = \sqrt{a^2 + b^2}$.

For example, if $z = 2 - 5i$, then $|z| = \sqrt{4 + 25} = \sqrt{29}$. Note that $|z|$ is a non-negative real number and generalizes the usual absolute value function for real numbers; that is, if $z = a + 0i$, then $|z| = |a| = \sqrt{a^2}$.

Properties of the Modulus

If z, z_1, and z_2 are complex numbers, then

- $|z| = 0$ if and only if $z = 0$
- $|z| = |\bar{z}|$
- $z\bar{z} = |z|^2$
- $|z_1 z_2| = |z_1||z_2|$

Proof of $|z_1 z_2| = |z_1||z_2|$.

If z_1 and z_2 are two complex numbers, then

$$
\begin{aligned}
|z_1 z_2|^2 &= (z_1 z_2)(\overline{z_1 z_2}) \quad \text{(using the property } |z|^2 = z\bar{z}) \\
&= (z_1 z_2)(\bar{z}_1 \bar{z}_2) \\
&= (z_1 \bar{z}_1)(z_2 \bar{z}_2) \quad \text{(by associativity)} \\
&= |z_1|^2 |z_2|^2
\end{aligned}
$$

Since the modulus is always non-negative, $|z_1 z_2| = |z_1||z_2|$.

The proofs of the remaining properties are left as an exercise.

We can find the reciprocal of the non-zero complex number z as follows. Start with

$$z\bar{z} = |z|^2$$

and divide by the non-zero real number $|z|^2$ to obtain

$$z\left(\frac{\bar{z}}{|z|^2}\right) = 1$$

$$z^{-1} = \frac{\bar{z}}{|z|^2}$$

Hence, the number in brackets is the reciprocal, z^{-1}, of z, since $zz^{-1} = 1$.

The **inverse** or **reciprocal** of the non-zero complex number $z = a + bi$ is

$$z^{-1} = \frac{\bar{z}}{|z|^2} = \frac{a - bi}{a^2 + b^2} = \frac{a}{a^2 + b^2} - \frac{b}{a^2 + b^2} i$$

Division of two complex numbers can now be defined. To divide any complex number w by the non-zero complex number z, multiply w by the reciprocal of z:

$$\frac{w}{z} = wz^{-1}$$

The easiest way to convert any quotient $\dfrac{w}{z}$ into standard form is to multiply both the numerator and denominator of $\dfrac{w}{z}$ by the conjugate, $\bar{z}$, of the denominator. If $w = a + bi$ and $z = c + di$, then

$$\begin{aligned}\frac{w}{z} &= \frac{a+bi}{c+di} \\ &= \left(\frac{a+bi}{c+di}\right)\left(\frac{c-di}{c-di}\right) \\ &= \frac{(ac+bd)+(bc-ad)i}{c^2+d^2}\end{aligned}$$

and the denominator is now real.

Example 3. If $z = 1 + 2i$, illustrate z and z^{-1} on the complex plane.

Solution.

$$\begin{aligned}z^{-1} &= \frac{1}{1+2i} \\ &= \frac{1-2i}{(1+2i)(1-2i)} \\ &= \frac{1-2i}{5} \\ &= \tfrac{1}{5} - \tfrac{2}{5}i\end{aligned}$$

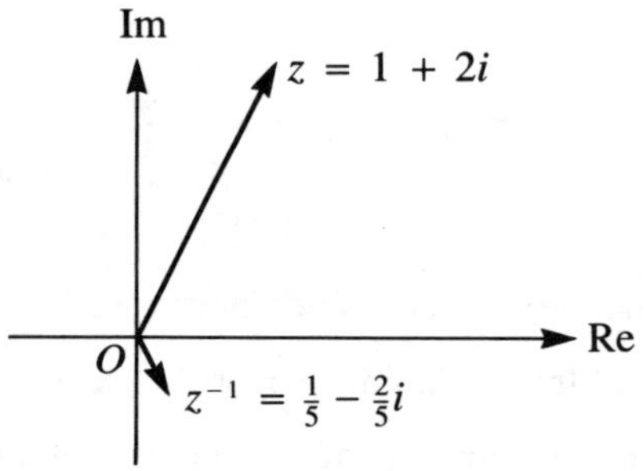

The vectors corresponding to z and z^{-1} are illustrated in the diagram. □

Note that the vector representing z^{-1} is in the same direction as the vector representing $\bar{z}$, but its magnitude is divided by $|z|^2$.

Example 4. Express $\dfrac{5-2i}{1+3i}$ and $\dfrac{2-i}{i}$ in standard form.

Solution.

$$\begin{aligned}\frac{5-2i}{1+3i} &= \frac{(5-2i)(1-3i)}{(1+3i)(1-3i)} \\ &= \frac{-1-17i}{10} \\ &= -\frac{1}{10} - \frac{17}{10}i\end{aligned}$$

$$\begin{aligned}\frac{2-i}{i} &= \frac{(2-i)(-i)}{(i)(-i)} \\ &= \frac{-1-2i}{1} \\ &= -1-2i\end{aligned}$$

□

Exercises 8.2

1. Plot the complex numbers $2 + 3i$, $5 - i$, -2, $-3 - 4i$, and $-3i$ in the complex plane as points and as vectors.

2. Find the magnitudes of the vectors in Exercise 1.

3. State the complex conjugate and modulus of each complex number.

   a. $2 + 9i$ **b.** $-i$ **c.** 3 **d.** $i(5 + 4i)$ **e.** $\sqrt{2} - 3\sqrt{7}i$

4. If $z_1 = 2 + 5i$, $z_2 = 4 + i$, and $z_3 = 6 - i$, illustrate the vector in the complex plane that corresponds to the given complex number.

   a. $z_1 + z_2$ **b.** $z_1 - z_2$ **c.** $z_1 + z_2 + z_3$ **d.** $2z_1 + 3z_2$

   e. $\bar{z}_1$ **f.** $\overline{z_1 + z_2}$ **g.** $z_1 + \bar{z}_1$ **h.** $z_2 - \bar{z}_2$

5. If $z = 3 + 5i$, plot z, iz, i^2z, i^3z, and i^4z on the same diagram.

6. If $z = 1 + \sqrt{3}i$, plot z, z^2, $2iz$, and $-iz$ on the same diagram.

7. If $z = -1 + i$, plot z, $\bar{z}$, and z^{-1} on the same diagram.

8. Express in standard form.

   a. $\dfrac{2 + i}{3 - i}$ **b.** $\dfrac{1 + 2i}{1 - 2i}$ **c.** $\dfrac{4 + 3i}{7i}$ **d.** $\dfrac{(2 + i)(1 + 2i)}{3 - 2i}$

9. If $z = 1 - 3i$, write in standard form.

   a. z^{-1} **b.** $(\bar{z})^{-1}$ **c.** z^{-2} **d.** $(z\bar{z})^{-1}$

10. If $z_1 = 5 + i$, $z_2 = 3 - i$, and $z_3 = -4 + 3i$, express the following in standard form.

    a. $(z_1 z_2)z_3$ **b.** $z_1(z_2 z_3)$ **c.** $z_1(z_2 + z_3)$

    d. $z_1 z_2 + z_1 z_3$ **e.** $z_1 + \bar{z}_1$ **f.** $\overline{z_2 + z_3}$

    g. $\bar{z}_2 + \bar{z}_3$ **h.** $\bar{z}_1 \bar{z}_2$ **i.** $\overline{z_1 z_2}$

11. Solve for z.

    a. $(2 - 3i)z = 5$ **b.** $(1 - 2i)z + 3 = -i$

12. **a.** Evaluate i^n for $n = 0, 1, 2, \ldots, 10$.

    b. Evaluate i^{4n}, i^{4n+1}, i^{4n+2}, i^{4n+3}, and i^{4n+4} for all positive integers n.

13. Show that $|z_1 - z_2|$ is the distance between the complex numbers z_1 and z_2 in the complex plane.

14. If z, z_1, and z_2 are complex numbers, prove each statement.

    a. $\bar{\bar{z}} = z$ **b.** $\overline{z_1 + z_2} = \bar{z}_1 + \bar{z}_2$

    c. $|z| = |\bar{z}|$ **d.** $z = \bar{z}$ if and only if $z \in R$

    e. $|z| = 0$ if and only if $z = 0$ **f.** $z + \bar{z} = 2\mathrm{Re}(z)$

15. Find the sum of the first ten terms of the arithmetic series with first term 3 and common difference $5i$.

Problems 8.2

1. Prove that $\text{Re}(z) = \dfrac{z + \bar{z}}{2}$ and $\text{Im}(z) = \dfrac{z - \bar{z}}{2i}$.

2. If z is a non-zero complex number, prove that z^{-1} can be represented by a vector in the direction of $\bar{z}$ and having a magnitude equal to the reciprocal of the magnitude of z.

3. Find the sum of the first seven terms of the geometric series with first term $1 + i$ and common ratio $2i$.

4. Use the Binomial Theorem to evaluate $(1 + i)^6$.

5. Use induction to prove that $\overline{z^n} = \bar{z}^n$ for all positive integers n.

6. If $a_1 + b_1 i = (a_2 + b_2 i)^n$, show that $a_1^2 + b_1^2 = (a_2^2 + b_2^2)^n$.

7. Find all complex numbers z such that $z^2 = \bar{z}$.

8.3 Quadratic Equations

The roots of the quadratic equation

$$ax^2 + bx + c = 0, \quad \text{where } a, b, c \in \mathbf{R}, \text{ and } a \neq 0$$

are $x = \dfrac{-b + \sqrt{b^2 - 4ac}}{2a}$ and $x = \dfrac{-b - \sqrt{b^2 - 4ac}}{2a}$. For example, the roots of

$2x^2 - 3x - 1 = 0$ are $x = \frac{3 + \sqrt{17}}{4}$ and $x = \frac{3 - \sqrt{17}}{4}$. The type of roots obtained depends on the sign of the discriminant $b^2 - 4ac$. If $b^2 - 4ac > 0$, there are two distinct real roots. If the discriminant is zero, there are two equal real roots, and if the discriminant is negative, there are no real roots. We are now able to consider this last case, where $b^2 - 4ac < 0$, and obtain complex roots of such a quadratic equation.

Recall how the quadratic formula was obtained. Divide the equation $ax^2 + bx + c = 0$ by a and complete the square in x to obtain

$$\left(x + \frac{b}{2a} \right)^2 = \frac{b^2 - 4ac}{4a^2}$$

If $b^2 - 4ac < 0$, then the right side has the two imaginary square roots $\dfrac{\pm \sqrt{b^2 - 4ac}}{2a}$,

and so we obtain the standard formula

$$x = \frac{-b \pm \sqrt{b^2 - 4ac}}{2a}$$

where x is now a complex number. For a negative discriminant, this formula can be written as

$$x = \frac{-b \pm \sqrt{(-1)(4ac - b^2)}}{2a} = \frac{-b \pm i\sqrt{4ac - b^2}}{2a} = \frac{-b}{2a} \pm \frac{\sqrt{4ac - b^2}}{2a}i;$$

which is a pair of conjugate complex numbers.

Example 1. Solve $x^2 + 2x + 4 = 0$.

Solution. By the quadratic formula,

$$\begin{aligned} x &= \frac{-2 \pm \sqrt{4 - 16}}{2} \\ &= \frac{-2 \pm \sqrt{(-1)12}}{2} \\ &= \frac{-2 \pm 2\sqrt{3}i}{2} \\ &= -1 \pm \sqrt{3}i \end{aligned}$$

Hence, the solutions are the complex conjugates $-1 + \sqrt{3}i$ and $-1 - \sqrt{3}i$. $\square$

The formula for finding the roots of a quadratic equation may also be used when the coefficients a, b, and c are complex numbers. In this case $\pm\sqrt{b^2 - 4ac}$ denotes the two complex square roots of the complex number $b^2 - 4ac$. In section 8.8 we shall see how to determine square roots of arbitrary complex numbers.

Example 2. Solve $x^2 - 4ix - 3 = 0$.

Solution. By the quadratic formula,

$$\begin{aligned} x &= \frac{4i \pm \sqrt{-16 + 12}}{2} \\ &= \frac{4i \pm \sqrt{-4}}{2} \\ &= \frac{4i \pm 2i}{2} \\ &= 2i \pm i \end{aligned}$$

Thus, the solutions are $3i$ and i.

We could also solve the equation by factoring the left side to obtain

$$(x - 3i)(x - i) = 0$$

so $x = i$ or $x = 3i$. $\square$

> ## Theorem
> For any complex numbers $a \neq 0$, b, and c, the sum of the roots of $ax^2 + bx + c = 0$ is $-\dfrac{b}{a}$ and the product of the roots is $\dfrac{c}{a}$.

Proof. If the roots of $ax^2 + bx + c = 0$ are the complex numbers r_1 and r_2, then the equation may be written as $(x - r_1)(x - r_2) = 0$. Hence,

$$x^2 - (r_1 + r_2)x + r_1 r_2 = 0$$

To compare this equation with $ax^2 + bx + c = 0$, we divide by a to obtain

$$x^2 + \frac{b}{a}x + \frac{c}{a} = 0$$

Hence, the sum of the roots is $r_1 + r_2 = -\frac{b}{a}$, and the product of the roots is $r_1 r_2 = \frac{c}{a}$. □

Example 3. Form a quadratic equation whose roots are $2 \pm 3i$.

Solution. The sum of the roots is $(2 + 3i) + (2 - 3i) = 4$, and the product of the roots is $(2 + 3i)(2 - 3i) = 13$. Hence, the equation $x^2 - 4x + 13 = 0$ has roots $2 \pm 3i$. □

Example 4. If the roots of a quadratic equation are complex conjugates, show that the equation can be written with real coefficients.

Solution. Let the conjugate roots be r_1 and $\bar{r}_1$. The equation can be written as

$$(x - r_1)(x - \bar{r}_1) = 0$$
$$x^2 - (r_1 + \bar{r}_1)x + r_1\bar{r}_1 = 0$$

By properties of the conjugate, $r_1 + \bar{r}_1$ and $r_1\bar{r}_1$ are both real, and so the equation has real coefficients. □

We have already seen that the converse of this result is true. If an equation with real coefficients has non-real roots, then the roots are complex conjugates.

Example 5. Form a quadratic equation whose roots are $(-3 \pm 2\sqrt{3})i$.

Solution. The sum of the roots is $(-3 + 2\sqrt{3})i + (-3 - 2\sqrt{3})i = -6i$. The product of the roots is $[(-3 + 2\sqrt{3})i][(-3 - 2\sqrt{3})i] = (9 - 12)(-1) = 3$. Therefore, an equation is $x^2 + 6ix + 3 = 0$. □

Some polynomial equations of higher degree can also be solved by a combination of factoring techniques and the quadratic formula.

Example 6. Solve $x^3 + 8 = 0$.

Solution. Factor the left side to obtain

$$(x + 2)(x^2 - 2x + 4) = 0$$

One root is -2. Solving $x^2 - 2x + 4 = 0$, we obtain $x = \frac{2 \pm \sqrt{4 - 16}}{2} = 1 \pm \sqrt{3}i$. Hence, the cubic equation has the three roots -2, $1 + \sqrt{3}i$, and $1 - \sqrt{3}i$. $\square$

Example 7. Solve $x^4 + 10x^2 + 24 = 0$.

Solution. Consider the equation as a quadratic in x^2 and factor the left side to obtain

$$(x^2 + 4)(x^2 + 6) = 0$$

Therefore, $x^2 + 4 = 0$ or $x^2 + 6 = 0$. Hence, $x^2 = -4$ or $x^2 = -6$ and the four roots are $\pm 2i$, $\pm \sqrt{6}i$. $\square$

There is no need to search beyond the set of complex numbers for solutions to polynomial equations. This is assured by the famous **Fundamental Theorem of Algebra**. The theorem states that any polynomial equation of degree $n > 1$,

$$a_n x^n + a_{n-1} x^{n-1} + \ldots + a_2 x^2 + a_1 x + a_0 = 0$$

in which the coefficients are complex numbers (which, of course, includes the real numbers) has at least one complex root. The proof of the theorem, which was first discovered by the great German mathematician Carl Friedrich Gauss in 1799, is beyond the scope of this book. A further consequence of the fundamental theorem of algebra is that every polynomial equation of degree n has exactly n complex roots, not necessarily all different. Some of these roots may be real.

Exercises 8.3

1. Solve each equation.

   a. $2x^2 + x + 2 = 0$

   b. $x^2 - 3x + 9 = 0$

   c. $x^2 - 2\sqrt{2}x - 6 = 0$

   d. $2\sqrt{3}x^2 - 3x - 3\sqrt{3} = 0$

2. Form a quadratic equation with the given roots.

   a. $5 - i, 5 + i$

   b. $\sqrt{2} + 2i, \sqrt{2} - 2i$

   c. $1 \pm \sqrt{5}i$

   d. $2 \pm (1 + \sqrt{2})i$

3. Solve each equation.

   a. $x^2 + 2ix + 3 = 0$

   b. $ix^2 + 7x - 10i = 0$

   c. $x^2 - 4x + 6i = 0$

   d. $x^2 - 5ix - (7 - i) = 0$

4. Form a quadratic equation with the given roots.

    a. $2i, -7i$ **b.** $1 + i, i$

    c. $2i - 1, i + 3$ **d.** $\sqrt{2} + i, -\sqrt{2} + 3i$

5. Solve $ix^2 - 6x + 3i = 0$ and verify, by substitution, that your roots satisfy the equation. Compare your answer with Example 5.

6. Solve each equation.

    a. $x^3 - 27 = 0$ **b.** $2x^4 + 7x^2 - 15 = 0$

7. By substitution, show that $-i$, $1 + 3i$, and $1 - 3i$ are roots of the equation

$$x^3 + (-2 + i)x^2 + (10 - 2i)x + 10i = 0$$

8. If m and n are the roots of $x^2 - 5x + 8 = 0$, find equations with the following roots.

    a. $m + 3, n + 3$ **b.** m^2, n^2 **c.** $\dfrac{m}{n}, \dfrac{n}{m}$ **d.** m^3, n^3

Problems 8.3

1. Solve the equation $x^4 - 6x^3 + 15x^2 - 18x + 10 = 0$.

2. If $p + qi$ is a solution to $x^3 + ax^2 + bx + c = 0$, where a, b, and c are real, show that its complex conjugate $p - qi$ is also a solution.

3. Prove that a polynomial equation of degree n can have at most n distinct roots.

4. In the quadratic equation $ax^2 + bx + c = 0$, the coefficients are all odd integers. Show that the roots are never rational.

5. Write a computer program to display the Mandelbrot set in the complex plane. An enlargement of this set near -1.76 is shown in the figure.

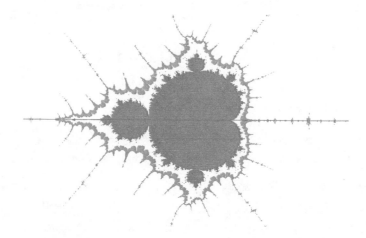

Introduce a scale so that the monitor represents the portion of the complex plane with real parts between -2 and $+1$ and imaginary parts between -1 and $+1$. Each pixel of the monitor corresponds to a complex number c. For each c, compute the sequence of complex numbers $w_0, w_1, \ldots, w_{10}$ defined recursively by $w_0 = 0$, $w_{n+1} = f(w_n) = w_n^2 + c$, but stop if $|w_n| > 2$. If $|w_{10}| \le 2$, colour the pixel, corresponding to c, white; otherwise colour the pixel a second colour if n is even, and a third colour if n is odd. The white region will depict the Mandelbrot set.

The Mandelbrot set consists of all the complex numbers c for which the Julia set of the function $f(z) = z^2 + c$ is connected. See Problem 6 in section 8.8 and also *The Fractal Geometry of Nature* by B.B. Mandelbrot (San Francisco: Freeman, 1982) for further information.

8.4 Further Properties of Complex Numbers (Optional)

Complex numbers satisfy the usual algebraic properties of addition, subtraction, multiplication, and division and can therefore be manipulated like other algebraic quantities.

Properties of Complex Numbers

If z_1, z_2, and z_3 are complex numbers, then:

- $z_1 + (z_2 + z_3) = (z_1 + z_2) + z_3$ (Associative Law of Addition)
- $z_1 + z_2 = z_2 + z_1$ (Commutative Law of Addition)
- There is a complex number 0 such that, for all complex numbers z,

$$z + 0 = z$$

- For each complex number z, there is a negative $-z$ such that

$$z + (-z) = 0$$

- $z_1(z_2 z_3) = (z_1 z_2)z_3$ (Associative Law of Multiplication)
- $z_1 z_2 = z_2 z_1$ (Commutative Law of Multiplication)
- There is a unit 1 such that $z1 = z$ for all complex numbers z.
- Each non-zero complex number z has an inverse z^{-1} such that

$$zz^{-1} = 1$$

- $z_1(z_2 + z_3) = z_1 z_2 + z_1 z_3$ (Distributive Law)

Proof of the Commutative Law of Addition.
Let $z_1 = a_1 + b_1 i$ and $z_2 = a_2 + b_2 i$. Then

$$
\begin{aligned}
z_1 + z_2 &= (a_1 + b_1 i) + (a_2 + b_2 i) \\
&= (a_1 + a_2) + (b_1 + b_2)i \\
&= (a_2 + a_1) + (b_2 + b_1)i \quad \text{(since real addition is commutative)} \\
&= (a_2 + b_2 i) + (a_1 + b_1 i) \\
&= z_2 + z_1
\end{aligned}
$$

The proofs of the remaining properties are left as an exercise.

An algebraic system involving addition and multiplication that satisfies the above properties is called a **field**. Other examples of fields, besides the set of complex numbers, are the set of real numbers, **R**, and the set of rational numbers.

Complex numbers lack one property that real numbers possess. The set of real numbers is "ordered" in the sense that we can determine if one real number is greater than another. The set of complex numbers cannot be ordered. The assumption "$i > 0$" leads to a contradiction, and the assumption "$i < 0$" also leads to a contradiction. For example, if "$i > 0$" then, on multiplying each side by i, we obtain "$i^2 > 0$." This is false since $i^2 = -1$. On the other hand, if we assume that "$i < 0$," then, on multiplying each side by i, we obtain "$i^2 > 0$," which is also false.

Even though we cannot use inequalities of complex numbers directly, we can have inequalities involving the modulus of a complex number, since the modulus is a real number.

The Triangle Inequality

For any complex numbers z_1 and z_2,

$$|z_1 + z_2| \leq |z_1| + |z_2|$$

Proof. Let the vectors $\overrightarrow{OP_1}$ and $\overrightarrow{OP_2}$ represent the complex numbers z_1 and z_2, respectively. Then $z_1 + z_2$ is represented by $\overrightarrow{OR}$, the diagonal from the origin in the parallelogram OP_1RP_2.

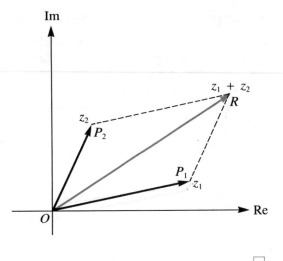

Since the sum of the two sides of the triangle OP_1R is greater than or equal to the third side,

$$|\overrightarrow{OR}| \le |\overrightarrow{OP_1}| + |\overrightarrow{P_1R}|$$

Now $|\overrightarrow{P_1R}| = |\overrightarrow{OP_2}| = |z_2|$, so that

$$|z_1 + z_2| \le |z_1| + |z_2|$$

Equality occurs whenever z_1 and z_2 are represented by vectors in the same direction or if z_1 or z_2 is zero.

□

Many interesting curves and regions can be obtained by looking at the graphs of equations or inequalities involving the modulus.

Example 1. Sketch the graph of $|z - i| = 2$ in the complex plane.

Solution. The expression $|z - i|$ is the distance from z to i in the complex plane. Hence, the graph is a circle of radius 2 centred at i.

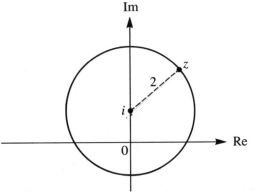

Alternative Solution. Let $z = x + yi$, so that

$$\begin{aligned}
|z - i| &= |x + yi - i| \\
&= |x + (y - 1)i| \\
&= \sqrt{x^2 + (y - 1)^2}
\end{aligned}$$

Hence, the equation is

$$x^2 + (y - 1)^2 = 2^2$$

which represents a circle of radius 2 with centre $(0, 1)$.

□

In general, if z_0 is a complex number and r is a positive real number, then $|z - z_0| = r$ is the circle with centre z_0 and radius r.

Example 2. Sketch the graph of $|z| \leq 3$ in the complex plane.

Solution. The graph of $|z| = 3$ is the circle with centre the origin and radius 3. The graph of $|z| \leq 3$ consists of all the points that are at a distance less than or equal to 3 from the origin, that is, all the points on and inside the circle.

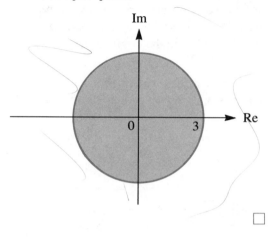

Example 3. Sketch the graph of $|z - 1| + |z + 1| = 4$ in the complex plane.

Solution. Let $z = x + yi$ so that the equation becomes

$$\sqrt{(x - 1)^2 + y^2} + \sqrt{(x + 1)^2 + y^2} = 4$$

$$\sqrt{(x + 1)^2 + y^2} = 4 - \sqrt{(x - 1)^2 + y^2}$$

Squaring both sides of the equation, we obtain

$$(x + 1)^2 + y^2 = 16 - 8\sqrt{(x - 1)^2 + y^2} + (x - 1)^2 + y^2$$

$$8\sqrt{(x - 1)^2 + y^2} = 16 - 4x$$

$$2\sqrt{(x - 1)^2 + y^2} = 4 - x$$

Squaring again, we get

$$4[(x - 1)^2 + y^2] = 16 - 8x + x^2$$

$$3x^2 + 4y^2 = 12$$

$$\frac{x^2}{4} + \frac{y^2}{3} = 1$$

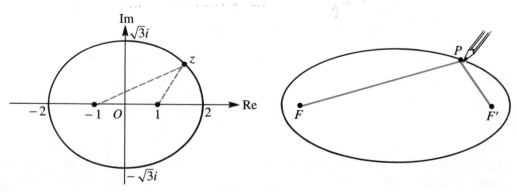

The graph is an ellipse with major axis of length 4 and minor axis of length $2\sqrt{3}$. Since $|z - 1|$ is the distance of the point z from 1 in the complex plane, and $|z + 1|$ is the distance of z from -1, this example shows that the ellipse is the locus of points for which the sum of its distances from 1 and -1 is the constant 4. ☐

More generally, any ellipse can be defined as the locus of points, P, for which the sum of its distances from two points, F and F', is constant; that is,

$$|FP| + |F'P| = 2a$$

The points F and F' are called the foci of the ellipse, and the constant, $2a$, is the length of the major axis. Such an ellipse can be drawn by taking a string of length $2a$, pinning the end points at the foci F and F', placing a pencil point, P, inside the string, and moving the pencil around so that the string is always taut.

Exercises 8.4

1. If z_1, z_2, and z_3 are any complex numbers, prove that

    [handwritten: ✓ easy Sub $z = a + bi$. $z_2 = a - bi$ $z_3 = a \pm 8bi$]

    a. $z_1 z_2 = z_2 z_1$ (Commutative Law of Multiplication)

    b. $z_1 + (z_2 + z_3) = (z_1 + z_2) + z_3$ (Associative Law of Addition)

    c. $z_1(z_2 z_3) = (z_1 z_2)z_3$ (Associative Law of Multiplication)

    d. $z_1(z_2 + z_3) = z_1 z_2 + z_1 z_3$ (Distributive Law)

2. If z_1 and z_2 are complex numbers and $|z_1| > |z_2|$, show geometrically that $|z_1| - |z_2| \le |z_1 - z_2|$.

3. Sketch the graphs in the complex plane.

a. $\quad |z| = 5$	**b.** $|z| < 5$	**c.** $|z| \ge 5$
d. $\quad 2 \le |z| \le 5$	**e.** $z\bar{z} = 3$	**f.** $|z + i| + |z - i| = 6$
g. $\quad \mathrm{Re}(z) \ge 3$	**h.** $\mathrm{Im}(z) < 1$	**i.** $|z| + |z - 1| = 2$
j. $\quad |\mathrm{Im}(z)| \le 2$	**k.** $\mathrm{Re}(\bar{z} - 4) = 1$	**l.** $\mathrm{Im}(z - i) \ge 3$
m. $|z - 2| = 5$	**n.** $|z + i| \le 3$	**o.** $|z - 2| + |z + 2| \le 6$

Problems 8.4

1. Sketch the graphs in the complex plane.

    a. $|z - 1 + i| = 7$ **b.** $|2z - i| = 4$ **c.** $\mathrm{Im}(z^2) = 4$ **d.** $\mathrm{Re}(z^2) = 4$

2. Describe the set of points satisfied by each equation.

    a. $z^2 + \bar{z}^2 = 8$ **b.** $|z + 1| = |z - 1|$ **c.** $|z + 2i| - |z - 2i| = 2$

3. If z_1 and z_2 are complex numbers, prove that

$$|z_1 + z_2|^2 = |z_1|^2 + |z_2|^2 + 2\mathrm{Re}(z_1 \bar{z}_2)$$

4. In 1843, Hamilton generalized the complex numbers to the quaternions, which consists of vectors $q = (a, b, c, d) \in \mathbf{R}^4$, or equivalently, quantities of the form $q = a + bi + cj + dk$, where $1, i, j,$ and k serve as basis vectors. Addition of quaternions is equivalent to vector addition. With two important exceptions, quaternions in the form $a + bi + cj + dk$ can be multiplied as if they were ordinary algebraic expressions. First, note that $i^2 = j^2 = k^2 = -1$, $ij = -ji = k$, $jk = -kj = i$, and $ki = -ik = j$. (See the postage stamps on page 1.) Also note that $i, j,$ and k are **different** square roots of -1 and that this multiplication is **not** commutative, so the order of the multiplication does matter. Multiplication is associative and is distributive over addition.

a. If $q_1 = 3 + 4i + j + k$ and $q_2 = 1 + i - j - 2k$, calculate $q_1 + q_2, q_1 q_2, q_2 q_1,$ and q_1^2.

b. Determine a conjugate, $\bar{q}$, of the quaternion q so that $q\bar{q} = \bar{q}q$ is real and non-negative. Then find the inverse of q.

c. Show that addition and multiplication of quaternions of the form $q = a + bi + cj + dk$ are equivalent to addition and multiplication of complex matrices of the form $\begin{bmatrix} s & t \\ -\bar{t} & \bar{s} \end{bmatrix}$, where $s = a + bi$ and $t = c + di$ are complex numbers.

8.5 Polar Coordinates

A point in the plane can be located by using the familiar rectangular Cartesian coordinate system and specifying its coordinates, x and y. In this section we describe an alternative coordinate system that will be useful in dealing with multiplication and powers of complex numbers. To use the **polar coordinate system** select a fixed point, O, in the plane, called the **pole** or origin, and a fixed horizontal ray Ox, called the **polar axis**. The position of a point P in the plane is given by the ordered pair of real numbers (r, θ), called its **polar coordinates**, where $|r|$ is the distance from O to P and θ is the angle, in radians, that OP makes with the polar axis.

The vector OP is called the **radius vector**, and θ is called the **vectorial angle**. By convention, the polar axis will always be selected in the direction of the positive x-axis, and the angle θ will be positive if measured in a counterclockwise direction from Ox, and negative if measured clockwise. Normally r is taken to be non-negative.

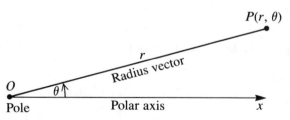

Example 1. Plot the points with these polar coordinates.

$$\left(3, \frac{\pi}{6}\right), \left(2, \frac{2\pi}{3}\right), (5, 0), (4, \pi), \left(3, \frac{-\pi}{4}\right), \left(3, \frac{5\pi}{4}\right)$$

Solution.

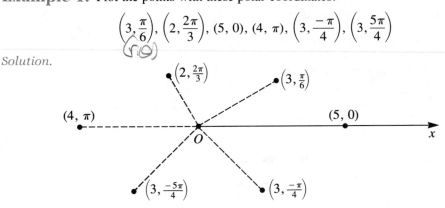

Example 2. Plot, in separate diagrams, the points with the following polar coordinates.

$$\left(3, \frac{\pi}{3}\right), \left(3, \frac{7\pi}{3}\right), \left(3, \frac{-5\pi}{3}\right)$$

Solution.

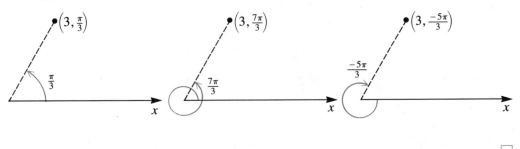

Example 2 illustrates the fact that the polar coordinates of a point are not unique. In general, the pair (r, θ) and the pair $(r, \theta + 2k\pi)$, where k is any integer, give the polar coordinates of the same point. For example, $\left(4, \frac{\pi}{9}\right)$, $\left(4, \frac{\pi}{9} + 2\pi\right)$, $\left(4, \frac{\pi}{9} - 2\pi\right)$, and $\left(4, \frac{\pi}{9} + 14\pi\right)$ all designate the same point. If $r = 0$, the point $(0, \theta)$ is the pole for every real value of θ.

Occasionally it is useful to allow r to be negative. In that case the point (r, θ) lies in the quadrant diagonally opposite to $(-r, \theta)$.

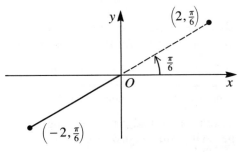

Given polar coordinates of a point, it is easy to calculate its Cartesian coordinates.

Let (r, θ) be polar coordinates of the point P, and let (x, y) be its Cartesian coordinates. Then, in the right-angled triangle,

$\cos \theta = \dfrac{x}{r}$ and $\sin \theta = \dfrac{y}{r}$.

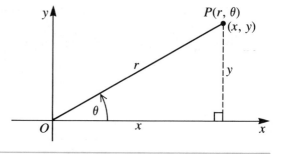

Changing from Polar to Cartesian Coordinates

$$x = r \cos \theta$$
$$y = r \sin \theta$$

Whenever you use a calculator in working with polar coordinates, make sure that all angles are measured in **radians** and not in degrees.

Example 3. Change the following polar coordinates to Cartesian form.

a. $\left(2, \dfrac{\pi}{3}\right)$ **b.** $\left(5, \dfrac{3\pi}{2}\right)$ **c.** $\left(-3, \dfrac{\pi}{6}\right)$

Solution.

a. $x = 2 \cos \dfrac{\pi}{3} = 2\left(\dfrac{1}{2}\right) = 1$, and $y = 2 \sin \dfrac{\pi}{3} = 2\left(\dfrac{\sqrt{3}}{2}\right) = \sqrt{3}$. Hence, the Cartesian

coordinates are $(1, \sqrt{3})$.

b. $x = 5 \cos \dfrac{3\pi}{2} = 5(0) = 0$, and $y = 5 \sin \dfrac{3\pi}{2} = 5(-1) = -5$. Hence, the Cartesian

coordinates are $(0, -5)$.

c. $x = -3 \cos \dfrac{\pi}{6} = -3\left(\dfrac{\sqrt{3}}{2}\right)$, and $y = -3 \sin \dfrac{\pi}{6} = -3\left(\dfrac{1}{2}\right) = -\dfrac{3}{2}$. Hence, the Cartesian

coordinates are $\left(-\dfrac{3\sqrt{3}}{2}, -\dfrac{3}{2}\right)$. $\square$

Given the Cartesian coordinates (x, y) of a point, it is slightly more difficult to find its polar coordinates (r, θ). By Pythagoras' Theorem in the previous diagram, we have $r^2 = x^2 + y^2$.

Using the same right-angled triangle, we have $\tan \theta = \dfrac{y}{x}$. We normally choose the positive

square root for r. There are two angles θ, in different quadrants, whose tangent is $\dfrac{y}{x}$. The

easiest way to find the correct angle is to plot the point first to ensure that the radius vector lies in the correct quadrant.

Changing from Cartesian to Polar Coordinates

$$r = \sqrt{x^2 + y^2}$$

$$\theta = \tan^{-1}\frac{y}{x} \quad \text{or} \quad \pi + \tan^{-1}\frac{y}{x}$$

Example 4. Change the following Cartesian coordinates to polar coordinates.

a. $(2, -2)$ **b.** $(-2, -2\sqrt{3})$

Solution.

a. The modulus is
$r = \sqrt{4 + 4} = \sqrt{8} = 2\sqrt{2}$ and
$\tan^{-1}\left(-\frac{2}{2}\right) = \tan^{-1}(-1) = -\frac{\pi}{4}$, so

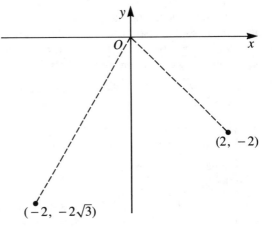

$\theta = -\frac{\pi}{4}$ or $\frac{3\pi}{4}$. We see from the diagram that the point is in the fourth quadrant, so $\theta = -\frac{\pi}{4}$. Hence, the polar coordinates are $\left(2\sqrt{2}, -\frac{\pi}{4}\right)$. Another answer is $\left(2\sqrt{2}, \frac{7\pi}{4}\right)$, since adding a multiple of 2π to the angle will not change the point.

b. The modulus is $r = \sqrt{4 + 12} = 4$, and $\tan^{-1}\left(\frac{-2\sqrt{3}}{-2}\right) = \tan^{-1}(\sqrt{3}) = \frac{\pi}{3}$, so $\theta = \frac{\pi}{3}$ or $\frac{4\pi}{3}$. We see from the diagram that θ must be $\frac{4\pi}{3}$. Hence, the polar coordinates are $\left(4, \frac{4\pi}{3}\right)$.

Equations can be converted between Cartesian and polar form by using the same transformations. Many curves can be described by a polar equation that is much simpler than the corresponding Cartesian equation.

Example 5. Describe the graph of the polar equation $r = 6$ and convert it to Cartesian form.

Solution. The polar equation does not contain θ explicitly, and so the locus consists of all the points that are a distance of 6 from the pole, that is, a circle of radius 6 with centre at the pole. To find the Cartesian form, replace r by $\sqrt{x^2 + y^2}$ to obtain $\sqrt{x^2 + y^2} = 6$. That is, $x^2 + y^2 = 36$ is the Cartesian equation.

Example 6. Convert $r = \dfrac{4}{2\sin\theta - 3\cos\theta}$ to Cartesian form.

Solution. Rewrite the equation as

$$2r\sin\theta - 3r\cos\theta = 4$$

and replace $r\cos\theta$ by x and $r\sin\theta$ by y to obtain

$$2y - 3x = 4$$

which is the Cartesian equation of a straight line. □

We conclude this section with a brief look at graphs of polar equations. The most naive way to graph polar equations, although not always the best way, is to construct a table of values and plot some points on the graph. To minimize the number of entries in the table of values, the student should also make use of the following rules of symmetry whenever possible. Note that these are sufficient conditions for symmetry but are not necessary conditions: that is, symmetry may exist even if these tests fail.

- Symmetry about the polar axis (that is, the x-axis): the equation is unchanged when θ is replaced by $-\theta$.

- Symmetry about the pole (that is, the origin): the equation is unchanged when r is replaced by $-r$ or when θ is replaced by $\pi + \theta$.

- Symmetry about the line $\theta = \dfrac{\pi}{2}$ (that is, the y-axis): the equation is unchanged when θ is replaced by $\pi - \theta$.

For example, the graph of $r = 4\cos\theta$ is symmetrical with respect to the polar axis because, when θ is replaced by $-\theta$, we obtain $r = 4\cos(-\theta) = 4\cos\theta$. The graph of $r^2 = \tan\theta$ is symmetrical with respect to the pole, since $(-r)^2 = r^2 = \tan\theta$. The graph of $r^3\sin\theta = 2$ is symmetrical with respect to the line $\theta = \dfrac{\pi}{2}$ since replacing θ by $\pi - \theta$ gives $r^3\sin(\pi - \theta) = r^3\sin\theta = 1$.

Example 7. Sketch the graph of $r = 3 + 5\cos\theta$.

Solution. First note that, if θ is replaced by $-\theta$, the equation is unchanged, and so there is symmetry about the polar axis. Hence, we only need to construct a table of values for θ between 0 and π.

θ	0	$\dfrac{\pi}{6}$	$\dfrac{\pi}{4}$	$\dfrac{\pi}{3}$	$\dfrac{\pi}{2}$	$\dfrac{2\pi}{3}$	$\dfrac{3\pi}{4}$	$\dfrac{5\pi}{6}$	π
$\cos\theta$	1	0.87	0.71	0.5	0	-0.5	-0.71	-0.87	-1
$r = 3 + 5\cos\theta$	8	7.33	6.54	5.5	3	0.5	-0.54	-1.33	-2

The dotted portion of the curve is obtained from the symmetry about the polar axis. This curve, illustrated in the diagram, is called a limaçon. □

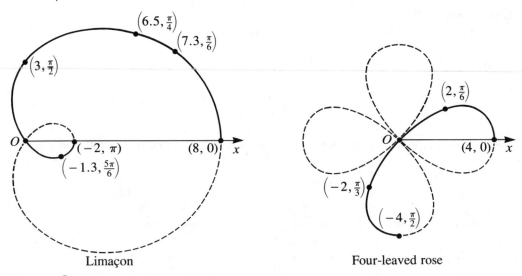

Limaçon   Four-leaved rose

Example 8. Sketch the graph of $r = 4 \cos 2\theta$.

Solution. If θ is replaced by $-\theta$, the equation is unchanged, so there is symmetry about the polar axis. If θ is replaced by $\pi - \theta$, the equation becomes

$$r = 4 \cos 2(\pi - \theta)$$
$$= 4 \cos(2\pi - 2\theta)$$
$$= 4 \cos(-2\theta)$$
$$= 4 \cos 2\theta$$

Hence, the graph is symmetrical about the line $\theta = \dfrac{\pi}{2}$. If θ is replaced by $\pi + \theta$, the equation becomes

$$r = 4 \cos 2(\pi + \theta)$$
$$= 4 \cos(2\pi + 2\theta)$$
$$= 4 \cos 2\theta$$

and so symmetry exists about the pole. Hence, we only need to construct a table of values for θ between 0 and $\dfrac{\pi}{2}$.

θ	0	$\dfrac{\pi}{12}$	$\dfrac{\pi}{6}$	$\dfrac{\pi}{4}$	$\dfrac{\pi}{3}$	$\dfrac{5\pi}{12}$	$\dfrac{\pi}{2}$
$\cos 2\theta$	1	$\dfrac{\sqrt{3}}{2}$	$\dfrac{1}{2}$	0	$-\dfrac{1}{2}$	$-\dfrac{\sqrt{3}}{2}$	-1
$r = 4 \cos 2\theta$	4	$2\sqrt{3}$	2	0	-2	$-2\sqrt{3}$	-4

The table of values is used to plot the solid part of the curve. The rest of the curve is obtained by using symmetry about the polar axis, the pole, and the line $\theta = \dfrac{\pi}{2}$. This curve, illustrated in the diagram, is called a four-leaved rose.   □

Exercises 8.5

1. Plot the points with the given polar coordinates.

    a. $\left(3, \dfrac{5\pi}{6}\right)$ **b.** $\left(4, -\dfrac{\pi}{3}\right)$ **c.** $\left(3, \dfrac{5\pi}{4}\right)$

    d. $\left(1, \dfrac{3\pi}{2}\right)$ **e.** $\left(-4, \dfrac{5\pi}{4}\right)$ **f.** $\left(3, \dfrac{13\pi}{6}\right)$

2. In each case, write two additional sets of polar coordinates that describe the same point.

    a. $(2, \pi)$ **b.** $\left(-3, \dfrac{2\pi}{3}\right)$ **c.** $\left(3, \dfrac{5\pi}{12}\right)$

3. Convert the following polar coordinates to Cartesian coordinates.

    a. $\left(2, \dfrac{\pi}{2}\right)$ **b.** $\left(\sqrt{2}, \dfrac{\pi}{4}\right)$ **c.** $\left(-5, \dfrac{\pi}{3}\right)$

    d. $\left(6, -\dfrac{5\pi}{6}\right)$ **e.** $\left(3, \dfrac{19\pi}{3}\right)$

4. Convert the following Cartesian coordinates to polar coordinates.

    a. $(2, 0)$ **b.** $(0, -5)$ **c.** $(4, -4)$

    d. $(-4, 4\sqrt{3})$ **e.** $(-\sqrt{2}, -\sqrt{2})$ **f.** $(-1, 2)$

5. Write each polar equation in Cartesian form.

    a. $r^2 = 5$ **b.** $r = 3 \cos \theta$ **c.** $\theta = \dfrac{2\pi}{3}$

    d. $r \sin^2 \theta = \cos \theta$ **e.** $r^2 = \dfrac{3}{\tan \theta}$

6. Write each Cartesian equation in polar form.

    a. $x^2 + y^2 = 9$ **b.** $y = 7$ **c.** $2xy = 5$

    d. $x^2 - 4y^2 = 4$ **e.** $x - 5y + 6 = 0$ **f.** $x^2 + y^2 - 2x + 6y = 0$

7. State the symmetry, if any, that exists for the following graphs with respect to the polar axis, the pole, and the line $\theta = \dfrac{\pi}{2}$.

    a. $r^2 = \cos \theta + \sin \theta$ **b.** $r = 8(1 - \cos \theta)$ **c.** $r = 4\theta$

    d. $r = \dfrac{2}{1 + \sin \theta}$ **e.** $r = 2 \cos\left(\theta - \dfrac{\pi}{6}\right)$

Don't have to do this.

8. Sketch the graphs of the polar equations.

a. $r = 5 \sin \theta$

b. $r = 8(1 + \cos \theta)$ *don't need to do this.*

c. $r = \dfrac{2}{1 - \cos \theta}$

d. $r = 2 \sec \theta$

9. Find, in polar form, the equation of the straight line with slope $-\dfrac{1}{\sqrt{3}}$ that passes through the point with Cartesian coordinates $(1, 2)$.

10. Find, in polar form, the equation of the circle whose centre has Cartesian coordinates $(3, -3)$ and that passes through the origin.

Problems 8.5

1. Sketch the graph of $(x^2 + y^2)^{3/2} - 4(x^2 - y^2) = 0$.

2. An equilateral triangle has its centroid at the pole and one vertex at the point with polar coordinates $(6, 0)$. Find the polar coordinates of the other two vertices.

3. Find the polar equation of the ellipse with eccentricity $\dfrac{OP}{QP} = \dfrac{3}{4}$, one focus at the pole, and the corresponding directrix perpendicular to the polar axis, through the point with polar coordinates $(8, \pi)$.

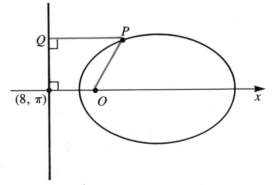

4. Write computer programs that will display the x-axis and y-axis in the plane and will plot the curves given by the following polar equations.

a. The cardioid $r = 1 - \cos \theta$, for $0 \le \theta \le 2\pi$

b. The three-leaved rose $r = \cos 3\theta$, for $0 \le \theta \le 2\pi$

c. The spiral $r = (1.05)^\theta$, for $-6\pi \le \theta \le 4\pi$

5. a. Show that the distance between the points with polar coordinates (r_1, θ_1) and (r_2, θ_2) is

$$\sqrt{r_1^2 + r_2^2 - 2r_1 r_2 \cos(\theta_2 - \theta_1)}$$

when r_1 and r_2 are positive.

b. Show that the polar equation of the circle with centre (r_1, θ_1) and radius a is

$$r^2 - 2rr_1 \cos(\theta - \theta_1) = a^2 - r_1^2$$

8.6 Complex Numbers in Polar Form

The complex number $z = x + yi$, written in standard form, can be represented by the point in the complex plane with Cartesian coordinates (x, y). Many problems in complex numbers, such as finding powers and roots, can be solved more easily by using the polar form of a complex number.

Let $z = x + yi$ be a complex number, and let (r, θ), where $r \geq 0$, be polar coordinates of the point representing z. Then $x = r \cos \theta$ and $y = r \sin \theta$ and

$$z = x + yi$$
$$= r \cos \theta + ri \sin \theta$$
$$= r(\cos \theta + i \sin \theta)$$

We often abbreviate $\cos \theta + i \sin \theta$ by cis θ.

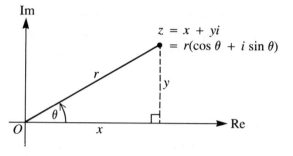

The Polar Form of a Complex Number

$$z = r(\cos \theta + i \sin \theta)$$
$$\text{or} \quad z = r \operatorname{cis} \theta, \quad \text{where } r \geq 0$$

The non-negative number $r = \sqrt{x^2 + y^2}$ is the **modulus** of the complex number z; that is, $r = |z|$. The angle θ, measured in radians, is called the **argument** of z and is often abbreviated as arg z. As we saw in the last section, the angle θ is not determined uniquely, but is defined only up to a multiple of 2π. In general, arg $z = \theta + 2k\pi$ for any integer k. Therefore,

$$z = r(\cos \theta + i \sin \theta) = r[\cos(\theta + 2k\pi) + i \sin(\theta + 2k\pi)]$$

or, equivalently,

$$z = r \operatorname{cis} \theta = r \operatorname{cis}(\theta + 2k\pi)$$

Example 1. Write the complex numbers in polar form.

a. $z_1 = -5 + 5i$ **b.** $z_2 = -3$ **c.** $z_3 = 2 + 5i$

Solution. Plot each of the numbers in the complex plane to help determine the correct arguments.

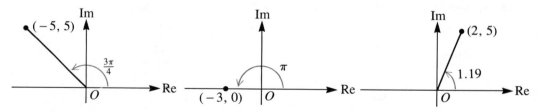

a. For $z_1 = -5 + 5i$, $r = \sqrt{25 + 25} = 5\sqrt{2}$ and $\tan^{-1}\left(\frac{5}{-5}\right) = \tan^{-1}(-1)$. Hence, the argument is either $\theta = -\frac{\pi}{4}$ or $\theta = \frac{3\pi}{4}$. We see from the diagram that the argument must be $\frac{3\pi}{4}$. Thus,

$$z_1 = 5\sqrt{2}\left(\cos\frac{3\pi}{4} + i\sin\frac{3\pi}{4}\right)$$
$$= 5\sqrt{2}\,\text{cis}\,\frac{3\pi}{4}$$

More generally, we could write

$$z_1 = 5\sqrt{2}\,\text{cis}\left(\frac{3\pi}{4} + 2k\pi\right), \quad \text{for any integer } k.$$

b. If $z_2 = -3$, then $r = |z_2| = 3$ and $\theta = \pi$, so

$$z_2 = 3(\cos\pi + i\sin\pi)$$
$$= 3\,\text{cis}\,\pi$$

c. If $z_3 = 2 + 5i$, then $r = |z_3| = \sqrt{4 + 25} = \sqrt{29}$ and $\theta = \tan^{-1}\left(\frac{5}{2}\right)$, which is approximately 1.19 radians. Hence,

$$z_3 \approx \sqrt{29}(\cos 1.19 + i\sin 1.19) = \sqrt{29}\,\text{cis}\,1.19 \qquad \square$$

Example 2. Write the complex numbers in standard form.

a. $z_1 = 8\left(\cos\frac{4\pi}{3} + i\sin\frac{4\pi}{3}\right)$ **b.** $z_2 = 2\,\text{cis}\left(-\frac{\pi}{6}\right)$ **c.** $z_3 = 5\,\text{cis}\,1$

Solution.

a. The real part of z_1 is $8\cos\frac{4\pi}{3} = 8\left(-\frac{1}{2}\right) = -4$, and the imaginary part is

$8\sin\frac{4\pi}{3} = 8\left(-\frac{\sqrt{3}}{2}\right) = -4\sqrt{3}$; therefore, the standard form is $z_1 = -4 - 4\sqrt{3}i$.

b. The real part of z_2 is $2\cos\left(-\frac{\pi}{6}\right) = 2\cos\frac{\pi}{6} = 2\left(\frac{\sqrt{3}}{2}\right) = \sqrt{3}$, and the imaginary part is

$2\sin\left(-\frac{\pi}{6}\right) = -2\sin\frac{\pi}{6} = -2\left(\frac{1}{2}\right) = -1$; therefore, the standard form is $z_2 = \sqrt{3} - i$.

c. The real part of z_3 is $5\cos 1 \approx 2.70$, and the imaginary part is $5\sin 1 \approx 4.21$; therefore, the standard form is $z_3 \approx 2.70 + 4.21i$. $\qquad \square$

Equality of Complex Numbers in Polar Form

Two complex numbers, $z_1 = r_1 \operatorname{cis} \theta_1$ and $z_2 = r_2 \operatorname{cis} \theta_2$, given in polar form with $r_1 \geq 0$ and $r_2 \geq 0$, are equal if and only if

$$r_1 = r_2 \text{ and } \theta_1 = \theta_2 + 2k\pi \quad \text{for some integer } k$$

For example, $3 \operatorname{cis} \dfrac{\pi}{12}$ and $3 \operatorname{cis} \dfrac{49\pi}{12}$ represent the same complex numbers and, for any integer k, $\operatorname{cis} 2k\pi = \operatorname{cis} 0 = 1$.

Complex Conjugate in Polar Form

If $z = r \operatorname{cis} \theta$, then $\bar{z} = r \operatorname{cis}(-\theta)$.

Proof. If $z = r \operatorname{cis} \theta = x + yi$, its complex conjugate is $\bar{z} = x - yi$. Geometrically, $\bar{z}$ is the reflection of z in the real axis. Hence, $\arg \bar{z} = -\arg z = -\theta$ and

$$\bar{z} = r \operatorname{cis}(-\theta)$$

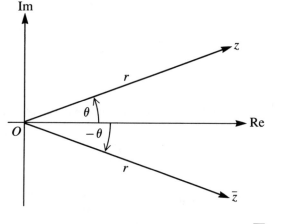

Complex Multiplication in Polar Form

If $z_1 = r_1 \operatorname{cis} \theta_1$ and $z_2 = r_2 \operatorname{cis} \theta_2$, then

$$z_1 z_2 = r_1 r_2 \operatorname{cis}(\theta_1 + \theta_2)$$

That is, to multiply complex numbers in polar form, we multiply their moduli and add their arguments.

Proof. Expanding and using the formulas for the sine and cosine of a sum of angles, we have

$$
\begin{aligned}
z_1 z_2 &= (r_1 \operatorname{cis} \theta_1)(r_2 \operatorname{cis} \theta_2) \\
&= [r_1(\cos \theta_1 + i \sin \theta_1)][r_2(\cos \theta_2 + i \sin \theta_2)] \\
&= r_1 r_2(\cos \theta_1 + i \sin \theta_1)(\cos \theta_2 + i \sin \theta_2) \\
&= r_1 r_2[(\cos \theta_1 \cos \theta_2 - \sin \theta_1 \sin \theta_2) + i(\sin \theta_1 \cos \theta_2 + \cos \theta_1 \sin \theta_2)] \\
&= r_1 r_2[\cos(\theta_1 + \theta_2) + i \sin(\theta_1 + \theta_2)] \\
&= r_1 r_2 \operatorname{cis}(\theta_1 + \theta_2) \qquad \square
\end{aligned}
$$

Complex Division in Polar Form

If $z_1 = r_1 \operatorname{cis} \theta_1$ and $z_2 = r_2 \operatorname{cis} \theta_2$, and $r_2 \neq 0$, then

$$
\frac{z_1}{z_2} = \frac{r_1}{r_2} \operatorname{cis}(\theta_1 - \theta_2)
$$

That is, to divide complex numbers in polar form, we divide their moduli and subtract their arguments.

Proof. Multiply numerator and denominator by $\overline{\operatorname{cis} \theta_2} = \operatorname{cis}(-\theta_2)$ to obtain

$$
\begin{aligned}
\frac{z_1}{z_2} &= \frac{r_1 \operatorname{cis} \theta_1}{r_2 \operatorname{cis} \theta_2} \\
&= \frac{r_1 \operatorname{cis} \theta_1 \operatorname{cis}(-\theta_2)}{r_2 \operatorname{cis} \theta_2 \operatorname{cis}(-\theta_2)} \\
&= \frac{r_1 \operatorname{cis}(\theta_1 - \theta_2)}{r_2 \operatorname{cis}(\theta_2 - \theta_2)} \\
&= \frac{r_1}{r_2} \frac{\operatorname{cis}(\theta_1 - \theta_2)}{\operatorname{cis} 0} \\
&= \frac{r_1}{r_2} \operatorname{cis}(\theta_1 - \theta_2) \quad \text{(since cis } 0 = 1) \qquad \square
\end{aligned}
$$

Example 3. If $z_1 = 2 \operatorname{cis} \dfrac{3\pi}{8}$ and $z_2 = 5 \operatorname{cis} \dfrac{2\pi}{3}$, calculate $z_1 z_2$ and $\dfrac{z_1}{z_2}$.

Solution.

$$
\begin{aligned}
z_1 z_2 &= (2)(5) \operatorname{cis}\left(\frac{3\pi}{8} + \frac{2\pi}{3}\right) \\
&= 10 \operatorname{cis} \frac{25\pi}{24} \\
\frac{z_1}{z_2} &= \frac{2}{5} \operatorname{cis}\left(\frac{3\pi}{8} - \frac{2\pi}{3}\right) \\
&= \frac{2}{5} \operatorname{cis}\left(-\frac{7\pi}{24}\right) \qquad \square
\end{aligned}
$$

If complex numbers are written in polar form, it is easy to illustrate their product geometrically. The magnitude of $z_1 z_2$ is the product of the magnitudes of z_1 and z_2, and the argument of $z_1 z_2$ is the sum of the arguments of z_1 and z_2. For example, multiplying a complex number by $i = 1 \text{ cis } \dfrac{\pi}{2}$ rotates the corresponding vector through a right angle in a counterclockwise direction, leaving its magnitude unchanged.

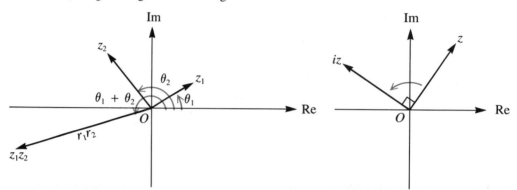

There is another convenient notation for $\cos \theta + i \sin \theta$ that is frequently used by mathematicians. This was introduced in the middle of the eighteenth century by Leonhard Euler when he was working with series of complex numbers. He denoted $\cos \theta + i \sin \theta$ by $e^{i\theta}$. His reason for doing so was that the argument of a product of complex numbers is the sum of the arguments, so that the argument acts like an exponent. The irrational number e is the base for natural logarithms and is approximately 2.718 28. The use of the number e can be justified by considering the infinite series expansions for e^z, $\cos \theta$, and $\sin \theta$, but they are beyond the scope of this book.

Euler's Formula

$$e^{i\theta} = \cos \theta + i \sin \theta$$

Any complex number can be written as

$$z = r(\cos \theta + i \sin \theta) = r \text{ cis } \theta = re^{i\theta}$$

The expression $re^{i\theta}$ is called the **exponential form** of the complex number z. As in the polar form, the value of θ is not unique. We have

$$z = re^{i\theta} = re^{i(\theta + 2k\pi)}, \quad \text{for any integer } k$$

Hence, $e^{2i\pi} = e^0 = 1$. Euler observed that $e^{i\pi} = \cos \pi + i \sin \pi = -1$, and obtained the famous formula

$$e^{i\pi} = -1$$

which connects the three mathematical quantities e, π and i, whose notations he established.

Example 4. Express $z = -2 - 2i$ in exponential form.

Solution.
The modulus is $r = \sqrt{4 + 4} = 2\sqrt{2}$, and
$\tan^{-1}\left(\dfrac{-2}{-2}\right) = \tan^{-1} 1 = \dfrac{\pi}{4}$. From the dia-

gram we see that $\theta = \pi + \dfrac{\pi}{4} = \dfrac{5\pi}{4}$ so that

$$z = 2\sqrt{2}e^{\frac{5i\pi}{4}}$$

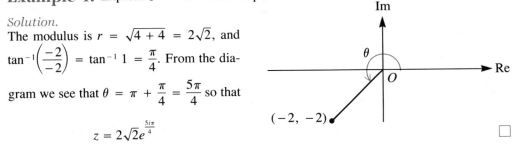

Example 5. Express $3e^{-\frac{i\pi}{3}}$ and e^{2i} in standard form.

Solution.

$$3e^{-\frac{i\pi}{3}} = 3\left[\cos\left(-\frac{\pi}{3}\right) + i \sin\left(-\frac{\pi}{3}\right)\right]$$

$$= 3 \cos \frac{\pi}{3} - 3i \sin \frac{\pi}{3}$$

$$= \frac{3}{2} - \frac{3\sqrt{3}}{2}i$$

$$e^{2i} = \cos 2 + i \sin 2$$

$$\approx -0.42 + 0.91i$$

The formulas for multiplication and division of complex numbers in exponential form are analogous to the standard formulas for multiplying and dividing exponentials. If $z_1 = re^{i\theta_1}$ and $z_2 = re^{i\theta_2}$, then

$$z_1 z_2 = (r_1 e^{i\theta_1})(r_2 e^{i\theta_2})$$

$$= r_1 r_2 e^{i\theta_1 + i\theta_2}$$

$$= r_1 r_2 e^{i(\theta_1 + \theta_2)}$$

$$\frac{z_1}{z_2} = \frac{r_1 e^{i\theta_1}}{r_2 e^{i\theta_2}}$$

$$= \frac{r_1}{r_2} e^{i(\theta_1 - \theta_2)}$$

Furthermore, the inverse of $z = re^{i\theta}$ is $z^{-1} = \dfrac{1}{r}e^{-i\theta}$.

Example 6. If $z_1 = 2e^{\frac{2i\pi}{3}}$ and $z_2 = 5e^{\frac{i\pi}{4}}$, find $z_1 z_2$, $\dfrac{z_1}{z_2}$ and z_2^{-1}.

Solution.

$$z_1 z_2 = (2)(5)e^{\frac{2i\pi}{3} + \frac{i\pi}{4}}$$

$$= 10e^{\frac{11i\pi}{12}}$$

$$\frac{z_1}{z_2} = \frac{2}{5}e^{\frac{2i\pi}{3} - \frac{i\pi}{4}}$$

$$= \frac{2}{5}e^{\frac{5i\pi}{12}}$$

$$z_2^{-1} = \frac{1}{5}e^{-\frac{i\pi}{4}}$$

Exercises 8.6

1. Convert the complex numbers to polar form.

   a. $1 + \sqrt{3}i$ **b.** $2i$ **c.** $-2\sqrt{2} - 2\sqrt{2}i$

   d. 4 **e.** $\dfrac{2}{1 + \sqrt{3}i}$ **f.** $3 - i$

   g. i^{15} **h.** $-\frac{1}{2} + \frac{\sqrt{3}}{2}i$ **i.** $\overline{(-\sqrt{3} - i)}$

2. Convert the complex numbers to standard form.

   a. $\cos\dfrac{3\pi}{2} + i\sin\dfrac{3\pi}{2}$ **b.** $4\operatorname{cis}\dfrac{7\pi}{4}$ **c.** $3\operatorname{cis}\dfrac{5\pi}{6}$

   d. $10(\cos 7\pi + i\sin 7\pi)$ **e.** $\frac{1}{2}\operatorname{cis}\left(-\dfrac{\pi}{3}\right)$ **f.** $2\operatorname{cis} 3.3$

3. Write each of the complex numbers in Exercise 1 in exponential form.

4. Write the complex numbers in standard form. ✓ $z = re^{i\theta}$

   a. $e^{\frac{i\pi}{2}}$ **b.** $4e^{\frac{-i\pi}{3}}$ **c.** $3e^{i}$ **d.** $-e^{-i\pi}$

5. If $z = \sqrt{2}\operatorname{cis}\dfrac{\pi}{12}$, find

   a. z^2.   **b.** $\bar{z}$.   **c.** z^{-1}.

6. Express each quantity as a complex number in polar form.

   a. $(1 - i)(1 + \sqrt{3}i)$ **b.** $\left(2e^{\frac{i\pi}{3}}\right)\left(5e^{\frac{2i\pi}{3}}\right)$ **c.** $\dfrac{-\sqrt{2} - \sqrt{2}i}{\sqrt{3} - i}$

   d. $(-6 + 6\sqrt{3}i)^2$ **e.** $\left[4\operatorname{cis}\left(-\dfrac{\pi}{6}\right)\right] \div \left(\dfrac{1}{2}\operatorname{cis}\dfrac{\pi}{2}\right)$

7. Illustrate the quotient $\dfrac{z_1}{z_2}$ geometrically.

8. If $z = r \operatorname{cis} \theta \neq 0$, prove that

$$\frac{\bar{z}}{z} = \cos^2 \theta - \sin^2 \theta - 2i \sin \theta \cos \theta$$

9. What is the locus of $z = e^{i\theta}$ for $\theta \in \mathbf{R}$?

Problems 8.6

1. If $z_1 = r_1 \operatorname{cis} \theta_1$, $z_2 = r_2 \operatorname{cis} \theta_2$, $\ldots$, $z_n = r_n \operatorname{cis} \theta_n$, prove by induction that

$$z_1 z_2 \ldots z_n = r_1 r_2 \ldots r_n \operatorname{cis}(\theta_1 + \theta_2 + \ldots + \theta_n)$$

2. If θ is not an odd multiple of π, prove that

$$\frac{1 + \cos \theta + i \sin \theta}{1 + \cos \theta - i \sin \theta} = \cos \theta + i \sin \theta$$

3. Use Euler's formula to prove that

a. $\cos \theta = \dfrac{e^{i\theta} + e^{-i\theta}}{2}$
　　　　　　　　　　　　　b. $\sin \theta \doteq \dfrac{e^{i\theta} - e^{-i\theta}}{2i}$

8.7 De Moivre's Theorem

The complex number $z = (1 + i)^{20}$ could be evaluated by using the Binomial Theorem, but it would be a laborious process. By changing $1 + i$ to its polar form and using the following theorem, it is easy to calculate $z = \left(\sqrt{2} \operatorname{cis} \dfrac{\pi}{2} \right)^{20}$.

De Moivre's Theorem

For any positive integer n,

$$(r \operatorname{cis} \theta)^n = r^n \operatorname{cis} n\theta$$

Proof. We shall prove the result by induction on n.

Step 1: When $n = 1$, the left side is $(r \operatorname{cis} \theta)^1$ and the right side is $r^1 \operatorname{cis} 1\theta$, and these quantities are clearly equal.

Step 2: As the induction hypothesis, assume that $z^k = r^k \operatorname{cis} k\theta$, for some positive integer k. Then

$$
\begin{aligned}
z^{k+1} &= z^k z \\
&= (r^k \operatorname{cis} k\theta)(r \operatorname{cis} \theta) \quad \text{(by the induction hypothesis)} \\
&= r^{k+1} \operatorname{cis}(k\theta + \theta) \\
&= r^{k+1} \operatorname{cis}(k + 1)\theta
\end{aligned}
$$

Hence, the result is valid for $n = k + 1$ whenever it is valid for $n = k$. Since it is valid for $n = 1$, it follows from the Principle of Mathematical Induction that it is valid for all positive integers n. □

The theorem is named after Abraham de Moivre (1667–1754), a French mathematician who did most of his work in England.

Example 1. Write $z = (1 + i)^{20}$ in standard form.

Solution. In polar form, $1 + i = \sqrt{2} \operatorname{cis} \dfrac{\pi}{4}$; therefore,

$$
\begin{aligned}
z &= \left(\sqrt{2} \operatorname{cis} \frac{\pi}{4} \right)^{20} \\
&= (\sqrt{2})^{20} \operatorname{cis}\left[20\left(\frac{\pi}{4}\right) \right] \\
&= 2^{10} \operatorname{cis} 5\pi \\
&= 2^{10} \operatorname{cis} \pi \\
&= -2^{10} \\
&= -1024
\end{aligned}
$$

□

When de Moivre's Theorem is rewritten in exponential form, it becomes a law of exponents.

De Moivre's Theorem

$$(re^{i\theta})^n = r^n e^{in\theta}$$

Example 2. If $z = 2e^{\frac{i\pi}{3}}$, find z^6 in standard form.

Solution.

$$
\begin{aligned}
z^6 &= 2^6 e^{\frac{6i\pi}{3}} \\
&= 64 e^{2i\pi} \\
&= 64 e^0 \\
&= 64
\end{aligned}
$$

□

De Moivre's Theorem for Negative Integers

$$(r \operatorname{cis} \theta)^{-n} = r^{-n} \operatorname{cis}(-n\theta)$$

Proof. If n is a positive integer, then

$$(r \operatorname{cis} \theta)^{-n} = \frac{1}{(r \operatorname{cis} \theta)^n}$$

$$= \frac{1}{r^n \operatorname{cis} n\theta} \quad \text{(by de Moivre's Theorem)}$$

$$= r^{-n} \operatorname{cis}(-n\theta) \quad \text{(by complex division in polar form)} \qquad \square$$

Example 3. Express $\left(-\dfrac{1}{2} - \dfrac{\sqrt{3}}{2}i\right)^{-13}$ in standard form.

Solution.

$$\left(-\frac{1}{2} - \frac{\sqrt{3}}{2}i\right)^{-13} = \left(1 \operatorname{cis} \frac{4\pi}{3}\right)^{-13}$$

$$= 1^{-13} \operatorname{cis}\left(-\frac{52\pi}{3}\right)$$

$$= \operatorname{cis} \frac{2\pi}{3}$$

$$= -\frac{1}{2} + \frac{\sqrt{3}}{2}i \qquad \square$$

De Moivre's Theorem can be used to find formulas for some trigonometric expressions of the form $\cos n\theta$ and $\sin n\theta$.

Example 4. Express $\cos 3\theta$ and $\sin 3\theta$ in terms of $\cos \theta$ and $\sin \theta$.

Solution. Use de Moivre's Theorem and then the Binomial Theorem to obtain

$$\cos 3\theta + i \sin 3\theta = (\cos \theta + i \sin \theta)^3$$
$$= \cos^3 \theta + 3i \cos^2 \theta \sin \theta + 3i^2 \sin^2 \theta \cos \theta + i^3 \sin^3 \theta$$
$$= (\cos^3 \theta - 3 \sin^2 \theta \cos \theta) + i(3 \cos^2 \theta \sin \theta - \sin^3 \theta)$$

Equate the real and imaginary parts of each side.

$$\cos 3\theta = \cos^3 \theta - 3 \sin^2 \theta \cos \theta$$
$$= \cos^3 \theta - 3(1 - \cos^2 \theta) \cos \theta$$
$$= 4 \cos^3 \theta - 3 \cos \theta$$
$$\sin 3\theta = 3 \cos^2 \theta \sin \theta - \sin^3 \theta$$
$$= 3(1 - \sin^2 \theta) \sin \theta - \sin^3 \theta$$
$$= 3 \sin \theta - 4 \sin^3 \theta \qquad \square$$

Exercises 8.7

1. Use de Moivre's Theorem to express each complex number in standard form.

a. $\left(2\operatorname{cis}\dfrac{\pi}{4}\right)^3$

b. $\left(\cos\dfrac{\pi}{12} + i\sin\dfrac{\pi}{12}\right)^8$

c. $(1 - i)^{16}$

d. $\left(e^{-\frac{2i\pi}{3}}\right)^7$

e. $\left(\dfrac{3\sqrt{3}}{2} + \dfrac{3i}{2}\right)^3$

f. $\left(\dfrac{1}{\sqrt{2}} + \dfrac{1}{\sqrt{2}}i\right)^9$

g. $\dfrac{1}{(\sqrt{3} - i)^{10}}$

h. $\dfrac{(-1 + i)^6(-1 - i)^4}{(\sqrt{2} + \sqrt{2}i)^3}$

i. $(-1 + i)^{-4}$

j. $(2 + 5i)^{-2}$

2. If $z = \operatorname{cis}\dfrac{2\pi}{9}$, plot z, z^2, z^3, . . . , z^9 in the complex plane.

3. If $z = 2\operatorname{cis}\dfrac{\pi}{3}$, plot z^{-1}, z^0, z, z^2, and z^3 in the complex plane.

4. Using de Moivre's Theorem, prove each statement.

a. $\cos 2\theta = 2\cos^2\theta - 1$
  $\sin 2\theta = 2\sin\theta\cos\theta$

b. $\cos 4\theta = 8\cos^4\theta - 8\cos^2\theta + 1$
  $\sin 4\theta = 4\sin\theta\cos\theta(1 - 2\sin^2\theta)$

5. Find the value in standard form.

a. $(1 + i)(-1 + i)^2(-1 - i)^3(1 - i)^4$

b. $(1 + i) + (-1 + i)^2 + (-1 - i)^3 + (1 - i)^4$

Problems 8.7

1. If n is a multiple of 4, prove that $(1 + i)^n = (-4)^k$, for some integer k.

2. If $z = \cos\theta + i\sin\theta$ and n is a positive integer, prove that

$$\left(z^n + \dfrac{1}{z^{2n}}\right)\left(z^{2n} - \dfrac{1}{z^n}\right) = 2i\sin 3n\theta$$

3. If n is an integer, find all possible values of $(1 + i^n)(1 + i^{2n})$.

4. Find all complex numbers z such that $\bar{z}z^{n-1} = 1$.

5. Use a computer to plot $(1 + 0.1i)^n$ in the complex plane, for $n = -100$ to 100.

8.8 Roots of Complex Numbers

One of the main reasons for studying complex numbers is to be able to find the roots of polynomial equations. In this section we will use de Moivre's Theorem to find all the square roots, cube roots, fourth roots, . . . of any real or complex number. That is, we will solve equations of the form $z^n = c$, where z and c are complex numbers and n is an integer.

Example 1. Find the cube roots of $125i$.

Solution. We have to solve the equation $z^3 = 125i$. Let $z = r \operatorname{cis} \theta$, and write $125i$ in its polar form so that the equation becomes $(r \operatorname{cis} \theta)^3 = 125 \operatorname{cis} \dfrac{\pi}{2}$. By de Moivre's Theorem the equation is $r^3 \operatorname{cis} 3\theta = 125 \operatorname{cis} \dfrac{\pi}{2}$. Two complex numbers are equal if and only if their moduli are equal and their arguments differ by a multiple of 2π. Hence, $r^3 = 125$ and $3\theta - \dfrac{\pi}{2} = 2k\pi$ for any integer k. Since r is real and non-negative, $r = 5$. Now $\theta = \dfrac{\pi}{6} + \dfrac{2k\pi}{3}$ and the cube roots are

$$z = 5 \operatorname{cis}\left(\frac{\pi}{6} + \frac{2k\pi}{3}\right), \quad \text{for any integer } k.$$

If $k = 0$, the root is $z_0 = 5 \operatorname{cis} \dfrac{\pi}{6}$.

If $k = 1$, the root is $z_1 = 5 \operatorname{cis}\left(\dfrac{\pi}{6} + \dfrac{2\pi}{3}\right) = 5 \operatorname{cis} \dfrac{5\pi}{6}$.

If $k = 2$, the root is $z_2 = 5 \operatorname{cis}\left(\dfrac{\pi}{6} + \dfrac{4\pi}{3}\right) = 5 \operatorname{cis} \dfrac{3\pi}{2}$.

If $k = 3$, $z_3 = 5 \operatorname{cis}\left(\dfrac{\pi}{6} + \dfrac{6\pi}{3}\right) = 5 \operatorname{cis}\left(\dfrac{\pi}{6} + 2\pi\right) = 5 \operatorname{cis} \dfrac{\pi}{6} = z_0$.

Similarly, $z_4 = z_1$, $z_5 = z_2$, and so on. Thus, there are only three distinct cube roots, namely, $z_0 = 5 \operatorname{cis} \dfrac{\pi}{6} = \dfrac{5\sqrt{3}}{2} + \dfrac{5i}{2}$, $z_1 = 5 \operatorname{cis} \dfrac{5\pi}{6} = -\dfrac{5\sqrt{3}}{2} + \dfrac{5i}{2}$, and $z_3 = 5 \operatorname{cis} \dfrac{3\pi}{2} = -5i$. $\square$

In Example 1, we used $k = 0, 1, 2$ to obtain the roots. Any three successive integral values of k would give the same three roots. Geometrically, z_0, z_1, and z_2 are three points on a circle, with centre at the origin and radius 5. The angles between the successive radius vector to these points are all $\dfrac{2\pi}{3}$.

Hence, z_0, z_1, and z_2 are the vertices of an equilateral triangle.

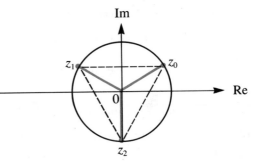

Complex Roots

All the complex nth roots of r cis θ are given by

$$\sqrt[n]{r}\,\text{cis}\left(\frac{\theta + 2k\pi}{n}\right), \quad \text{for } k = 0, 1, 2, \ldots, n - 1$$

Proof. We have to solve $z^n = r$ cis θ. Put $z = s$ cis ϕ so that $(s\,\text{cis}\,\phi)^n = r$ cis θ. By de Moivre's Theorem, s^n cis $n\phi = r$ cis θ. The moduli of these two complex numbers must be equal; therefore, $s^n = r$ and $s = r^{\frac{1}{n}} = \sqrt[n]{r}$, the positive real nth root of r. The arguments of the two complex numbers may differ by a multiple of 2π so $n\phi - \theta = 2k\pi$, for any integer k. Hence, $\phi = \left(\frac{\theta + 2k\pi}{n}\right)$ and the nth roots are

$$z = \sqrt[n]{r}\,\text{cis}\left(\frac{\theta + 2k\pi}{n}\right), \quad \text{for any integer } k.$$

Two of these arguments, $\left(\frac{\theta + 2k_1\pi}{n}\right)$ and $\left(\frac{\theta + 2k_2\pi}{n}\right)$, represent the same complex number if and only if they differ by a multiple of 2π, that is, if and only if

$$\left(\frac{\theta + 2k_1\pi}{n}\right) - \left(\frac{\theta + 2k_2\pi}{n}\right) = 2q\pi, \quad \text{for some integer } q.$$

This is equivalent to $k_1 - k_2 = qn$; that is, k_1 and k_2 differ by a multiple of n. Hence, all the different roots can be obtained by letting $k = 0, 1, 2, 3, \ldots, n - 1$; the roots obtained by letting $k = n, n + 1, \ldots$, etc. would be the same as those obtained by letting $k = 0, 1, \ldots$, etc. Therefore, there are precisely n distinct nth roots of z. $\qquad\square$

These n distinct nth roots are evenly spaced on a circle with centre at the origin and radius $\sqrt[n]{r}$. Hence, they form the vertices of a regular n-sided polygon.

In the particular case $n = 2$, each non-zero complex number has precisely two square roots whose arguments differ by π. That is, one square root is the negative of the other. Hence, the quadratic equation, $ax^2 + bx + c = 0$, with complex coefficients, will have the two roots $x = \dfrac{-b \pm \sqrt{b^2 - 4ac}}{2a}$, where $\pm\sqrt{b^2 - 4ac}$ denotes the two square roots of the complex number $b^2 - 4ac$, found using the above result.

Example 2. Solve the equation

$$z^4 + 2\sqrt{2} - 2\sqrt{2}i = 0$$

Solution. Write the equation as $z^4 = -2\sqrt{2} + 2\sqrt{2}i$. The polar coordinates of the point on the right side are given by $r = \sqrt{8 + 8} = 4$ and $\theta = \pi + \tan^{-1}(-1) = \dfrac{3\pi}{4}$. Hence, $z^4 = 4$ cis $\dfrac{3\pi}{4}$ and, by the above result, the fourth roots are

$$z = 4^{\frac{1}{4}} \operatorname{cis} \frac{1}{4}\left(\frac{3\pi}{4} + 2k\pi\right) = \sqrt{2}\operatorname{cis}\left(\frac{3\pi}{16} + \frac{k\pi}{2}\right), \quad \text{where } k = 0, 1, 2, 3$$

If $k = 0$, then $z_0 = \sqrt{2}\operatorname{cis}\dfrac{3\pi}{16}$.

If $k = 1$, then $z_1 = \sqrt{2}\operatorname{cis}\dfrac{11\pi}{16}$.

If $k = 2$, then $z_2 = \sqrt{2}\operatorname{cis}\dfrac{19\pi}{16}$.

If $k = 3$, then $z_3 = \sqrt{2}\operatorname{cis}\dfrac{27\pi}{16}$.

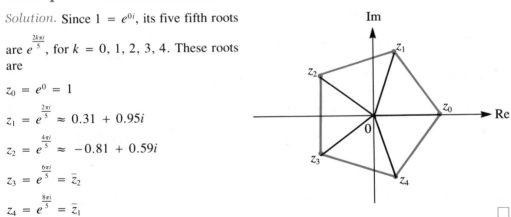

The roots lie at the vertices of a square.

Instead of using the polar form of the roots, we could just as easily have used the exponential form. The n distinct nth roots of $re^{i\theta}$ are

$$r^{\frac{1}{n}}e^{\frac{\theta i + 2ki\pi}{n}}, \text{ where } k = 0, 1, 2, \ldots, n - 1$$

Example 3. Find all the fifth roots of the number 1.

Solution. Since $1 = e^{0i}$, its five fifth roots are $e^{\frac{2k\pi i}{5}}$, for $k = 0, 1, 2, 3, 4$. These roots are

$z_0 = e^0 = 1$

$z_1 = e^{\frac{2\pi i}{5}} \approx 0.31 + 0.95i$

$z_2 = e^{\frac{4\pi i}{5}} \approx -0.81 + 0.59i$

$z_3 = e^{\frac{6\pi i}{5}} = \bar{z}_2$

$z_4 = e^{\frac{8\pi i}{5}} = \bar{z}_1$

Exercises 8.8

1. Find all the roots in polar form and illustrate each geometrically.

    a. the cube roots of 8

    b. the fourth roots of i

    c. the square roots of $-i$

    d. the fifth roots of $32\operatorname{cis}\dfrac{5\pi}{6}$

    e. the sixth roots of 1

    f. the fifth roots of -32

2. Solve the equations and express your answers in standard form.

    a. $z^4 - 16 = 0$ **b.** $z^3 = 64i$

    c. $z^4 + 1 = 0$ **d.** $z^4 + 8 - 8\sqrt{3}i = 0$

    e. $z^2 - (2 + 2i)z + i = 0$ **f.** $z^2 + 2z - \sqrt{3}i = 0$

3. Use the complex exponential to solve the equations; leave your answers in exponential form.

    a. $z^4 + \dfrac{1}{\sqrt{2}} + \dfrac{i}{\sqrt{2}} = 0$ **b.** $z^5 - 243 = 0$

4. Solve $z^2 = -5 + 12i$, giving answers in both standard and polar form.

5. If $3e^{\frac{2i\pi}{15}}$ represents one vertex of a regular hexagon with centre at the origin, state the other five vertices.

6. Solve the equation $(1 + z)^3 = (1 - z)^3$.

Problems 8.8

1. Show that the inverse of an nth root of 1 is also an nth root of 1.

2. If n is a positive integer, prove that the product of the roots of $z^n = r \operatorname{cis} \theta$ is $r \operatorname{cis}(\theta + n\pi - \pi)$.

3. a. If $z_0, z_1, z_2, \ldots, z_{n-1}$ are the nth roots of 1, prove that

$$z_0 + z_1 + z_2 + \ldots + z_{n-1} = 0$$

    b. Prove that $1 + \cos\dfrac{2\pi}{n} + \cos\dfrac{4\pi}{n} + \ldots + \cos\dfrac{(n-1)2\pi}{n} = 0$ and that

$$\sin\dfrac{2\pi}{n} + \sin\dfrac{4\pi}{n} + \ldots + \sin\dfrac{(n-1)2\pi}{n} = 0.$$

4. Find the solution to $z^2 - 4z + 6i = 0$ in standard form to two decimal places.

5. Solve $z^4 + z^2 + 1 + i = 0$.

6. The Julia set of a complex quadratic function $f(z) = z^2 + c$ describes an intriguing region of the complex plane. The Julia set is the set of points z in the complex plane for which the values of $f(z)$ do not converge to any point or diverge to infinity under repeated iterations of the function $f(z) = z^2 + c$. For example, the Julia set of $f(z) = z^2$ is the unit circle $|z| = 1$. The Julia set is much more complicated for all other fixed values of the complex number c, especially those values of c near the boundary of the Mandelbrot set (see Problem 5 of section 8.3). The figure that follows the Julia set for $f(z) = z^2 + 0.378 - 0.307i$, but it was computed using a much more time-consuming program than the one described below.

Write a computer program to display the Julia set for a fixed complex number c. The function $f(z) = z^2 + c$ has an inverse $g(z) = \pm\sqrt{z - c}$. Pick any complex number z_0 as a starting value and compute the sequence of complex numbers, $z_0, z_1, z_2, \ldots, z_n, \ldots$ defined recursively by

$$z_{n+1} = \pm\sqrt{z_n - c}$$

(Choose either root randomly.) Plot the values of z_n in the complex plane for $n > 50$; these points will approach the Julia set. Try $c = 0, i,$ or -1.

Review Exercises

1. If $z_1 = 3 + 5i$ and $z_2 = 2 - 3i$, compute each quantity.

   a. $z_1 + 2z_2$ **b.** $z_1 - 4\bar{z}_2$ **c.** $|z_1|$ **d.** $z_1 z_2$

   e. $z_1 \div z_2$ **f.** $[\text{Re}(z_1)][\text{Im}(z_2)]$ **g.** z_2^{-1} **h.** $z_1 \bar{z}_1$

2. Find real numbers x and y satisfying each equation.

   a. $3x - 4yi = 11 + 7i$ **b.** $x^2 + xi = y^2 + 2yi + 3i$

3. Write in standard form.

   a. $\dfrac{6 - 3i}{-i}$ **b.** $\dfrac{100i}{7 - i}$

   c. $i(1 + i)(1 + 2i)(1 + 3i)$ **d.** $(1 - i)^3 - (1 - i)^2 + (1 - i)$

4. If $x = \dfrac{1 - i}{i}$, compute $x^2 - 3x + 2i$.

5. If $z_1 = 5 - 2i$ and $z_2 = 2 + 4i$, plot each expression in the complex plane.

   a. $\bar{z}_1$ **b.** $z_1 + z_2$ **c.** $z_1 - z_2$ **d.** iz_2

6. Sketch the graph of each relation in the complex plane.

   a. $|z| = 3$ **b.** $|z + i| \le 4$ **c.** $\{z \mid \text{Re}(z) \ge 1 \text{ and } \text{Im}(z) \ge 2\}$

7. Find the quadratic equation whose roots are $5 + 7i$ and $5 - 7i$.

8. Solve the following equations.

   a. $5x^2 + 2x + 3 = 0$ **b.** $x^2 - 5ix - 4i = 0$

9. If m and n are the roots of $2x^2 + 7x + 8 = 0$, find the quadratic equation whose roots are m^2n and mn^2.

10. Convert the Cartesian coordinates to polar coordinates.

   a. $(-5\sqrt{3}, -5)$ **b.** $(7, -7)$ **c.** $(-5, 0)$

11. Convert the polar coordinates to Cartesian coordinates.

   a. $\left(12, \dfrac{3\pi}{4}\right)$ **b.** $\left(4, \dfrac{3\pi}{2}\right)$ **c.** $(2, 1.3)$

12. Write the Cartesian equations in polar form.

   a. $5x^2 + 2y^2 = 9$ **b.** $2x + 3y = 7$

13. Write the polar equations in Cartesian form and sketch their graphs.

   a. $r^2 \cos^2 \theta - 16 = 0$ **b.** $r = -6 \sin \theta$

14. Write the complex numbers in polar and exponential forms.

   a. $-2\sqrt{3} - 2i$ **b.** $3i$ **c.** $-8 + 15i$

15. Write the complex numbers in standard form.

   a. $3 \operatorname{cis}\left(-\dfrac{3\pi}{4}\right)$ **b.** $2e^{\frac{i\pi}{2}}$ **c.** $\left(2 \operatorname{cis} \dfrac{\pi}{6}\right)\left(15 \operatorname{cis} \dfrac{7\pi}{6}\right)$

   d. $(2 - 2i)^6$ **e.** $e^{-5\pi i}$ **f.** $(\sqrt{3} + i)^{-3}$

16. Find all the complex solutions to each equation.

   a. $z^3 + i = 0$ **b.** $z^5 = 16 - 16\sqrt{3}i$ **c.** $z^8 - 1 = 0$

Answers

Chapter 1

Exercises 1.1

2. Parts c, d, f, h, and k are vectors and the others are scalars. **3. c.** When A and C are the same **d.** Always **e.** When A and C are diametrically opposite **f.** When A and C differ by one quarter of a revolution **g.** The acceleration points towards the centre of the circle.

Problems 1.1

1. $D(11, 11)$, $F(-12, 3)$, $G(-5, -5)$, $H(-8, -12)$, $I(7, -3)$, $J(4, -10)$

Exercises 1.2

1. a.

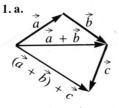

b.

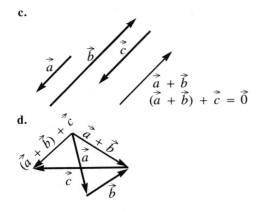

c.

d.

2. a. $\overrightarrow{QS}$ **b.** $\overrightarrow{QS}$ **c.** $\overrightarrow{RP}$ **d.** $\overrightarrow{PR}$

4. a. $|\vec{F_1}| + |\vec{F_2}|$ **b.** $-(\vec{F_1} + \vec{F_2})$
c. The magnitude is $\left||\vec{F_1}| - |\vec{F_2}|\right|$ and the force required is $-(\vec{F_1} + \vec{F_2})$.
5. b. $\sqrt{|\vec{F_1}|^2 + |\vec{F_2}|^2 + 2|\vec{F_1}||\vec{F_2}|\cos\theta}$
6. 34 km/h
7. a. $\vec{s}$ **b.** $-\vec{t}$ **c.** $-\vec{u}$ **d.** $\vec{s} - \vec{u}$
e. $\vec{t} + \vec{u}$ **f.** $-\vec{t} - \vec{u}$ **g.** $\vec{s} + \vec{u}$ **h.** $-\vec{s}$
i. $\vec{s} + \vec{u}$ **j.** $\vec{s} - \vec{t}$ **9. a.** $\overrightarrow{QY}$ **b.** $\overrightarrow{TX}$
10. a. $\overrightarrow{CA}$ **b.** $\vec{0}$ **11.** $\left||\vec{a}| - |\vec{b}|\right|$

Exercises 1.3

3. $k = 3, -3$ **4.** 1.61 units
5. 1.64 units **6. a.** $\overrightarrow{OA} = 4\vec{i}$,
$\overrightarrow{OB} = 4\vec{i} + 5\vec{j}$, $\overrightarrow{BC} = -4\vec{i}$,
$\overrightarrow{CA} = 4\vec{i} - 5\vec{j}$ **b.** $\frac{4}{\sqrt{41}}\vec{i} + \frac{5}{\sqrt{41}}\vec{j}$,
$\frac{4}{\sqrt{41}}\vec{i} - \frac{5}{\sqrt{41}}\vec{j}$, $-\vec{j}$ **9.** DE is parallel to and one
half the length of BC. **10.** $\vec{z} = \dfrac{\vec{x} + \vec{y}}{2}$

Problems 1.3

1. a. $-\vec{a}$ **b.** $-\vec{b}$ **c.** $\vec{b} - \vec{a}$ **d.** $2\vec{b} - \vec{a}$
2. $\overrightarrow{AC} = 2\vec{y} - 2\vec{x}$, $\overrightarrow{OM} = \vec{x} + 2\vec{y}$,
$\overrightarrow{ON} = 3\vec{x} + \vec{y}$

Exercises 1.4

2. a. $\overrightarrow{AG}$ **b.** $\overrightarrow{AH}$ **3. a.** $5\vec{i} - 2\vec{j} - \vec{k}$
b. $-2\vec{i} - \vec{j} + 12\vec{k}$ **c.** $-4\vec{i} + 2\vec{j} + 11\vec{k}$
4. $\vec{x} = \frac{2}{11}\vec{a} + \frac{1}{11}\vec{b}$, $\vec{y} = \frac{5}{22}\vec{a} - \frac{3}{22}\vec{b}$
8. a. $\overrightarrow{AC}$ **b.** $\overrightarrow{ED}$ **c.** $\vec{0}$ **d.** $\overrightarrow{DE}$

Problems 1.4

2. 20 units **3.** $\vec{0}$
4. $\overrightarrow{TO} = \frac{1}{b+1}\overrightarrow{TX} + \frac{b}{b+1}\overrightarrow{TZ}$

Exercises 1.5

2. a. $\vec{i} + 3\vec{j} + 2\vec{k}$ **b.** $\vec{i} + 5\vec{k}$
c. $-6\vec{i} - 8\vec{j} + 11\vec{k}$ **d.** $9\vec{i} - 6\vec{j} + 2\vec{k}$
3. a. $(3, -2, 7)$ **b.** $(-9, 3, 14)$
c. $(1, 1, 0)$ **d.** $(2, 0, -9)$ **4. a.** $6\vec{i} - \vec{j}$
b. $6\vec{i} - 18\vec{j} + 18\vec{k}$ **c.** $-5\vec{i} + 2\vec{k}$
d. $90\vec{i} - 35\vec{j} - 35\vec{k}$ **5. a.** On the xy-plane
b. On the xz-plane **c.** On the yz-plane

Exercises 1.6

1. a. $(3, 3)$ **b.** $(5, 20)$ **c.** $(0, 0)$
d. $(1, -7)$ **e.** $(0, 0, -6)$ **f.** $(2, 2, -8)$
g. $(6, -2, 0)$ **h.** $(-8, 11, 3)$ **i.** $(0, 2, 5)$

j. $(4, -6, 8)$ **k.** $(-12, -42, -20)$
l. $(21, 6, 32)$ **2. a.** $(1, -10, 14)$
b. $(-1, -9, -10)$ **c.** $(-5, -15, 16)$
d. $(13, 11, 0)$ **e.** $(-5, 8, -15)$
f. $(6, -18, 29)$ **3. a.** $6\vec{i} + 7\vec{k}$
b. $2\vec{i} + 2\vec{j} + 5\vec{k}$ **c.** $2\vec{i} - 4\vec{j} - 3\vec{k}$
d. $-2\vec{i} + 4\vec{j} + 3\vec{k}$ **4. a.** $\sqrt{11}$ **b.** $3\sqrt{3}$
c. $\sqrt{149}$ **5. a.** $5\sqrt{2}$ **b.** $\sqrt{30}$
c. $(-5, -3, 0)$ **d.** $\sqrt{34}$ **e.** $(5, 3, 0)$
f. $\sqrt{34}$ **6. a.** $\sqrt{17}$ **b.** $\left(\frac{2}{\sqrt{17}}, \frac{3}{\sqrt{17}}, -\frac{2}{\sqrt{17}}\right)$

7. $\left(\frac{3}{13}, \frac{4}{13}, \frac{12}{13}\right)$ **8. a.** Same length
b. Neither **c.** Parallel and same length
9. $(-13, -5)$
10. $(-3, -7), (17, -9), (-7, 13)$
11. $(6, 4, -3), (5, 10, -1), (7, 6, 0),$
$(9, 10, -2)$ **12. a.** $\left(1, -\frac{1}{3}\right)$ **b.** $\left(\frac{15}{4}, 1\right)$
c. $\left(\frac{1}{3}, \frac{1}{3}, \frac{1}{3}\right)$ **d.** $\left(\frac{1}{4}, \frac{1}{4}, \frac{1}{4}\right)$ **13. a.** $\left(\frac{8}{11}, -\frac{41}{11}\right)$
b. $\left(\frac{2}{11}, -\frac{17}{11}, \frac{72}{11}\right)$ **14. b.** $\sqrt{82}$
c. $7 + 2\sqrt{2} + \sqrt{41}$ **d.** $(1, 5, 4)$
15. a. $x = 2, y = 1$ **b.** $x = -5, y = -\frac{1}{3}$,
$z = -20$ **17.** $(0, 1, 0)$

Problems 1.6

1. 24 **2.** $\left(\frac{6}{7}, \frac{2}{7}, -\frac{3}{7}\right)$ **3. a.** $\frac{5}{2}$ **b.** $\frac{5}{3}$

Exercises 1.7

1. a. $6\sqrt{2}$ **b.** 15 **c.** $-9\sqrt{2}$ **d.** 0
2. a. 0, perpendicular **b.** -29
c. 0, perpendicular **d.** -28 **3.** $-|\vec{a}||\vec{b}|$
5. a. 0, perpendicular **b.** -14 **c.** 0,
perpendicular **d.** 1 **e.** 6 **f.** -113
6. a. $(3, 2), (-3, -2), (6, 4)$, etc.
b. $(3, 2, 0), (1, 0, -2), (1, 1, 1)$, etc.
c. two **d.** an infinite number **7. a.** -6
b. $\frac{106}{3}$ **8. a.** 0.99 **b.** 0 **c.** 0.58
d. 0.29 **9.** $89°$ **10.** $3y + 4z + 20 = 0$
11. $(-16, 2, 3)$ **12.** $p = 4$ or $\frac{-44}{65}$
13. $\lambda = 1$ **14.** $\$3520$ **15. b.** Pythagoras'
Theorem **16.** $\frac{5\sqrt{3}}{2}$, $49°$, $131°$

Problems 1.7

1. $71°$ **3.** $\frac{3}{5}\vec{i} + \frac{4}{5}\vec{j}$ **6. a.** $(0, 0, 0)$,

$(0, 1, 0), \left(\frac{\sqrt{3}}{2}, \frac{1}{2}, 0\right), \left(\frac{\sqrt{3}}{6}, \frac{1}{2}, \frac{\sqrt{6}}{3}\right)$ **b.** $\left(\frac{\sqrt{3}}{6}, \frac{1}{2}, \frac{\sqrt{6}}{12}\right)$
c. $\frac{\sqrt{6}}{4}$

Exercises 1.8

3. $|\vec{a}|^2 - |\vec{b}|^2$
4. $\vec{a} \cdot \vec{c} + \vec{a} \cdot \vec{d} + \vec{b} \cdot \vec{c} + \vec{b} \cdot \vec{d}$
5. a. $8|\vec{a}|^2 + 15|\vec{b}|^2 + 22\vec{a} \cdot \vec{b}$
b. $4|\vec{a}|^2 - |\vec{b}|^2$ **c.** $2|\vec{a}|^2 + 2\vec{a} \cdot \vec{b}$
6. 13 **7.** $60°$ **8.** $-\frac{3}{2}$ **9.** $-\frac{11}{2}$ **10.** 84

Problems 1.8

1. $-\frac{29}{2}$ **2. b.** The Cosine Law

Exercises 1.9

1. a. $\frac{16}{\sqrt{13}}, \left(\frac{48}{13}, \frac{32}{13}\right)$ **b.** $\frac{14}{\sqrt{13}}, \left(-\frac{42}{13}, \frac{28}{13}\right)$
c. $-\frac{10}{\sqrt{89}}, \left(\frac{40}{89}, -\frac{30}{89}, \frac{80}{89}\right)$ **d.** $-4, (0, 0, -4)$
2. a. $\vec{a}$ is perpendicular to $\vec{b}$ **b.** Yes
3. $2, 2\vec{i}; 3, 3\vec{j}; -4, -4\vec{k}$ **4.** $61°, 43°, 119°$
5. $\frac{a}{\sqrt{a^2 + b^2 + c^2}}, \frac{b}{\sqrt{a^2 + b^2 + c^2}}, \frac{c}{\sqrt{a^2 + b^2 + c^2}}$
6. $60°, 45°$; one answer **7.** $90°, 0°, 90°$
8. 1 **9.** $-3, -3\vec{i}; -1, -\vec{j}; 0, \vec{0}$ **10. a.** $\frac{1}{\sqrt{2}}$
b. 1

Problems 1.9

1. a. $55°$ **b.** $125°$ **2.** $\left(\frac{2}{\sqrt{6}}, -\frac{1}{\sqrt{6}}, -\frac{1}{\sqrt{6}}\right)$
3. $(2, 2, -1)$ etc.

Review Exercises

1. a. $(2, 2, 3), (6, -4, 3), (-6, 4, -3),$
$(6, 1, 6)$ **b.** $\sqrt{17}, \sqrt{61}, \sqrt{61}, \sqrt{73}$
2. a. $-6\vec{j} + 16\vec{k}$ **b.** $-\vec{i} - \vec{j} - \vec{k}$
c. $-\vec{i} - 3\vec{j}$ **d.** $-10\vec{j}$ **3. a.** $\left(-\frac{1}{\sqrt{5}}, \frac{2}{\sqrt{5}}\right)$
b. $\left(\frac{1}{\sqrt{21}}, \frac{4}{\sqrt{21}}, \frac{2}{\sqrt{21}}\right)$ **c.** $\left(-\frac{1}{\sqrt{26}}, \frac{3}{\sqrt{26}}, \frac{4}{\sqrt{26}}\right)$
4. $\sqrt{|\vec{F_1}|^2 + |\vec{F_2}|^2}$ **5.** $\left(\frac{4}{5}, \frac{3}{5}\right), \left(-\frac{4}{5}, -\frac{3}{5}\right)$
6. a. $\frac{2}{5}$ **b.** $-\frac{5}{2}$ **c.** $\frac{7}{3}$ **7.** $(1, -2, 13)$
8. a. $\frac{1}{\sqrt{2}}, \left(-\frac{1}{2}, \frac{1}{2}\right)$ **b.** $\frac{11}{\sqrt{53}}, \left(\frac{44}{53}, \frac{66}{53}, -\frac{11}{53}\right)$
9. $68°$ **10.** $54°, 38°, 79°$
11. $\vec{p} = \left(\frac{3}{2}, \frac{1}{2}, 0\right)$ **13. a.** $\vec{p}$ **b.** $\vec{p}$ **c.** $2\vec{p}$

-3 + 1 +0
2q+1 +0

14. $\vec{a}$, $\vec{b}$, and $\vec{c}$ are unit vectors; $\vec{a}$, $\vec{b}$, and $\vec{d}$ are mutually perpendicular   **15. a.** 52°, 72°, 56°   **b.** 40°, 50°, 90°   **19.** 44°, 68°, 84°, or their supplements

Chapter 2

Exercises 2.1

1. a. Resultant of $10\sqrt{2}$ N acting northwest; equilibrant of $10\sqrt{2}$ N acting southeast.
b. Resultant of 2 N acting south; equilibrant of 2 N acting north.   **c.** Resultant of 15 N acting 37° east of south; equilibrant of 15 N acting 37° west of north.   **2. a.** 1.93 N
b. 0.52 N   **3.** b and c   **5.** 24.5 N
6. Magnitude is $\sqrt{|F_1|^2 + |F_2|^2}$
7. 5 N   **8.** $\sqrt{189}$ N   **9.** $10\sqrt{3}$ N   **10.** 82°
11. 71.7 N, 87.9 N   **12.** 192 N, 56 N

Problems 2.1
1. At an angle of 80° to the positive x-axis

Exercises 2.2

1. 100 J   **2. a.** $\frac{5}{2}$ J   **b.** $\frac{5\sqrt{390}}{2}$ J   **c.** 0 J
d. $30\sqrt{5}$ J   **3.** $60\sqrt{2}$ J   **4.** $-19\sqrt{30}$ J

Problems 2.2
1. a. 105 J   **b.** 105 J

Exercises 2.3
2. a. 0.6 km   **b.** 6 min   **3. a.** 1383 km
b. 13° east of north   **4. a.** 4° north of east
b. 65 min   **5.** 291 km/h   **6. a.** 66 m
b. 100 seconds   **7.** 2.5 m/s in a direction 56° west of north   **8.** 13 m/s   **9. a.** 63°
b. 27°

Exercises 2.4
1. a. $3\vec{i} + 4\vec{j}$ **b.** $-7\vec{i} + 8\vec{j}$ **c.** $5\vec{i} - 9\vec{j}$
2. a, b, g, and h are dependent, and c, d, e, and f are independent   **4. a.** $s = t = 0$
b. $s = 5, t = 3$ **c.** $s = 2, t = -1$
d. $s = 5, t = 7$ **5. a.** Yes
b. $100\vec{u} - 199\vec{v}$ **6.** Yes, $\vec{u}$ and $\vec{v}$ are linearly independent   **7.** a, b, and c
8. a. Yes   **b.** No   **9. a.** $r = 0, s = \frac{1}{2}$,
$t = -\frac{1}{2}$ **b.** $r = 2, s = -3, t = \frac{2}{3}$
10. Linearly dependent

Problems 2.4
1. Linearly independent   **3. a.** $a = 2$,
$b = 2, c = -1$ **b.** $a = -1, b = 1, c = 3$
5. a. $t = -1$ **b.** $t = 2$ **6.** $s = 2$ or -1

Exercises 2.5
1. a. 3:1   **b.** 3:5   **c.** 4:−1 or −4:1
d. 4:−3 or −4:3   **e.** 1:−2 or −1:2
2.

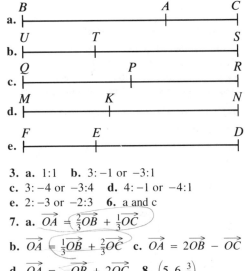

3. a. 1:1   **b.** 3:−1 or −3:1
c. 3:−4 or −3:4   **d.** 4:−1 or −4:1
e. 2:−3 or −2:3   **6.** a and c
7. a. $\overrightarrow{OA} = \frac{2}{3}\overrightarrow{OB} + \frac{1}{3}\overrightarrow{OC}$
b. $\overrightarrow{OA} = \frac{1}{3}\overrightarrow{OB} + \frac{2}{3}\overrightarrow{OC}$ **c.** $\overrightarrow{OA} = 2\overrightarrow{OB} - \overrightarrow{OC}$
d. $\overrightarrow{OA} = -\overrightarrow{OB} + 2\overrightarrow{OC}$ **8.** $\left(5, 6, \frac{3}{2}\right)$
9. (4, 4, 5) and (5, 2, 2)   **10. a.** $\left(\frac{11}{6}, \frac{15}{2}\right)$
b. (0, −20)   **c.** $\left(\frac{10}{3}, 30\right)$ **d.** $\left(\frac{9}{5}, 7\right)$

Exercises 2.6
1. a. $\left(\frac{5}{2}, -3\right), \left(\frac{7}{2}, -3\right), (1, 0); \left(\frac{7}{3}, -2\right)$
b. $\left(5, 4, \frac{1}{2}\right), \left(3, 0, \frac{3}{2}\right), (2, 3, 3); \left(\frac{10}{3}, \frac{7}{3}, \frac{5}{3}\right)$
11. a. and **b.** All ratios are 1:2
12. R divides CQ in the ratio 14:9 and BP in the ratio 21:2.

Problems 2.6
1. K divides AC in the ratio 1:1 and BE in the ratio 1:3.   **2. a.** D divides AE in the ratio 2:1 and BF in the ratio 5:4.   **b.** $\frac{22}{45}$

Exercises 2.7
1. a. (1, 0, 0)   **b.** (10, −1, −9)

c. $(1, 0, 1)$, etc.   **d.** $(45, -18, 20)$
2. a. 2   **b.** $(-2, -5, -3)$ **c.** -1
d. $(-4, -3, 1)$ **e.** $(4, 3, -1)$ **f.** -14
g. -14 **h.** 14   **i.** -14 **3.** a is
meaningless; b is a scalar; c, d, e, and f are

vectors   **4.** $\left(\frac{6}{\sqrt{61}}, -\frac{4}{\sqrt{61}}, \frac{3}{\sqrt{61}}\right)$ **5.** 1 N·m

6. $fl \sin \theta$; maximum when $\theta = 90°$

8. $\sqrt{65}$ **9. a.** $\frac{49}{2}$ **b.** $\frac{\sqrt{3}}{2}$

Review Exercises
1. 502 N and 615 N   **2.** 93 N and 80 N
3. 10° to the starboard   **4. a.** 14 J
b. -5 J   **5. a.** $t = 1$ **b.** $t = 2$
c. $t = -5$ **6.** a, b, and c are linearly
dependent; d and e are linearly independent

7. $\frac{3}{2}$ **9. a.** 1:1   **b.** 5:-4 or -5:4

11. K divides AF in the
ratio 4:19 and DE in the ratio 20:3

13. a. $(1, 1, 3)$ **b.** $\frac{9}{2}\sqrt{13}$

14. a. $(-4, -1, -5)$ **b.** $(15, -16, -10)$
15. 1 unit   **16. a.** $(-22, -14, 6)$
b. $(22, 14, -6)$ **c.** Anti-commutative Law
17. a. 15   **b.** $(3, -5, -4)$ **c.** $(13, -9, 11)$
d. $(4, -16, 4)$ **18.** $\left(\frac{1}{\sqrt{14}}, -\frac{3}{\sqrt{14}}, \frac{2}{\sqrt{14}}\right)$,
$\left(-\frac{1}{\sqrt{14}}, \frac{3}{\sqrt{14}}, -\frac{2}{\sqrt{14}}\right)$

Chapter 3
Exercises 3.1
1. a. $\vec{r} = (-2, 7) + t(3, -4), t \in R$;
$x = -2 + 3t, y = 7 - 4t, t \in R$; $(1, 3)$,
$(4, -1)$ **b.** $\vec{r} = (0, 7) + t(-5, 2), t \in R$;
$x = -5t, y = 7 + 2t, t \in R$; $(-5, 9)$,
$(-10, 11)$ **c.** $\vec{r} = (\sqrt{2}, -1) + t(0, 6), t \in R$;
$x = \sqrt{2}, y = -1 + 6t, t \in R$; $(\sqrt{2}, 5)$,
$(\sqrt{2}, 11)$ **d.** $\vec{r} = t(2, 7), t \in R$;
$x = 2t, y = 7t, t \in R$; $(2, 7)$, $(4, 14)$
2. a. $\vec{r} = (0, 5) + t(-6, 0), t \in R$; $x = -6t$,
$y = 5, t \in R$ **b.** $\vec{r} = (\sqrt{3}, -1) + t(\sqrt{3}, -1)$,
$t \in R$; $x = \sqrt{3} + \sqrt{3}t, y = -1 - t, t \in R$
c. $\vec{r} = (0, k) + t(k, -k), t \in R$;
$x = kt, y = k - kt, t \in R$
d. $\vec{r} = \left(2, \frac{1}{3}\right) + t\left(-\frac{9}{4}, -\frac{1}{3}\right), t \in R$;
$x = 2 - \frac{9}{4}t, y = \frac{1}{3} - \frac{1}{3}t, t \in R$
3. a. $(2, 3)$, $(-2, 4)$, $(-6, 5)$

b. $(0, 3)$, $(5, -1)$, $(10, -5)$
c. $(3, 7)$, $(2, 7)$, $(1, 7)$
4. a. $\vec{r} = \left(5, -\frac{1}{2}\right) + t(9, 2), t \in R$;
$x = 5 + 9t, y = -\frac{1}{2} + 2t, t \in R$
b. $\vec{r} = \left(5, -\frac{1}{2}\right) + t(1, 0), t \in R$;
$x = 5 + t, y = -\frac{1}{2}, t \in R$
c. $\vec{r} = \left(5, -\frac{1}{2}\right) + t(-3, 7), t \in R$;
$x = 5 - 3t, y = -\frac{1}{2} + 7t, t \in R$
5. b. $b = -1$ **6. a.** yes   **b.** yes   **c.** no
7. a. $\vec{m} = (-1, 10)$; $P_1(0, 8)$
b. $\vec{m} = (4, 3)$; $P_1(1, 0)$ **c.** $\vec{m} = (6, -2)$;
none   **8. a.** neither   **b.** parallel
c. perpendicular   **9.** $\vec{r} = (4, 5) + t(-7, 3)$,
$t \in R$ **10. a.** $(11, 0)$, $\left(0, \frac{11}{3}\right)$ **b.** $(-7, 0)$,
$(0, 35)$ **c.** $(6, 0)$, no point
11. a. $x = x_1 + t, y = y_1, t \in R$ **b.** $x = x_1$,
$y = y_1 + t, t \in R$ **12.** 87°   **13.** 41°

Problems 3.1
1. b. $x = 7 + 2t, y = 3 - 5t, -1 \le t \le 5$
2. b. $0 \le t \le 1$
3. $\vec{r} = (2, -3) + u\left(\frac{1}{\sqrt{2}} - \frac{1}{\sqrt{10}}, \frac{1}{\sqrt{2}} + \frac{3}{\sqrt{10}}\right), u \in R$,
and $\vec{r} = (2, -3) + v\left(\frac{1}{\sqrt{2}} + \frac{1}{\sqrt{10}}, \frac{1}{\sqrt{2}} - \frac{3}{\sqrt{10}}\right)$,
$v \in R$

Exercises 3.2
1. a. $2x + 5y + 2 = 0$ **b.** $2x - 1 = 0$
c. $x + y = 0$ **d.** $y - \sqrt{3} = 0$
2. a. $\vec{n} = (3, 4), \vec{m} = (-4, 3), P_1(4, 0)$
b. $\vec{n} = (2, -1), \vec{m} = (1, 2), P_1(9, 0)$
c. $\vec{n} = (1, 0), \vec{m} = (0, 1), P_1(3, 5)$
d. $\vec{n} = (5, -1), \vec{m} = (1, 5), P_1(1, -5)$
3. a. $2x - 3y + 3 = 0$ **b.** $y + 3 = 0$
c. $5x + 2y + 36 = 0$ **d.** $x - 3y - 3 = 0$
e. $x - y + 3 = 0$ **4. a.** $3x - 2y - 13 = 0$
b. $x - 1 = 0$ **c.** $x - y - 6 = 0$
d. $y + 5 = 0$ **5. a.** $k = 3$ **b.** $k = -\frac{3}{2}$
c. $k = \pm 3$ **6. a.** $5x - 2y - 23 = 0$
b. $y = 0$ **c.** $x = 3$ **d.** $7x + 2y = 0$
7. a. $\vec{r} = (0, 1) + t(1, 2), t \in R$
b. $\vec{r} = (0, 4) + t(1, 0), t \in R$
c. $\vec{r} = (3, 0) + t(3, 2), t \in R$

Problems 3.2
1. 75°

Exercises 3.3

1. a. $\vec{r} = (2, 4, 6) + t(-1, -3, 2), t \in \mathbf{R}$;
$x = 2 - t, y = 4 - 3t, z = 6 + 2t, t \in \mathbf{R}$;
$\frac{x-2}{-1} = \frac{y-4}{-3} = \frac{z-6}{2}$; $P_2(1, 1, 8), P_3(0, -2, 10)$
b. $\vec{r} = (0, 1, 0) + t(1, 0, 0), t \in \mathbf{R}$; $x = t$,
$y = 1, z = 0, t \in \mathbf{R}$; $P_2(1, 1, 0), P_3(2, 1, 0)$
c. $\vec{r} = \left(\frac{1}{2}, \frac{1}{3}, 0\right) + t(2, 0, 1), t \in \mathbf{R}$;
$x = \frac{1}{2} + 2t, y = \frac{1}{3}, z = t, t \in \mathbf{R}$;
$P_2\left(\frac{5}{2}, \frac{1}{3}, 1\right), P_3\left(\frac{9}{2}, \frac{1}{3}, 2\right)$ **d.** $\vec{r} = t(1, -1, 1)$,
$t \in \mathbf{R}; x = t, y = -t, z = t, t \in \mathbf{R}$;
$\frac{x}{1} = \frac{y}{-1} = \frac{z}{1}$; $P_2(1, -1, 1), P_3(2, -2, 2)$
2. a. P, S **b.** $a = -8$
3. a. $\vec{r} = (1, -1, 1) + t(3, 1, 7), t \in \mathbf{R}$;
$x = 1 + 3t, y = -1 + t, z = 1 + 7t, t \in \mathbf{R}$;
$\frac{x-1}{3} = \frac{y+1}{1} = \frac{z-1}{7}$
b. $\vec{r} = \left(6, 0, -\frac{1}{2}\right) + t(0, 0, 1), t \in \mathbf{R}$;
$x = 6, y = 0, z = -\frac{1}{2} + t, t \in \mathbf{R}$
c. $\vec{r} = (5, 5, -4) + t(5, 2, 0), t \in \mathbf{R}$;
$x = 5 + 5t, y = 5 + 2t, z = -4, t \in \mathbf{R}$
d. $\vec{r} = (-3, 4, 0) + t(5, -3, -8), t \in \mathbf{R}$;
$x = -3 + 5t, y = 4 - 3t, z = -8t, t \in \mathbf{R}$;
$\frac{x+3}{5} = \frac{y-4}{-3} = \frac{z}{-8}$
e. $\vec{r} = (1, 1, -2) + t(-1, 0, 0), t \in \mathbf{R}$;
$x = 1 - t, y = 1, z = -2, t \in \mathbf{R}$
4. $\vec{r} = (0, -1, 1) + t\left(3, 2, \frac{1}{2}\right), t \in \mathbf{R}$
or $\vec{r} = (0, -1, 1) + t(6, 4, 1), t \in \mathbf{R}$
5. $\vec{r} = t(-6, -7, 2), t \in \mathbf{R}$ **7. a.** A line
that passes through the point $(1, 2, 0)$,
parallel to the z-axis **b.** A line that passes
through the points $(2, 4, 5)$ and $(3, 11, 5)$
(parallel to the xy-plane) **c.** A line that
passes through the points $(-3, 0, 5)$ and
$(-1, 0, 7)$ (in the xz-plane) **9.** $\cos \alpha = \frac{1}{2}$,
$\cos \beta = -\frac{\sqrt{3}}{2}, \cos \gamma = 0; \alpha = 60°, \beta = 150°$,
$\gamma = 90°$ **10. a.** $\vec{r} = \left(2, 0, \frac{1}{2}\right) + t(-3, 12, 4)$,
$t \in \mathbf{R}$ **b.** $-3, 12, 4$ **c.** $103°, 23°, 72°$
d. $a = -20, b = -\frac{37}{6}$

Problems 3.3

1. $k = -4$ or $k = 1$ **2.** $\frac{x-2}{-34} = \frac{y+5}{25} = \frac{z}{13}$

3. b. $x = 3t, y = t, z = 2 + 6t$,
$-3 \le t \le 2$ **4.** $s = -1, t = 2$
5. b. $P_1(-10, 1, 2), P_2(-1, -2, -3)$

Exercises 3.4

1. a. $\vec{r} = (2, 1, 5) + s(0, 1, 7) +$
$t(5, -2, 1), s, t \in \mathbf{R}; x = 2 + 5t$,
$y = 1 + s - 2t, z = 5 + 7s + t, s, t \in \mathbf{R}$;
$(2, 1, 5), (2, 2, 12), (7, -1, 6)$
b. $\vec{r} = s(1, 1, 1) + t(-1, 1, 1), s, t \in \mathbf{R}$;
$x = s - t, y = s + t, z = s + t, s, t \in \mathbf{R}$;
$(0, 0, 0), (1, 1, 1), (0, 2, 2)$
c. $\vec{r} = (0, 1, -2) + s(-3, 0, 1) +$
$t(-3, -5, 7), s, t \in \mathbf{R}; x = -3s - 3t$,
$y = 1 - 5t, z = -2 + s + 7t, s, t \in \mathbf{R}$;
$(0, 1, -2), (-3, -4, 5), (-3, 1, -1)$
d. $\vec{r} = (1, 0, 1) + s(1, 2, 0) + t(1, 1, -1)$,
$s, t \in \mathbf{R}; x = 1 + s + t, y = 2s + t$,
$z = 1 - t, s, t \in \mathbf{R}$
2. $\vec{r} = (5, 4, 3) + s(0, 1, 0) + t(0, 0, 1)$,
$s, t \in \mathbf{R}$ **3.** $x = 5 + s - 3t$,
$y = -1 + 2t, z = 7 + 2s + 2t, s, t \in \mathbf{R}$
4. $\vec{r} = (7, 0, -7) + s(-1, -2, 1) +$
$t(0, 0, 1), s, t \in \mathbf{R}; x = 7 - s, y = -2s$,
$z = -7 + s + t, s, t \in \mathbf{R}$ **5. a.** yes **b.** no
c. no **6. a.** yes **b.** no **7. a.** a plane
that passes through the point $(0, 4, 0)$, parallel
to the xz-plane **b.** the yz-plane **c.** a plane
that passes through the point $(1, 0, 0)$, parallel
to the yz-plane

Problems 3.4

1. $k = -12$ **2. b.** All points in and on the
parallelogram whose vertices have position
vectors $\vec{a}, \vec{b}, -\vec{a} + \vec{b} + \vec{c}$, and $\vec{c}$

Exercises 3.5

1. a. $7x + y - z - 18 = 0$ **b.** $x - 5 = 0$
c. $2x + 3z + 6 = 0$ **d.** $2x - y + 4z = 0$
2. a. $x - y - 2z - 5 = 0$ **b.** $z + 3 = 0$
c. $x + y + z = 0$ **3. a.** coincident
b. perpendicular **c.** none **d.** parallel and
distinct **4. a.** $11x + 8y - 2z - 21 = 0$
b. $x + 3y + z = 0$ **c.** $y - 1 = 0$
5. $x - 4z = 0$
6. $8x + 11y - 10z - 46 = 0$
7. $x = s, y = -24 + 2s + 3t, z = t, s, t \in \mathbf{R}$
8. $5x + 11y + 2z - 21 = 0$
10. a. parallel and lying in the plane
b. parallel and not lying in the plane
c. not parallel **11. a.** $25°$ **b.** $17°$

c. $90°$ **12.** $x + y + 3z - 5 = 0$
13. $17x - 11y + z + 66 = 0$
14. a. $6x - 4y + 8z - 3 = 0$ **b.** a plane midway between P_1 and P_2 and perpendicular to P_1P_2

Problems 3.5
2. b. $53°$ **3.** $3x + 5y + kz - 15 = 0$ for any fixed value of k; the points are collinear.
4. a. $(-1, 3, 4, 5) \cdot (\vec{r} - (2, 7, 3, 0)) = 0$ or $x_1 - 3x_2 - 4x_3 - 5x_4 + 31 = 0$
b. $(3, 1, 2, 2) \cdot (\vec{r} - (4, 1, 2, -3)) = 0$ or $3x_1 + x_2 + 2x_3 + 2x_4 - 11 = 0$
c. $(2, 3, -4, -2, 6) \cdot (\vec{r} - (0, 3, 0, 0, 0)) = 0$

Problems 3.6
1. a. two planes, $x = 2$ and $x = -2$ **b.** the three coordinate planes **c.** two planes, $z = -1$ and $z = 4$ **d.** the line $x = 3$, $y = -4$, $z = t$, $t \in R$ **e.** two planes, $x = 3$ and $y = 0$ **d.** two planes, $x = 2$ and $x - y = 0$

Review Exercises
1. a. $\vec{r} = (1, 7) + t(-10, -4)$, $t \in R$; $x = 1 - 10t$, $y = 7 - 4t$, $t \in R$
b. $\vec{r} = (-2, 0) + t(0, 5)$, $t \in R$; $x = -2$, $y = 5t$, $t \in R$ **c.** $\vec{r} = \left(\frac{1}{2}, 3\right) + t(1, 4)$, $t \in R$; $x = \frac{1}{2} + t$, $y = 3 + 4t$, $t \in R$
2. a. $\vec{r} = (0, -1, 2) + t(2, 5, -1)$, $t \in R$; $x = 2t$, $y = -1 + 5t$, $z = 2 - t$, $t \in R$; $\frac{x}{2} = \frac{y+1}{5} = \frac{z-2}{-1}$
b. $\vec{r} = (1, 2, -5) + t(0, 1, 0)$, $t \in R$; $x = 1$, $y = 2 + t$, $z = -5$, $t \in R$;
c. $\vec{r} = (0, 0, 1) + t(1, 0, -1)$, $t \in R$; $x = t$, $y = 0$, $z = 1 - t$, $t \in R$;
d. $\vec{r} = \left(\frac{3}{2}, 0, -2\right) + t(2, -1, 2)$, $t \in R$; $x = \frac{3}{2} + 2t$, $y = -t$, $z = -2 + 2t$, $t \in R$; $\frac{x - \frac{3}{2}}{2} = \frac{y}{-1} = \frac{z+2}{2}$ **3. a.** $\vec{r} = (-1, -1, 2) + s(5, 4, 2) + t(0, 0, 1)$, $s, t \in R$; $x = -1 + 5s$, $y = -1 + 4s$, $z = 2 + 2s + t$, $s, t \in R$
b. $\vec{r} = (1, 1, 0) + s(-3, -1, 3) + t(0, 1, 0)$, $s, t \in R$; $x = 1 - 3s$, $y = 1 - s + t$, $z = 3s$, $s, t \in R$
c. $\vec{r} = (-2, 0, 0) + s(2, -3, 0) + t(2, 0, 4)$, $s, t \in R$;

$x = -2 + 2s + 2t$, $y = -3s$, $z = 4t$, $s, t \in R$ **d.** $\vec{r} = (1, 1, 1) + s(-1, -1, -1) + t(3, 4, 5)$, $s, t \in R$; $x = 1 - s + 3t$, $y = 1 - s + 4t$, $z = 1 - s + 5t$, $s, t \in R$ **e.** $\vec{r} = (3, -1, 2) + s(4, 0, 1) + t(4, 0, 2)$, $s, t \in R$; $x = 3 + 4s + 4t$, $y = -1$, $z = 2 + s + 2t$, $s, t \in R$ **4. a.** $3x - 4y - 5 = 0$
b. $x + 2y + 1 = 0$ **c.** $4x - y = 0$
5. a. $x + 3y + 5z - 67 = 0$
b. $2x - 3y - 11z + 33 = 0$
c. $y + z - 6 = 0$
d. $8x + 2y + z - 18 = 0$ **e.** $z - 7 = 0$
f. $x - 3y - 3 = 0$ **6. a.** $x = 6 + 5t$, $y = 4 - 2t$, $z = -3t$, $t \in R$
b. $\frac{x-6}{5} = \frac{y-4}{-2} = \frac{z}{-3}$ **c.** $m = 8$, $n = 6$
7. $\vec{r} = (1, 2, 1) + t(2, 1, 0)$, $t \in R$
8. a. coincident **b.** perpendicular
c. parallel and distinct **d.** none
9. a. $k = \frac{1}{3}$ **b.** $k = 5$ or $k = -4$
10. a. $\vec{r} = (1, 4, 4) + t(2, 0, -3)$, $t \in R$
b. $\left(\frac{11}{3}, 4, 0\right)$ **c.** $56°, 90°, 146°$
11. $7x + 2y - 4z - 13 = 0$
12. $(-5, 0, 0)$, $(0, -4, 0)$, $(0, 0, 20)$
13. $(0, 4, 6)$, $(8, 0, 22)$, $\left(-3, \frac{11}{2}, 0\right)$
14. a. $5x + y - 13 = 0$
b. $\vec{r} = (-2, 0) + t(2, 5)$, $t \in R$
c. $x = 9 + s - t$, $y = s$, $z = t$, $s, t \in R$
d. $2x + y + 7z + 24 = 0$ **15. a.** $46°$
b. $90°$ **c.** $74°$ **d.** $35°$ **e.** $39°$
16. $\vec{r} = s(2, -3, 2) + t(1, 2, -1)$, $s, t \in R$
17. $2x - y = 0$
18. $x - 3y + 2z - 14 = 0$
19. $17x - 7y + 13z - 23 = 0$
20. a. $54x + 55y - 16z - 56 = 0$
b. $\left(0, 0, -\frac{7}{2}\right)$ **21. a.** the point $(0, 1, 2)$

b. plane with x-intercept $\frac{3}{2}$, y-intercept 3, z-intercept 3 **c.** line through the point $(0, 5, 4)$, parallel to the x-axis **d.** plane parallel to the x-axis with y-intercept 4 and z-intercept 5 **e.** plane parallel to the xy-plane with z-intercept 3 **f.** line in the xy-plane passing through $(0, 0, 0)$ and $(1, 1, 0)$

Chapter 4

Exercises 4.1

1. a. $(4, 6, -2)$ **b.** $(1, 1, 2)$

c. No intersection

d. $(x, y, z) = (2 - t, 14 - t, 1 + t), t \in \mathbf{R}$

e. $(5, 15, -5)$ **2. a.** $(9, 14, 0)$

b. $\left(-\frac{3}{2}, 0, \frac{7}{2}\right)$ **c.** $(0, 2, 3)$

3. a. Yes **b.** No **4. a.** $(2, 0, 0)$

b. $(0, -3, 0)$ **c.** $\left(0, 0, -\frac{6}{7}\right)$ **5.** $\left(0, 0, -\frac{7}{2}\right)$

6. $\left(\frac{3}{2}, -1, \frac{7}{2}\right)$ **7. a.** $(8, 2, 3)$ **b.** $(-1, 1, 1)$

c. no intersection; lines are skew

d. $(x, y, z) = (1, 1, 1) + t(1, 2, -3), t \in \mathbf{R}$;

lines coincide

e. no intersection; lines are parallel and

distinct **8.** $(2, 3, 1)$ **9. a.** $(-2, -3, 0)$

b. $\vec{r} = (-2, -3, 0) + t(1, -2, 1), t \in \mathbf{R}$

10. $c = 3$

Problems 4.1

2. a. No intersection; lines are parallel and

distinct **b.** No intersection; lines are skew

3. $\frac{x}{2} = \frac{y - 1}{1} = \frac{z - 2}{-2}$

4. $\vec{r} = (2, 0, -1) + t(-34, -26, 19), t \in \mathbf{R}$

5. $(1, 2, 1)$ and $(2, -1, -1)$

6. a. No value **b.** $k = 9$ **c.** $k \neq 9$

Exercises 4.2

1. a, d, and h are linear; b, c, e, f, and g are

non-linear **2. b.** $\left(\frac{1}{2}, -1\right)$

4. a. $(x, y) = (3, 2)$ **b.** $(x, y, z) = (0, 0, 0)$

5. a. $(x, y) = (4, -1)$ **b.** No solution

c. $(x, y) = (8 - 2t, t), t \in \mathbf{R}$

d. $(x, y) = \left(\frac{1}{2}, \frac{2}{3}\right)$ **e.** $(x, y, z) = (-1, 2, 0)$

f. $(x, y, z) = (5, -3, -2)$

g. $(x, y, z) = (4, 2, 6)$

Problems 4.2

1. $(x, y) = \left(\frac{-3a + 2b}{9}, \frac{6a - b}{9}\right)$

2. $ad - bc \neq 0$ **3. a.** $c = -4$

b. $c = 4$ **c.** $c \neq \pm 4$

Exercises 4.3

1. a. $\begin{bmatrix} 1 & 3 \\ 2 & -4 \end{bmatrix}, \begin{bmatrix} 1 & 3 & | & 8 \\ 2 & -4 & | & 7 \end{bmatrix}$

b. $\begin{bmatrix} 3 & 4 & -1 \\ 0 & 1 & 3 \\ 1 & -1 & 0 \end{bmatrix}, \begin{bmatrix} 3 & 4 & -1 & | & 1 \\ 0 & 1 & 3 & | & 5 \\ 1 & -1 & 0 & | & -7 \end{bmatrix}$

c. $\begin{bmatrix} 1 & 2 \\ 1 & -2 \\ 1 & 1 \end{bmatrix}, \begin{bmatrix} 1 & 2 & | & 0 \\ 1 & -2 & | & 0 \\ 1 & 1 & | & 0 \end{bmatrix}$

2. a. $x - 2y = 1$
     $3x + 4y = 0$

b. $2x + y + 7z = 1$ **c.** $x + y + z = 0$
     $3y + 4z = 7$ $5y + 6z = 0$
     $6z = -5$

3. a. In row-echelon form

b. $\begin{bmatrix} 1 & 4 & -6 & | & 3 \\ 0 & 1 & -7 & | & \frac{1}{2} \\ 0 & 0 & 0 & | & 0 \end{bmatrix}$ **c.** In row-echelon form

d. $\begin{bmatrix} 1 & 3 & | & -3 \\ 0 & 1 & | & 4 \end{bmatrix}$ **e.** $\begin{bmatrix} 1 & -3 & 40 & | & 5 \\ 0 & 1 & 4 & | & 3 \\ 0 & 0 & -19 & | & -12 \end{bmatrix}$

f. $\begin{bmatrix} 1 & 1 & 1 & | & 0 \\ 0 & 2 & 1 & | & 0 \\ 0 & 0 & \frac{3}{2} & | & 0 \end{bmatrix}$ **4. a.** $(x, y) = (-1, 2)$

b. $(x, y, z) = (6, 3, -5)$ **c.** No solution

d. $(x, y, z) = (0, 0, 0)$

e. $(x, y, z) = \left(\frac{5}{3}, \frac{2}{3}, \frac{2}{3}\right)$ **f.** No solution

5. a. $(x, y, z) = (-2 - 5t, 2 + 2t, t), t \in \mathbf{R}$;
$(-2, 2, 0), (-7, 4, 1)$

b. $(x, y, z) = (1 - t, -2 - 4t, t), t \in \mathbf{R}$;
$(1, -2, 0), (0, -6, 1)$

c. $(x, y, z) = \left(\frac{-5t + 8}{11}, \frac{7t + 13}{11}, t\right), t \in \mathbf{R}$;

$\left(\frac{8}{11}, \frac{13}{11}, 0\right), \left(\frac{3}{11}, \frac{20}{11}, 1\right)$ **6. a.** $(x, y, z) = (0, 2, 4)$

b. $(x, y, z) = (2, 6 - 3t, t), t \in \mathbf{R}$

c. $(x, y, z) = \left(2, 0, \frac{1}{2}\right)$

Problems 4.3

1. $(x, y, z) = \left(1, -1, \frac{1}{2}\right)$ **2.** If $k = 1$ then

$(x, y, z) = \left(\frac{4 + 4t}{7}, \frac{3 + 3t}{7}, t\right), t \in \mathbf{R}$;

no solution if $k \neq 1$ **3.** $k \neq \frac{12}{5}$;

$(x, y, z) = \left(\frac{5t + 252}{5k - 12}, \frac{15t - 3}{5k - 12}, \frac{-165}{5k - 12}\right), t \in \mathbf{R}$

4. $(x_1, x_2, x_3, x_4) = (1, 2, 4, 3)$

Exercises 4.4

1. a. $x = 7 + 5t, y = -3 - 2t, z = t, t \in R$

b. Parallel and distinct **c.** $x = \frac{3}{10} + \frac{7}{10}t,$

$y = \frac{11}{10} - \frac{1}{10}t, z = t, t \in R$

d. $x = 0, y = 1 - t, z = t, t \in R$

e. Parallel and coincident

2. a. $\vec{r} = (10, -3, 0) + t(-27, 10, 1), t \in R$

b. $\vec{r} = \left(\frac{5}{9}, -\frac{10}{9}, 0\right) + t(-3, 0, 1), t \in R$

c. $\vec{r} = \left(\frac{13}{4}, 0, \frac{1}{4}\right) + t(-4, 1, 0), t \in R$

3. $(4, -2, 0), \left(\frac{32}{9}, 0, \frac{10}{9}\right), (0, 16, 10)$

6. $5x - y - 3z + 8 = 0$

Problems 4.4

1. $60°$ **2.** $48°$ **3. b.** $4x + 5y - 14z = 0$

c. $8x - 8y - 12z + 15 = 0$

Exercises 4.5

1. a. Three planes intersecting at the origin. **b.** Four coincident planes intersecting in the plane $x - y + 2z = 3$
c. Three planes intersecting in the line $(x, y, z) = (2 - 3t, 7 - 4t, t), t \in R$
2. a. Unique solution; point $(x, y, z) = (2, 3, 4)$ **b.** No solution; three distinct parallel planes **c.** Infinite number of solutions; line $(x, y, z) = (7 - t, t, 2), t \in R$
d. Infinite number of solutions; three coincident planes, $x - 2y - 3z = 1$
e. No solution; two of the planes parallel and distinct **f.** No solution; two planes coincident, third parallel and distinct
g. Infinite number of solutions; line $(x, y, z) = \left(6 + \frac{1}{2}t, -1 - \frac{1}{2}t, t\right), t \in R$
h. No solution; triangular prism
i. Unique solution; origin $(x, y, z) = (0, 0, 0)$

Problems 4.5

1. a. They are parallel. **b.** Cannot be a unique point **2.** $k = 3$

Exercises 4.6

1. a. $\frac{7}{\sqrt{13}}$ **b.** 0 **c.** $\frac{12}{\sqrt{53}}$ **d.** $\frac{17}{\sqrt{10}}$ **e.** 2

f. 6 **2. a.** $\sqrt{\frac{11}{6}}$ **b.** $3\sqrt{2}$ **c.** $\sqrt{\frac{7}{3}}$

d. $\sqrt{\frac{73}{2}}$ **3. a.** $\frac{7}{5}$ **b.** $\frac{11}{\sqrt{10}}$ **c.** $\sqrt{\frac{134}{45}}$

5. $\sqrt{\frac{61}{14}}$ **6. a.** $\frac{29}{2\sqrt{2}}$ **b.** $\frac{2}{\sqrt{13}}$ **c.** $\sqrt{\frac{1555}{74}}$ **d.** 0

7. $5x - y + 3\sqrt{34} = 0, 5x - y - 3\sqrt{34} = 0$

8. $(0, -3)$ and $(0, 9)$ **9.** $\sqrt{\frac{2}{3}}$

Problems 4.6

1. b. $\frac{3}{\sqrt{52}}$

2. $(x + y - 8)(3x - 3y + 4) = 0$

3. $y^2 = 8x$ **4.** $\sqrt{\frac{456}{17}}$

Exercises 4.7

1. a. 0 **b.** 2 **c.** $\frac{7}{\sqrt{13}}$ **d.** 7 **e.** 4

2. a. $x - 2y + 5z - 33 = 0$ **b.** $\frac{33}{\sqrt{30}}$

3. $\frac{30}{19}$ **4.** $\sqrt{\frac{30}{13}}$ **5.** $\frac{12}{7}$ **6. a.** $\frac{1}{\sqrt{6}}$ **b.** $2\sqrt{6}$

c. $\frac{19}{14}$ **7.** $4x - 3y + 2z \pm 3\sqrt{29} = 0$

8. a. $\frac{1}{3}$; same side **b.** $\frac{5}{3}$; same side **c.** 0;

in plane **d.** $\frac{1}{3}$; opposite side **e.** 0; in plane

f. $\frac{2}{3}$; same side **9.** $(1, 3, 3); (5, 3, 5)$

Problems 4.7

1. b. $\frac{\sqrt{26}}{6}$

3. $\vec{r} = (2, 0, 1) + t(3, 1, -1), t \in R$

Exercises 4.8

1. a. $\sqrt{3}$ **b.** 6 **c.** 0 **d.** $\frac{\sqrt{6}}{3}$ **2.** $\frac{9}{\sqrt{10}}$

3. a. $\frac{12}{5}$ **b.** $\frac{3}{\sqrt{10}}$

Problems 4.8

1. a. $(1, 1, 1), (0, 1, 2); \sqrt{2}$ **b.** $(2, 0, 1),$

$(3, 4, -1); \sqrt{21}$ **2.** $\frac{x + \frac{7}{13}}{4} = \frac{y - \frac{25}{13}}{1} = \frac{z - \frac{25}{13}}{-3}$

4. $x - 5y + 22z - 114 = 0$

5. $4x + 2y - 5z - 15 = 0$

Review Exercises

1. a. $(0, 0, 2)$ **b.** None **c.** None

d. $(15, -11, 21)$

e. $\vec{r} = \left(-9, \frac{13}{3}, 0\right) + t\left(-3, \frac{5}{3}, 1\right), t \in R$

f. $\vec{r} = \left(-5, 0, -\frac{8}{5}\right) + t(-2, 1, 0), t \in \mathbf{R}$

4. a. $k \neq \frac{9}{2}$ **b.** No values **c.** $k = \frac{9}{2}$

5. a. $3x + 4y - z - 1 = 0$
b. $\vec{r} = (0, 3, 3) + t(-3, -4, 1), t \in \mathbf{R}$

c. $\left(-\frac{12}{13}, \frac{23}{13}, \frac{43}{13}\right)$

6. $27x + 11y + 7z - 53 = 0$
7. a. $4x - y + z = 0$

8. a. Line $(x, y, z) = \left(\frac{1}{2}, \frac{3}{2}, t\right), t \in \mathbf{R}$

b. No solution; parallel planes

c. Line $(x, y, z) = \left(-1 + \frac{6}{7}t, 1 + \frac{5}{7}t, t\right), t \in \mathbf{R}$

d. Point $(2, 3, -1)$
e. No solution; triangular prism
f. Line $(x, y, z) = (5 - 3t, 1, t), t \in \mathbf{R}$

g. Line $(x, y, z) = \left(1 + \frac{1}{5}t, -2 - \frac{3}{5}t, t\right), t \in \mathbf{R}$

h. Planes coincident with $x - z = 4$
i. No solution; two of the planes are parallel
and distinct **9. a.** $(2, 1, -3)$; unique
b. $(1, 3, -2)$; unique
c. $(x, y, z) = (1, 1, 0) + t(1, -1, 1), t \in \mathbf{R}$;
infinite number; $(1, 1, 0), (2, 0, 1), (0, 2, -1)$
10. Point $(2, -1, 1)$ **11. a.** $3\sqrt{5}$ **b.** $\frac{22}{\sqrt{13}}$

c. $\sqrt{2}$ **d.** $\frac{5}{\sqrt{3}}$ **e.** $\frac{54}{\sqrt{37}}$ **f.** $\frac{4}{\sqrt{14}}$ **g.** $\frac{2}{\sqrt{5}}$

h. $\frac{3}{\sqrt{120}}$ **12.** $\frac{22}{7}$ **13. a.** $\frac{10\sqrt{6}}{9}$ **b.** $\sqrt{\frac{216}{29}}$

14. $(4, -1, 5)$

Chapter 5

Exercises 5.1
1. c, d, h, and i are linear **2. a.** No
b. Yes **3. a.** 1.26 times **b.** 10 times
c. Approximately 3 dB

Problems 5.1
1. Yes **2. a.** $y = kp^x$ **b.** $y = kx^m$

Exercises 5.2
1. a. $\begin{bmatrix} 6 & 0 \\ -3 & 2 \end{bmatrix}$ **b.** $\begin{bmatrix} 6 & \sqrt{2} & 6 \\ 4 & 4\sqrt{3} & 0 \end{bmatrix}$

2. a. $\begin{bmatrix} 3 & 12 \\ -6 & 15 \end{bmatrix}$ **b.** $\begin{bmatrix} 0 & 4 \\ -2 & 4 \end{bmatrix}$ **c.** $\begin{bmatrix} 1 & -2 \\ 12 & 9 \end{bmatrix}$

d. B **e.** $\begin{bmatrix} 0 & 3 \\ -7 & -2 \end{bmatrix}$ **f.** $\begin{bmatrix} 4 & 25 \\ -29 & 14 \end{bmatrix}$

g. $\begin{bmatrix} 5 & 0 \\ 0 & 5 \end{bmatrix}$ **h.** $\begin{bmatrix} 2 & 1 \\ 5 & 8 \end{bmatrix}$ **6.** $a = \frac{1}{3}, b = -\frac{10}{3}$,

$c = \frac{19}{3}$ **7.** $p = \frac{1}{2}, q = -\frac{3}{2}$

8. a. $\begin{bmatrix} 8 \\ -1 \end{bmatrix}$ **b.** $\begin{bmatrix} -3 \\ -21 \end{bmatrix}$ **c.** $\begin{bmatrix} 0 \\ 0 \end{bmatrix}$ **d.** $\begin{bmatrix} 9 \\ -18 \end{bmatrix}$

9. $x = \frac{16}{11}, y = -\frac{23}{11}$

Problems 5.2
1. $A = \begin{bmatrix} -17 & 4 \\ -8 & -5 \end{bmatrix}, B = \begin{bmatrix} 13 & -3 \\ 6 & 4 \end{bmatrix}$

2. $A = \begin{bmatrix} -8 & 7 \\ -9 & 8 \end{bmatrix}$

Exercises 5.3
1. a. Projection onto the y-axis; linear
b. Reflection in the line $y = x$; linear
c. Zero transformation; linear
d. Every point maps to $(4, 2)$; non-linear
e. Translation along $(-3, -2)$; non-linear
f. Points map to the positive x-axis with the
distance from the origin perserved; non-linear
2. a. $T(x, y) = (0, y)$; projection on the
y-axis **b.** $T(x, y) = (3x, 3y)$; magnification
by a factor of 3
c. $T(x, y) = (x, 4y)$; vertical stretch
d. $T(x, y) = (x - y, y)$; horizontal shear
e. $T(x, y) = (-x, y)$; reflection in the y-axis
f. $T(x, y) = \left(\frac{x+y}{2}, \frac{x+y}{2}\right)$; projection

onto the line $y = x$ **g.** $T(x, y) = (5x, 2y)$;
two-way stretch **h.** $T(x, y) = (-x, 4y)$;
vertical stretch combined with a reflection
in the y-axis **3. a.** $(0, 1), (0, -3)$
b. $(6, 3), (-9, -9)$ **c.** $(2, 4), (-3, -12)$
d. $(1, 1), (0, -3)$ **e.** $(-2, 1), (3, -3)$
f. $\left(\frac{3}{2}, \frac{3}{2}\right), (-3, -3)$ **g.** $(10, 2), (-15, -6)$
h. $(-2, 4), (3, -12)$ **4. a.** Non-linear

b. $\begin{bmatrix} 1 & 2 \\ 1 & 2 \end{bmatrix}$ **c.** $\begin{bmatrix} -2 & 3 \\ 0 & 7 \end{bmatrix}$ **d.** Non-linear

5. $\begin{bmatrix} 0 & 1 \\ -1 & 0 \end{bmatrix}$ **6. a.** x-axis; y-axis;

$3x - 10y = 30$ **b.** $7x - 4y = 0$;
$x + 3y = 0$; $11x - 17y + 150 = 0$
c. $2x - y = 0$; $2x - y = 0$; $2x - y = 0$

7. Ellipse $\frac{x^2}{49} + \frac{y^2}{9} = k^2$ **8. a.** Square with vertices $(0, 0)$, $(1, 0)$, $(1, -1)$, $(0, -1)$
b. Parallelogram with vertices $(0, 0)$, $(0, -1)$, $(3, 0)$, $(3, 1)$ **c.** Parallelogram with vertices $(0, 0)$, $(3, 2)$, $(7, 3)$, $(4, 1)$

9. T is represented by $\begin{bmatrix} -\frac{7}{2} & \frac{7}{2} \\ -4 & 3 \end{bmatrix}$

10. a. Transformation represented by $\begin{bmatrix} 2 & 5 \\ 1 & -3 \end{bmatrix}$ **b** and **c.** Not possible

11. a. Plane R^2 **b.** Line $x + y = 0$
c. Origin   **d.** Line $3x - 2y = 0$
12. Straight line; ellipse

Problems 5.3
2. $16x^2 - 24xy + 9y^2 - 75x - 100y = 0$

Exercises 5.4
2. a. $\begin{bmatrix} 9 & -1 \\ 2 & 5 \end{bmatrix}$ **b.** $\begin{bmatrix} 15 & -4 \\ -7 & 3 \end{bmatrix}$ **c.** $\begin{bmatrix} 17 & 7 \\ 0 & 1 \end{bmatrix}$

d. $\begin{bmatrix} 32 & 3 \\ -7 & 4 \end{bmatrix}$ **e.** $\begin{bmatrix} 17 & 1 \\ -7 & 2 \end{bmatrix}$ **f.** $\begin{bmatrix} 17 & 1 \\ -7 & 2 \end{bmatrix}$

g. A **h.** O **i.** $\begin{bmatrix} -8 & 3 \\ 6 & 2 \end{bmatrix}$ **j.** $\begin{bmatrix} -8 & 3 \\ 6 & 2 \end{bmatrix}$

k. $\begin{bmatrix} 4 & 3 \\ -3 & -2 \end{bmatrix}$ **l.** O **3.** $\begin{bmatrix} 0 & -1 \\ -1 & 0 \end{bmatrix}$

5. b, d, e, f, and g are defined
6. a. $\begin{bmatrix} 21 & 3 & 6 \\ -35 & -5 & -10 \end{bmatrix}$ **g.** $\begin{bmatrix} 4 & 1 & 22 \\ -13 & 4 & 30 \end{bmatrix}$

h. $\begin{bmatrix} 204 & 29 & 60 \\ 207 & 28 & 52 \end{bmatrix}$ The remainder are not

defined.   **7. a.** $\begin{bmatrix} a^n & 0 \\ 0 & a^n \end{bmatrix}$ **b.** $\begin{bmatrix} 1 & 0 \\ 0 & 1 \end{bmatrix}$,

if $n = 4k$; $\begin{bmatrix} 0 & -1 \\ 1 & 0 \end{bmatrix}$, if $n = 4k + 1$; $\begin{bmatrix} -1 & 0 \\ 0 & -1 \end{bmatrix}$,

if $n = 4k + 2$; $\begin{bmatrix} 0 & 1 \\ -1 & 0 \end{bmatrix}$, if $n = 4k + 3$

c. $\begin{bmatrix} 0 & 0 \\ 0 & 1 \end{bmatrix}$ **d.** $\begin{bmatrix} 1 & nb \\ 0 & 1 \end{bmatrix}$

Problems 5.4
1. $5^{n-1}A$ **2.** $\begin{bmatrix} a & -\frac{a}{m} \\ am & -a \end{bmatrix}$ or $\begin{bmatrix} 0 & b \\ 0 & 0 \end{bmatrix}$ or $\begin{bmatrix} 0 & 0 \\ c & 0 \end{bmatrix}$

3. No   **4.** No

Exercises 5.5
1. a. -81 **b.** 0 **c.** -28 **d.** -40
e. -66 **4.** $2, 3$ **5. a.** $x = \frac{12}{7}, y = \frac{17}{7}$
b. $x = \frac{1}{k+4}, y = \frac{2}{k+4}$ **c.** $x = 2, y = 1,$
$z = 1$ **d.** $x = \frac{17}{8}, y = -\frac{3}{4}, z = \frac{7}{8}$
e. Does not have a unique solution
f. $x = 0, y = 0, z = 0$

Problems 5.5
1. a. 0 **b.** -120 **c.** 0 **2.** 0
4. $f(x) = 2x^2 + 3x - 1$

Exercises 5.6
1. a. 9 **b.** 16 **c.** 0 **2.** $\frac{27}{2}$ **3. a.** 24
b. 144 **c.** 0 **4.** $-\frac{3}{2}$ **5.** $t \neq 3$
6. a. $-2x + 5y - 9z + 11 = 0$
b. $x + 2y + 1 = 0$ **7.** $1, 0, a^2, ad,$
$-1, 1, 1, ad - bc$ **8. a.** 1
b. -1; reflection   **c.** 49

Problems 5.6
1. $\frac{197}{3}$ **2.** 13 **3.** πabc

Exercises 5.7
1. a. $\begin{bmatrix} -4 & 7 \\ -3 & 5 \end{bmatrix}$ **b.** $\frac{1}{14}\begin{bmatrix} 1 & 4 \\ -3 & 2 \end{bmatrix}$
c. Inverse does not exist
d. $\begin{bmatrix} 1 & 0 & 0 \\ -3 & 1 & 0 \\ 1 & -1 & 1 \end{bmatrix}$ **e.** $\frac{1}{35}\begin{bmatrix} 12 & -7 & -4 \\ 3 & 7 & -1 \\ -7 & 7 & 14 \end{bmatrix}$

f. $\begin{bmatrix} \frac{1}{2} & 0 & \frac{1}{2} & \frac{1}{2} \\ 0 & -1 & 0 & 1 \\ 0 & 1 & 0 & 0 \\ \frac{1}{2} & 1 & -\frac{1}{2} & -\frac{1}{2} \end{bmatrix}$

2. a. $x = -34, y = -25$
b. $x = 23, y = 17$ **3.** $\frac{1}{20}\begin{bmatrix} 6 & 2 \\ -1 & 3 \end{bmatrix}$

Problems 5.7
1. $t \neq \pm 2$

Review Exercises

1. a. $\begin{bmatrix} -3 & -10 \\ 4 & 37 \end{bmatrix}$ **b.** $\begin{bmatrix} -6 & 12 \\ -21 & -3 \end{bmatrix}$

c. Not defined **d.** $\begin{bmatrix} 8 \\ -2 \end{bmatrix}$ **e.** $\begin{bmatrix} 0 \\ 0 \end{bmatrix}$

f. $\begin{bmatrix} -10 & -16 \\ 13 & -9 \end{bmatrix}$ **g.** $\begin{bmatrix} 13 \\ -12 \end{bmatrix}$ **h.** Not defined

2. a. Translation along $(1, -5)$; not linear

b. Magnification by a factor of 7; $\begin{bmatrix} 7 & 0 \\ 0 & 7 \end{bmatrix}$

c. Reflection combined with a magnification by a factor of $\sqrt{2}$; $\begin{bmatrix} 1 & 1 \\ 1 & -1 \end{bmatrix}$

d. Projection on the x-axis; $\begin{bmatrix} 1 & 0 \\ 0 & 0 \end{bmatrix}$

3. a. $(9, 12), (-5, -1)$ **b.** $(0, 5), (0, 1)$
c. $(-27, 17), (-19, 0)$ **d.** $(-17, 34)$,
$(-17, 34)$ **4.** Vertical shear; triangle with vertices $(1, -3), (2, -6), (2, -5)$

5. Circle $x^2 + y^2 = 36$ **7.** $\begin{bmatrix} -1 & 0 \\ 0 & -1 \end{bmatrix}$

8. $\begin{bmatrix} b & b^2 + 1 \\ b^2 + 1 & b^3 + 2b \end{bmatrix}$ **9.** No

10. $\begin{bmatrix} -14 + 2\sqrt{2} \\ -4 + 2\sqrt{2} \end{bmatrix}$ **11.** $\begin{bmatrix} \frac{3}{2} & -\frac{1}{2} \\ -\frac{1}{2} & \frac{7}{2} \end{bmatrix}$

12. a. 71 **b.** -51 **c.** 0 **d.** 1 **e.** $2t^3$
f. -20 **13.** $0, -1, -2$ **14.** 31
16. $x + y + z - 3 = 0$ **17. a.** $x = 5$,
$y = -2$ **b.** $x = 1, y = -6, z = 10$
18. a. $x = -11, y = -9$ **b.** $x_1 = 5$,
$x_2 = -2, x_3 = -2$ **19. a.** $\begin{bmatrix} 3 & 2 \\ 1 & 1 \end{bmatrix}$

b. $\begin{bmatrix} 2 & 3 \\ 1 & 2 \end{bmatrix}$ **c.** $\begin{bmatrix} 0 & -1 \\ 1 & 1 \end{bmatrix}$ **d.** $\begin{bmatrix} 3 & -2 \\ 2 & -1 \end{bmatrix}$

Chapter 6

Exercises 6.1

1. a. $(-2, -1)$ **b.** $(-9, 1)$ **c.** $(-8, 8)$

d. $(-7, 8)$ **e.** $(1, 7)$ **f.** $(0, 0)$ **g.** $(1, 11)$
2. a. $(-1, -1)$ **b.** $(0, 0)$ **c.** $(-4, 15)$
d. $(12, -8)$ **e.** $(6, 5)$ **f.** $(-4, 2)$
3. a. $5x - 2y + 26 = 0$
b. $x + 3y - 1 = 0$ **c.** $x = 9$
d. $2x - 5 = 0$ **4. a.** $(-2, 4)$
b. $Q'(-5, 8), R'(2, 3)$ **c.** $|P'Q'| = \sqrt{106}$,
$|P'R'| = 2\sqrt{5}, |Q'R'| = \sqrt{74}$
d. $\angle P' = 56°, \angle Q' = 25°, \angle R' = 99°$
e. 19 **f.** $\sqrt{85}$ **g.** $\left(1, -\frac{2}{3}\right), \left(-1, \frac{10}{3}\right)$
5. $P''(-3, -3), Q''(-8, 6), R''(-1, 1)$;
$(x, y) \rightarrow (x - 5, y + 2)$ **6.** a and j; f, i,
and l; g and k **7. a.** $(-1, 1)$
b. $(5, 1)$ **c.** $(2, -2)$ **d.** $(3, -1)$
8. $2x - 3y - 17 = 0$
9. $x - 2y + 11 = 0$
10. $f \circ g(x, y) = g \circ f(x, y) = (x - 3, y + 2)$
11. The translation along $(2, -5)$

Problems 6.1

1. a. and b. $T \circ S(x, y) = S \circ T(x, y) =$
$(x + m + p - a - c, y + n + q - b - d)$
3. a. Translations along $\left(-\frac{3}{2}, \frac{\sqrt{3}}{2}\right)$,
$\left(\frac{3}{2}, \frac{\sqrt{3}}{2}\right), (3, \sqrt{3}), (-3, -\sqrt{3}), (3, 0)$
b. Translations along $\left(\frac{3}{2}m, \frac{\sqrt{3}}{2}m + \sqrt{3}n\right)$ for all
integers m and n **4.** $\vec{n} \cdot \vec{a} = 0$

Exercises 6.2

1. a. $a = 2, b = -5, f = -6, g = -5$,
$c = -27$ **b.** $a = 3, b = -5, f = 6$,
$g = 20, c = -68$ **c.** $a = \frac{1}{9}, b = \frac{1}{4}, f = 0$,
$g = 0, c = -1$ **d.** not possible **e.** $a = 4$,
$b = 0, f = \frac{3}{2}, g = -\frac{1}{2}, c = -5$
f. not possible **2. a.** Circle; $ab > 0$;
radius 4; original centre $(0, 0)$; image centre
$(-3, 4)$ **b.** Ellipse; $ab > 0$; original centre
$(0, 0)$; image centre $(-5, 3)$; original vertices
$(4, 0), (-4, 0)$; image vertices $(-1, 3), (9, 3)$
c. Hyperbola; $ab < 0$; original centre $(0, 0)$;
image centre $(3, 1)$; original vertices $(5, 0)$,
$(-5, 0)$; image vertices $(8, 1), (-2, 1)$;
original asymptotes $2x - 5y = 0$,
$2x + 5y = 0$; image asymptotes
$2x - 5y - 1 = 0, 2x + 5y - 11 = 0$

d. Hyperbola; $ab < 0$; original centre $(-2, 3)$; image centre $(0, 0)$; original vertices $(2, 3)$, $(-6, 3)$; image vertices $(4, 0)$, $(-4, 0)$; original asymptotes $x + y - 1 = 0$, $x - y + 5 = 0$; image asymptotes $x + y = 0$, $x - y = 0$
e. Ellipse; $ab > 0$; original centre $(1, 3)$; image centre $(0, 0)$; original vertices $(1, 2)$, $(1, -8)$; image vertices $(0, 5)$, $(0, -5)$
f. Parabola; $ab = 0$; original vertex $(3, -5)$; image vertex $(0, 0)$ **g.** Circle; $ab > 0$; radius $\frac{5}{3}$; original centre $(1, -2)$; image centre $(0, 0)$ **h.** Two intersecting lines; $ab < 0$; original lines intersect at $(-2, 5)$; image intersection $(0, 0)$ **i.** Imaginary circle; $ab > 0$ **3.** $y^2 - 4px - 2ky + k^2 + 4ph = 0$

Problems 6.2

1. Parabola if $ab = 0$; ellipse if $ab > 0$ (circle if $a = b$); hyperbola if $ab < 0$
2. a. $xy + 2x - 5y - 11 = 0$
b. $y = x^3 + 3x^2 + 3x + 4$
c. $y = \sin\left(x + \frac{\pi}{4}\right) + 3$ **d.** $y = 2^{x-5} - 3$

Exercises 6.3

1. a. $(1, -2)$, 3 **b.** $(-3, 4)$, $2\sqrt{3}$
c. $(2, -4)$, $\frac{5}{2}$ **d.** $(-2, -2)$, $2\sqrt{2}$
e. $(0, -2)$, $\frac{\sqrt{5}}{3}$ **f.** Imaginary circle
2. a. $(h, k) = (-1, 3)$, $4x^2 + 9y^2 = 36$
b. $(h, k) = (-1, 3)$, $y^2 = 8x$
c. $(h, k) = (3, 3)$, $4x^2 - y^2 = -4$
d. $(h, k) = (-1, 2)$, $4x^2 - y^2 = -16$
3. a. Along $(2, 2)$, $4x^2 - y^2 = -4$
b. Along $(-5, 3)$, $x^2 = 8y$
c. Along $(-3, -3)$, $x^2 + 9y^2 = 9$
d. Along $(2, 1)$, $5x^2 = -2y$
4. a. Parabola, vertex $(2, -5)$ **b.** Ellipse, centre $(5, -3)$, vertices $(5, 2)$, $(5, -8)$
c. Point circle, centre $(5, -3)$, radius 0
d. Circle, centre $\left(-\frac{1}{2}, \frac{3}{4}\right)$, radius 1
e. Parabola, vertex $(1, -3)$ **f.** Ellipse, centre $(-5, 2)$, vertices $(-5, 4)$, $(-5, 0)$
g. Hyperbola, centre $(0, -3)$, vertices $(2, -3)$, $(-2, -3)$

Problems 6.3

1. a. Hyperbola, centre $(-1, 5)$, asymptotes $x = -1$, $y = 5$ **b.** Two parallel lines with slope -1 **2.** $2x - 3y + 9 = 0$, $2x + 3y + 3 = 0$ **3.** Centre is $(1, -3, -1)$

Exercises 6.4

1. All pairs except d and f
2. a. $\left(\frac{3 + 2\sqrt{3}}{2}, \frac{-2 + 3\sqrt{3}}{2}\right)$
b. $(1 + 3\sqrt{3}, -3 + \sqrt{3})$ **c.** $\left(\frac{1}{\sqrt{2}}, \frac{9}{\sqrt{2}}\right)$
d. $(3, -7)$ **e.** $(\sqrt{3}, -1)$
f. $(-2 - 2\sqrt{3}, -2 + 2\sqrt{3})$
3. b. $\frac{1}{\sqrt{10}}\begin{bmatrix} 1 & -3 \\ 3 & 1 \end{bmatrix}$ **c.** $72°$

6. $\left(\frac{3 + 4\sqrt{3}}{2}, \frac{-4 + 3\sqrt{3}}{2}\right)$, $\left(\frac{-2 + \sqrt{3}}{2}, \frac{-1 - 2\sqrt{3}}{2}\right)$, $\left(\frac{5\sqrt{3}}{2}, -\frac{5}{2}\right)$ **7. a.** $\begin{bmatrix} 0 & -1 \\ 1 & 0 \end{bmatrix}$
b. $\frac{1}{2\sqrt{2}}\begin{bmatrix} 1 - \sqrt{3} & -1 - \sqrt{3} \\ 1 + \sqrt{3} & 1 - \sqrt{3} \end{bmatrix}$
c. $\frac{1}{2\sqrt{2}}\begin{bmatrix} 1 + \sqrt{3} & 1 - \sqrt{3} \\ -1 + \sqrt{3} & 1 + \sqrt{3} \end{bmatrix}$
8. a. $\frac{1}{2}\begin{bmatrix} -\sqrt{3} & 1 \\ 1 & \sqrt{3} \end{bmatrix}$ **b.** $\frac{1}{2}\begin{bmatrix} -\sqrt{3} & -1 \\ -1 & \sqrt{3} \end{bmatrix}$
c. $\frac{1}{2}\begin{bmatrix} 1 & \sqrt{3} \\ -\sqrt{3} & 1 \end{bmatrix}$ **d.** $\frac{1}{\sqrt{2}}\begin{bmatrix} -1 & -1 \\ -1 & 1 \end{bmatrix}$
e. $\begin{bmatrix} \sqrt{2} & 0 \\ \sqrt{2} & \sqrt{2} \end{bmatrix}$
9. a. $\begin{bmatrix} \cos(\theta + \phi) & -\sin(\theta + \phi) \\ \sin(\theta + \phi) & \cos(\theta + \phi) \end{bmatrix}$ and $\begin{bmatrix} 1 & 0 \\ 0 & 1 \end{bmatrix}$

Problems 6.4

1. $3x - y + 5 = 0$
3. b. $\begin{bmatrix} \cos\theta & 0 & -\sin\theta \\ 0 & 1 & 0 \\ \sin\theta & 0 & \cos\theta \end{bmatrix}$
4. $(x, y) \to ((x - a)\cos\theta - (y - b)\sin\theta + a, (x - a)\sin\theta + (y - b)\cos\theta + b)$

Exercises 6.5

1. a. $\begin{bmatrix} 2 & -1 \\ 7 & 3 \end{bmatrix}$ **b.** $\begin{bmatrix} 5 & 2 \\ 0 & -1 \end{bmatrix}$ **c.** $\begin{bmatrix} 3 & -2 \end{bmatrix}$
d. $\begin{bmatrix} -4 \\ 5 \end{bmatrix}$ **e.** $\begin{bmatrix} 24 & 1 \\ -7 & -3 \end{bmatrix}$ **f.** $\begin{bmatrix} 24 & 1 \\ -7 & -3 \end{bmatrix}$

g. $[-13]$ **h.** $[29]$ **i.** $[-22]$ **j.** $[-22]$

k. $\begin{bmatrix} 53 & 19 \\ 19 & 10 \end{bmatrix}$ **l.** $\begin{bmatrix} 5 & 11 \\ 11 & 58 \end{bmatrix}$ **m.** $[-91 \quad 13]$

n. $\begin{bmatrix} -91 \\ 13 \end{bmatrix}$ **o.** $\begin{bmatrix} -12 & 8 \\ 15 & -10 \end{bmatrix}$ **p.** $\begin{bmatrix} 122 & -41 \\ -1 & 3 \end{bmatrix}$

2. a. $[x \quad y] \begin{bmatrix} 3 & 0 \\ 0 & 5 \end{bmatrix} \begin{bmatrix} x \\ y \end{bmatrix} = 16$

b. $[x \quad y] \begin{bmatrix} 3 & -2 \\ -2 & 5 \end{bmatrix} \begin{bmatrix} x \\ y \end{bmatrix} = 1$

c. $[x \quad y] \begin{bmatrix} 1 & \frac{1}{2} \\ \frac{1}{2} & -2 \end{bmatrix} \begin{bmatrix} x \\ y \end{bmatrix} = 0$

d. $[x \quad y] \begin{bmatrix} 0 & \frac{1}{2} \\ \frac{1}{2} & 0 \end{bmatrix} \begin{bmatrix} x \\ y \end{bmatrix} = 8$

3. a. $5x^2 + 2\sqrt{3}xy + 5y^2$
b. $-3x^2 - xy + y^2$ **c.** $x^2 + 4xy$
4. a. $(5\sqrt{3} + 3)x + (-5 + 3\sqrt{3})y + 30 = 0$
b. $10x^2 - 12xy + 10y^2 = 9$
c. $x^2 - 10\sqrt{3}xy + 11y^2 = -64$
d. $x^2 - y^2 = 8$
e. $x^2 + 2\sqrt{3}xy + 3y^2 + 32\sqrt{3}x - 32y = 0$
f. $x^2 - 5y^2 = -20$

Problems 6.5

1. The final image is the hyperbola $x^2 - 4y^2 = -6$.

Exercises 6.6

1. a. $\frac{1}{2}\begin{bmatrix} \sqrt{3} & 1 \\ -1 & \sqrt{3} \end{bmatrix}$ **b.** $\frac{1}{\sqrt{2}}\begin{bmatrix} 1 & 1 \\ -1 & 1 \end{bmatrix}$

c. $\frac{1}{2}\begin{bmatrix} 1 & \sqrt{3} \\ -\sqrt{3} & 1 \end{bmatrix}$ **d.** $\frac{1}{2}\begin{bmatrix} \sqrt{3} & 1 \\ -1 & \sqrt{3} \end{bmatrix}$

e. $\frac{1}{2}\begin{bmatrix} 1 & \sqrt{3} \\ -\sqrt{3} & 1 \end{bmatrix}$ **f.** $\frac{1}{\sqrt{2}}\begin{bmatrix} 1 & 1 \\ -1 & 1 \end{bmatrix}$

g. $\frac{1}{\sqrt{2}}\begin{bmatrix} 1 & 1 \\ -1 & 1 \end{bmatrix}$ **h.** $\frac{1}{2}\begin{bmatrix} 1 & \sqrt{3} \\ -\sqrt{3} & 1 \end{bmatrix}$

i. $\frac{1}{\sqrt{5}}\begin{bmatrix} 2 & 1 \\ -1 & 2 \end{bmatrix}$ **j.** $\frac{1}{5}\begin{bmatrix} 3 & 4 \\ -4 & 3 \end{bmatrix}$

2. a. $x^2 + 3y^2 = 18$ **b.** $3x^2 - y^2 = 16$
c. $x^2 - y^2 = -2$ **d.** Two lines $x^2 - y^2 = 0$
e. $2x^2 + 5y^2 = 2$
f. $3x^2 + 7y^2 = 0$, the point $(0, 0)$
g. $x^2 - y^2 = 8$ **h.** $4x^2 + 9y^2 = 36$
i. $8x^2 + 3y^2 = 240$

j. $12x^2 - 13y^2 + 468 = 0$

Problems 6.6

1. a. Hyperbola with asymptotes $x = -3$ and $y = 1$ **b.** Parabola with vertex $(-1, \sqrt{3})$

Exercises 6.7

1. a. $\frac{1}{\sqrt{10}}\begin{bmatrix} 3 & 1 \\ -1 & 3 \end{bmatrix}$ **b.** $\frac{1}{\sqrt{13}}\begin{bmatrix} 3 & 2 \\ -2 & 3 \end{bmatrix}$

c. $\frac{1}{\sqrt{29}}\begin{bmatrix} 2 & 5 \\ -5 & 2 \end{bmatrix}$ **d.** $\frac{1}{5}\begin{bmatrix} 3 & 4 \\ -4 & 3 \end{bmatrix}$ **e.** $\frac{1}{\sqrt{2}}\begin{bmatrix} 1 & 1 \\ -1 & 1 \end{bmatrix}$

f. $\frac{1}{\sqrt{2}}\begin{bmatrix} 1 & 1 \\ -1 & 1 \end{bmatrix}$ **g.** $\frac{1}{5}\begin{bmatrix} 4 & 3 \\ -3 & 4 \end{bmatrix}$

2. a is an ellipse; d and f are hyperbolas; the others are parabolas **3. a.** $6x^2 + y^2 = 9$
b. Two lines $y^2 = 4$ **c.** Line $x^2 = 0$
d. $2x^2 - 3y^2 = -6$ **e.** $x^2 = 4y$
f. $x^2 - y^2 = -16$ **g.** $x^2 = -8y$

Problems 6.7

1. Vertices are $\left(\frac{4}{\sqrt{5}}, -\frac{7}{\sqrt{5}}\right)$, $(-4\sqrt{5}, \sqrt{5})$;
asymptotes are $x + 7y + 3\sqrt{5} = 0$,
$5x + 5y + 9\sqrt{5} = 0$ **2. a.** Hyperbola
$x^2 + 2xy - y^2 - 4x + 4 = 0$ **b.** Parabola
$x^2 - 2xy + y^2 - 10x + 2y = 0$

Review Exercises

1. a. $(5, -6)$ **b.** $(1, 2)$ **c.** $(5, -8)$
d. $\left(-2 + \frac{3\sqrt{3}}{2}, -3 - \sqrt{3}\right)$
2. a. $(x - 1, y - 2)$
b. $(x + 5, y - 6)$ **c.** $(x + 3, y - 5)$
d. $(x + 7, y)$ **3.** $\ell_1{:}2x - y + 7 = 0$
and $\ell_2{:}2x - y - 1 = 0$
4. a. $x^2 + y^2 - 4x - 10y + 25 = 0$
b. $x^2 - 4x + 8y - 36 = 0$
c. $25x^2 + 4y^2 - 100x - 40y + 100 = 0$
d. $xy - 5x - 2y + 22 = 0$
5. a. $(x, y) \rightarrow (x - 1, y + 1)$
b. $(x, y) \rightarrow (x + 2, y - 5)$
c. $(x, y) \rightarrow \left(x + 1, y - \frac{1}{2}\right)$
d. $(x, y) \rightarrow (x + 1, y)$, etc.
6. a. Ellipse with vertices $(2, 2)$ and $(2, -8)$
b. Circle centre $(2, -3)$ and radius 5
c. Parabola with vertex $(2, 2)$
d. Point $(-3, 1)$ **e.** Hyperbola with vertices

$(3, -4)$ and $(3, -6)$ **7. a.** $\begin{bmatrix} 3 & -1 \\ -1 & 5 \end{bmatrix}$

b. $\begin{bmatrix} 1 & 2 \\ 2 & 0 \end{bmatrix}$ **c.** $\begin{bmatrix} 1 & \sqrt{3} \\ \sqrt{3} & 1 \end{bmatrix}$ **d.** $\begin{bmatrix} 0 & \frac{1}{2} \\ \frac{1}{2} & 0 \end{bmatrix}$

8. a. $3x^2 + 2xy + 2y^2$ **b.** $4x^2 - 6xy$

c. $2x^2 + 3\sqrt{3}xy - y^2$ **9. a.** $\frac{1}{2}\begin{bmatrix} \sqrt{3} & 1 \\ -1 & \sqrt{3} \end{bmatrix}$;

ellipse with vertices $\pm\left(\frac{3\sqrt{2}}{2}, \frac{3\sqrt{6}}{2}\right)$

b. $\frac{1}{\sqrt{2}}\begin{bmatrix} 1 & 1 \\ -1 & 1 \end{bmatrix}$; hyperbola with vertices

$\pm(\sqrt{2}, \sqrt{2})$ **c.** $\frac{1}{\sqrt{5}}\begin{bmatrix} 2 & 1 \\ -1 & 2 \end{bmatrix}$; ellipse

with vertices $\pm\left(\frac{3}{\sqrt{5}}, -\frac{3}{2\sqrt{5}}\right)$

d. $\frac{1}{2}\begin{bmatrix} 1 & \sqrt{3} \\ -\sqrt{3} & 1 \end{bmatrix}$; parallel lines through

$\pm(1, 0)$ with slope $-\sqrt{3}$ **e.** $\frac{1}{\sqrt{13}}\begin{bmatrix} 2 & 3 \\ -3 & 2 \end{bmatrix}$;

ellipse with vertices $\pm(3\sqrt{13}, 2\sqrt{13})$

f. $\frac{1}{\sqrt{2}}\begin{bmatrix} 1 & 1 \\ -1 & 1 \end{bmatrix}$; point $(0, 0)$

10. a. Hyperbola with vertices $\left(\frac{3}{\sqrt{2}}, \frac{5}{\sqrt{2}}\right)$,

$\left(-\frac{3}{\sqrt{2}}, -\frac{1}{\sqrt{2}}\right)$ **b.** Ellipse with vertices

$\left(3 + \frac{\sqrt{3}}{2}, \frac{1}{2} - 3\sqrt{3}\right)$, $\left(-1 + \frac{\sqrt{3}}{2}, \frac{1}{2} + \sqrt{3}\right)$

c. Hyperbola with vertices $\left(-\frac{1}{5}, -\frac{7}{5}\right)$,

$\left(-\frac{13}{5}, -\frac{9}{5}\right)$ **d.** Parabola with vertex $(0, 0)$

11. -6

Chapter 7

Exercises 7.1

1. a. $1^2 = \frac{1 \cdot 2 \cdot 3}{6}$, $1^2 + 2^2 + 3^2 = \frac{3 \cdot 4 \cdot 7}{6}$

b. $\frac{1}{2} = \frac{1}{2}$, $\frac{1}{2} + \frac{1}{6} + \frac{1}{12} = \frac{3}{4}$ **c.** A one element
set has 2 subsets; a three element set has
8 subsets. **d.** $2 + 3 + 1$ is divisible by 6;
$2 \cdot 3^3 + 3 \cdot 3^2 + 3$ is divisible by 6.

e. $2 \le 1 + 1$, $\sqrt[3]{2} \le 1 + \frac{1}{3}$ **f.** One line

divides the plane into at most 2 regions;
three lines divide the plane into at most
7 regions. **3. a.** $k^2 + 2k$

b. $(-1)^k(2k + 1)$ **c.** $(2k + 5)(7k - 17)$

Problems 7.1

1. $2^{-(n-1)/2} L$, $2^{-(n-1)} L^2$ **2.** Segment has
length $3^{-(n-1)}l$; perimeter is $3\left(\frac{4}{3}\right)^{n-1}l$

Exercises 7.2

5. a. True **b.** False **c.** True

Problems 7.2

2. $\frac{10}{7} - \frac{5}{7 \cdot 2^{3n-1}}$

Exercises 7.3

4. a. $\frac{2047}{1024}$ **b.** 3.60 **c.** 1 **d.** 2 505 503

7. a. 480 **b.** 65 651 332

Exercises 7.4

5. b is true

Problems 7.4

2. $\frac{n(n-3)}{2}$

Exercises 7.5

1. a. 2 500 **b.** 210 **c.** 40 **d.** 0

e. 29 652 480 **f.** 280 **4. a.** $64a^6 + 192a^5b$
$+ 240a^4b^2 + 160a^3b^3 + 60a^2b^4 + 12ab^5 + b^6$

b. $a^5 - 5a^4 + 10a^3 - 10a^2 + 5a - 1$

c. $x^8 - 8x^6 + 28x^4 - 56x^2 + 70 - 56x^{-2} +$
$28x^{-4} - 8x^{-6} + x^{-8}$ **d.** $256x^8 - 786x^6y^3 +$
$864x^4y^6 - 432x^2y^9 + 81y^{12}$ **5.** $99 - 70\sqrt{2}$

7. -467 and 0 **8.** 2 446 875

Review Exercises

2. a, c, f, g, and i are true **3. a.** 65 600

b. 1 589 525 **7. a.** 61 236 **b.** 122 472

c. $20a^3b^3$ **d.** 0 **10.** n^2

Chapter 8

Exercises 8.1

1. a. 6, 11 **b.** 0, -7 **c.** 14, 0

d. -1, -2 **2. a.** $3 + 4i$, $-1 + 5i$

b. 4, 5 **c.** $4 + 6i$, $-5 + 4i$ **d.** $6 - 6i$,

$48 + 46i$ **e.** $(2 + \sqrt{5}) - 6i$, $2\sqrt{5} - 6\sqrt{5}i$

f. $-5 + i$, $10 - 10i$ **3. a.** $0 + 2i$

b. $9 + 3i$ **c.** $-25 + 0i$ **d.** $17 + 0i$
e. $0 + 0i$ **f.** $(\pi^2 - 3) - 2\sqrt{3}\pi i$

g. $10 + 0i$ **h.** $\frac{1}{2} - \frac{1}{36}i$ **4. a.** $2 - 9i$

b. $3 + 6i$ **5. a.** $0 \pm \sqrt{3}i$ **b.** $\frac{1}{\sqrt{2}} + \frac{1}{\sqrt{2}}i$,

$-\frac{1}{\sqrt{2}} - \frac{1}{\sqrt{2}}i$ **c.** $\pm\sqrt{7} + 0i$

6. When $a = \frac{2}{3}b$ **7.** When $a = -\frac{5}{4}b$

Problems 8.1
2. a. $1 + 2i$ **b.** $0 + 0i$ **c.** $1 + 0i$
d. $4 + 4i$

Exercises 8.2
1.

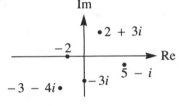

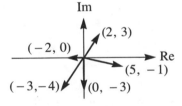

2. $\sqrt{13}, \sqrt{26}, 2, 5, 3$ **3. a.** $2 - 9i, \sqrt{85}$
b. $i, 1$ **c.** $3, 3$ **d.** $-4 - 5i, \sqrt{41}$
e. $\sqrt{2} + 3\sqrt{7}i, \sqrt{65}$

4.

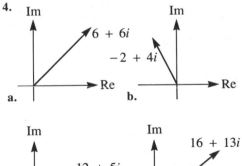

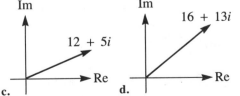

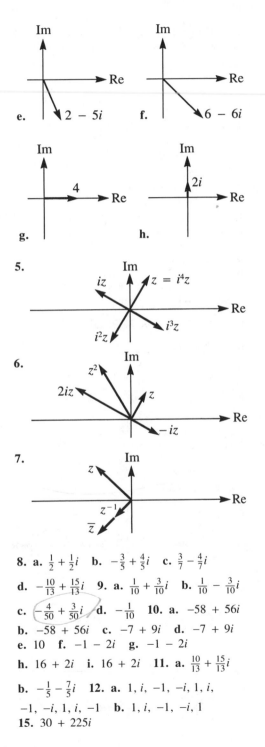

8. a. $\frac{1}{2} + \frac{1}{2}i$ **b.** $-\frac{3}{5} + \frac{4}{5}i$ **c.** $\frac{3}{7} - \frac{4}{7}i$

d. $-\frac{10}{13} + \frac{15}{13}i$ **9. a.** $\frac{1}{10} + \frac{3}{10}i$ **b.** $\frac{1}{10} - \frac{3}{10}i$

c. $-\frac{4}{50} + \frac{3}{50}i$ **d.** $-\frac{1}{10}$ **10. a.** $-58 + 56i$

b. $-58 + 56i$ **c.** $-7 + 9i$ **d.** $-7 + 9i$
e. 10 **f.** $-1 - 2i$ **g.** $-1 - 2i$

h. $16 + 2i$ **i.** $16 + 2i$ **11. a.** $\frac{10}{13} + \frac{15}{13}i$

b. $-\frac{1}{5} - \frac{7}{5}i$ **12. a.** $1, i, -1, -i, 1, i,$

$-1, -i, 1, i, -1$ **b.** $1, i, -1, -i, 1$
15. $30 + 225i$

Problems 8.2

3. $-77 - 25i$ **4.** $0 - 8i$ **7.** $0 + 0i$,

$1 + 0i$, $-\frac{1}{2} + \frac{\sqrt{3}}{2}i$, $-\frac{1}{2} - \frac{\sqrt{3}}{2}i$

Exercises 8.3

1. a. $-\frac{1}{4} \pm \frac{\sqrt{15}}{4}i$ **b.** $\frac{3}{2} \pm \frac{3\sqrt{3}}{2}i$

c. $-\sqrt{2}, 3\sqrt{2}$ **d.** $\sqrt{3}, -\frac{\sqrt{3}}{2}$

2. a. $x^2 - 10x + 26 = 0$

b. $x^2 - 2\sqrt{2}x + 6 = 0$

c. $x^2 - 2x + 6 = 0$

d. $x^2 - 4x + 7 + 2\sqrt{2} = 0$

3. a. $i, -3i$ **b.** $2i, 5i$ **c.** $2 \pm \sqrt{4 - 6i}$

d. $1 + 2i, -1 + 3i$

4. a. $x^2 + 5ix + 14 = 0$

b. $x^2 - (1 + 2i)x - 1 + i = 0$

c. $x^2 - (2 + 3i)x - 5 + 5i = 0$

d. $x^2 - 4ix - 5 + 2\sqrt{2}i = 0$

5. $(-3 \pm 2\sqrt{3})i$ **6. a.** $3, -\frac{3}{2} \pm \frac{3\sqrt{3}}{2}i$

b. $\pm\frac{\sqrt{6}}{2}, \pm\sqrt{5}i$ **8. a.** $x^2 - 11x + 32 = 0$

b. $x^2 - 9x + 64 = 0$

c. $8x^2 - 9x + 8 = 0$

d. $x^2 - 5x + 512 = 0$

Problems 8.3

1. $1 \pm i, 2 \pm i$

Exercises 8.4

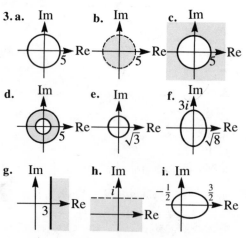

3. a. Im   **b.** Im   **c.** Im

d. Im   **e.** Im   **f.** Im

g. Im   **h.** Im   **i.** Im

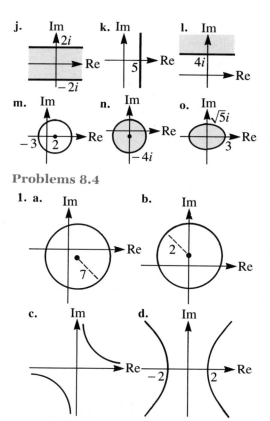

j. Im   **k.** Im   **l.** Im

m. Im   **n.** Im   **o.** Im

Problems 8.4

1. a. Im   **b.** Im

c. Im   **d.** Im

2. a. The hyperbola illustrated in Problem 1d.
b. The y-axis.   **c.** One branch of a hyperbola
with vertex at i.   **4. a.** $4 + 5i + 0j - k$,
$2 + 6i + 7j - 10k$, $2 + 8i - 11j + 0k$,
$-9 + 24i + 6j + 6k$

b. $\bar{q} = a - bi - cj - dk$,
$q\bar{q} = \bar{q}q = a^2 + b^2 + c^2 + d^2$,

$q^{-1} = \dfrac{\bar{q}}{a^2 + b^2 + c^2 + d^2}$

Exercises 8.5

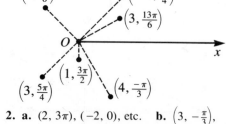

1. $\left(3, \frac{5\pi}{6}\right)$ $\left(-4, \frac{5\pi}{4}\right)$ $\left(3, \frac{13\pi}{6}\right)$

O x

$\left(3, \frac{5\pi}{4}\right)$ $\left(1, \frac{3\pi}{2}\right)$ $\left(4, \frac{-\pi}{3}\right)$

2. a. $(2, 3\pi), (-2, 0)$, etc.   **b.** $\left(3, -\frac{\pi}{3}\right)$,

$\left(3, \frac{5\pi}{3}\right)$, etc.   **c.** $\left(3, \frac{29\pi}{12}\right), \left(3, -\frac{19\pi}{12}\right)$, etc.

3. a. $(0, 2)$ **b.** $(1, 1)$ **c.** $\left(-\frac{5}{2}, -\frac{5\sqrt{3}}{2}\right)$

d. $(-3\sqrt{3}, -3)$ **e.** $\left(\frac{3}{2}, \frac{3\sqrt{3}}{2}\right)$ **4. a.** $(2, 0)$

b. $\left(5, \frac{3\pi}{2}\right)$ **c.** $\left(4\sqrt{2}, -\frac{\pi}{4}\right)$ **d.** $\left(8, \frac{2\pi}{3}\right)$

e. $\left(2, \frac{5\pi}{4}\right)$ **f.** $(\sqrt{5}, \pi - \tan^{-1}(2)) \approx (\sqrt{5}, 2.03)$

5. a. $x^2 + y^2 = 5$ **b.** $x^2 + y^2 - 3x = 0$
c. $y = -\sqrt{3}x$ **d.** $y^2 = x$
e. $x^2y + y^3 = 3x$ **6. a.** $r = 3$
b. $r = 7 \csc \theta$ **c.** $r^2 = 5 \csc 2\theta$

d. $r^2 = \dfrac{4}{1 - 5\sin^2\theta}$ **e.** $r = \dfrac{6}{5\sin\theta - \cos\theta}$

f. $r = 2\cos\theta - 6\sin\theta$

7. a. Symmetry with respect to the pole

b. Symmetry with respect to the polar axis

c. Symmetry with respect to the line $\theta = \frac{\pi}{2}$

d. Symmetry with respect to the line $\theta = \frac{\pi}{2}$

e. No symmetry with respect to the pole, polar axis, or line $\theta = \frac{\pi}{2}$

8. a.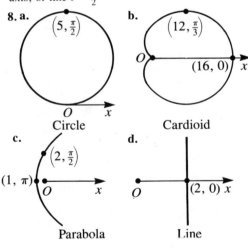

Circle

b. Cardioid

c. Parabola

d. Line

9. $r = \dfrac{1 + 2\sqrt{3}}{\sqrt{3}\sin\theta + \cos\theta}$

10. $r = 6(\cos\theta + \sin\theta)$

Problems 8.5
1. The polar equation is $r = 4\cos 2\theta$. Its graph is the four-leaved rose shown in Example 8.   **2.** $\left(6, \frac{2\pi}{3}\right), \left(6, \frac{4\pi}{3}\right)$

3. $r = \dfrac{24}{4 - 3\cos\theta}$

Exercises 8.6
1. a. $2 \operatorname{cis} \frac{\pi}{3}$ **b.** $2 \operatorname{cis} \frac{\pi}{2}$ **c.** $4 \operatorname{cis} \frac{5\pi}{4}$

d. $4 \operatorname{cis} 0$ **e.** $\operatorname{cis}\left(-\frac{\pi}{3}\right)$

f. $\sqrt{10} \operatorname{cis}(-0.32)$ **g.** $\operatorname{cis} \frac{3\pi}{2}$

h. $\operatorname{cis} \frac{2\pi}{3}$ **i.** $2 \operatorname{cis} \frac{5\pi}{6}$ **2. a.** $-i$

b. $2\sqrt{2} - 2\sqrt{2}i$ **c.** $-\frac{3\sqrt{3}}{2} + \frac{3}{2}i$ **d.** -10

e. $\frac{1}{4} - \frac{\sqrt{3}}{4}i$ **f.** $-1.97 - 0.31i$ **3. a.** $2e^{\frac{i\pi}{3}}$

b. $2e^{\frac{i\pi}{2}}$ **c.** $4e^{\frac{5i\pi}{4}}$ **d.** $4e^{0i}$ **e.** $e^{-\frac{i\pi}{3}}$

f. $\sqrt{10}e^{-0.32i}$ **g.** $e^{\frac{3i\pi}{2}}$ **h.** $e^{\frac{2i\pi}{3}}$ **i.** $2e^{\frac{5i\pi}{6}}$
4. a. $0 + i$ **b.** $2 - 2\sqrt{3}i$ **c.** $1.62 + 2.52i$

d. 1 **5. a.** $2 \operatorname{cis} \frac{\pi}{6}$ **b.** $\sqrt{2} \operatorname{cis}\left(-\frac{\pi}{12}\right)$

c. $\frac{1}{\sqrt{2}} \operatorname{cis}\left(-\frac{\pi}{12}\right)$ **6. a.** $2\sqrt{2} \operatorname{cis}\left(-\frac{\pi}{12}\right)$

b. $10 \operatorname{cis} \pi$ **c.** $\operatorname{cis} \frac{17\pi}{12}$ **d.** $144 \operatorname{cis} \frac{4\pi}{3}$

e. $8 \operatorname{cis} \frac{4\pi}{3}$ **9.** A circle with centre the origin and radius 1.

Exercises 8.7
1. a. $-4\sqrt{2} + 4\sqrt{2}i$ **b.** $-\frac{1}{2} + \frac{\sqrt{3}}{2}i$

c. $256 + 0i$ **d.** $-\frac{1}{2} - \frac{\sqrt{3}}{2}i$ **e.** $0 + 27i$

f. $\frac{1}{\sqrt{2}} + \frac{1}{\sqrt{2}}i$ **g.** $\frac{1}{2048} - \frac{\sqrt{3}}{2048}i$

h. $-2\sqrt{2} + 2\sqrt{2}i$ **i.** $-\frac{1}{4} + 0i$

j. $-0.025 - 0.024i$

2.

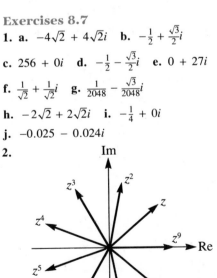

3.

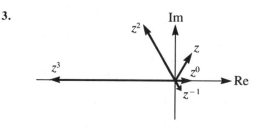

5. a. $32i$ **b.** $-1 - 3i$

Problems 8.7

3. 0 or 4 **4.** If $n \neq 2$, $z = \text{cis} \frac{2k\pi}{n-2}$, for any integer k; if $n = 2$, $z = \text{cis}\,\theta$, for any θ.

Exercises 8.8

1. a. 2, $2\,\text{cis}\,\frac{2\pi}{3}$, $2\,\text{cis}\,\frac{4\pi}{3}$ **b.** $\text{cis}\,\frac{\pi}{8}$, $\text{cis}\,\frac{5\pi}{8}$,

$\text{cis}\,\frac{9\pi}{8}$, $\text{cis}\,\frac{13\pi}{8}$ **c.** $\text{cis}\,\frac{3\pi}{4}$, $\text{cis}\,\frac{7\pi}{4}$ **d.** $2\,\text{cis}\,\frac{\pi}{6}$,

$2\,\text{cis}\,\frac{17\pi}{30}$, $2\,\text{cis}\,\frac{29\pi}{30}$, $2\,\text{cis}\,\frac{41\pi}{30}$, $2\,\text{cis}\,\frac{53\pi}{30}$

e. $\text{cis}\,0$, $\text{cis}\,\frac{\pi}{3}$, $\text{cis}\,\frac{2\pi}{3}$, $\text{cis}\,\pi$, $\text{cis}\,\frac{4\pi}{3}$, $\text{cis}\,\frac{5\pi}{3}$

f. $2\,\text{cis}\,\frac{\pi}{5}$, $2\,\text{cis}\,\frac{3\pi}{5}$, $2\,\text{cis}\,\pi$, $2\,\text{cis}\,\frac{7\pi}{5}$, $2\,\text{cis}\,\frac{9\pi}{5}$

2. a. 2, $2i$, -2, $-2i$ **b.** $2\sqrt{3} + 2i$,

$-2\sqrt{3} + 2i$, $-4i$ **c.** $\frac{1}{\sqrt{2}} + \frac{1}{\sqrt{2}}i$, $-\frac{1}{\sqrt{2}} + \frac{1}{\sqrt{2}}i$,

$-\frac{1}{\sqrt{2}} - \frac{1}{\sqrt{2}}i$, $\frac{1}{\sqrt{2}} - \frac{1}{\sqrt{2}}i$

d. $\sqrt{3} + i$, $-1 + \sqrt{3}i$, $-\sqrt{3} - i$, $1 - \sqrt{3}i$

e. $\left(1 + \frac{1}{\sqrt{2}}\right) + \left(1 + \frac{1}{\sqrt{2}}\right)i$, $\left(1 - \frac{1}{\sqrt{2}}\right) + \left(1 - \frac{1}{\sqrt{2}}\right)i$

f. $\left(-1 + \frac{\sqrt{6}}{2}\right) + \frac{1}{\sqrt{2}}i$, $\left(-1 - \frac{\sqrt{6}}{2}\right) - \frac{1}{\sqrt{2}}i$

3. a. $e^{\frac{5i\pi}{16}}$, $e^{\frac{13i\pi}{16}}$, $e^{\frac{21i\pi}{16}}$, $e^{\frac{29i\pi}{16}}$

b. 3, $3e^{\frac{2i\pi}{5}}$, $3e^{\frac{4i\pi}{5}}$, $3e^{\frac{6i\pi}{5}}$, $3e^{\frac{8i\pi}{5}}$

4. $2 + 3i$, $-2 - 3i$, $3.61\,\text{cis}\,0.98$, $3.61\,\text{cis}\,7.27$

5. $3e^{\frac{7i\pi}{15}}$, $3e^{\frac{4i\pi}{5}}$, $3e^{\frac{17i\pi}{15}}$, $3e^{\frac{22i\pi}{15}}$, $3e^{\frac{9i\pi}{5}}$

6. 0, $\sqrt{3}i$, $-\sqrt{3}i$

Problems 8.8

4. $4.37 - 1.27i$, $-0.37 + 1.27i$ **5.** $\text{cis}\,\frac{3\pi}{4}$,

$\text{cis}\,\frac{7\pi}{4}$, $\sqrt[4]{2}\,\text{cis}\,\frac{3\pi}{8}$, $\sqrt[4]{2}\,\text{cis}\,\frac{11\pi}{8}$

Review Exercises

1. a. $7 - i$ **b.** $-5 - 7i$ **c.** $\sqrt{34}$

d. $21 + i$ **e.** $-\frac{9}{13} + \frac{19}{13}i$ **f.** -9

g. $\frac{2}{13} + \frac{3}{13}i$ **h.** 34 **2. a.** $x = \frac{11}{3}$, $y = -\frac{7}{4}$

b. $x = -3$, $y = -3$; $x = 1$, $y = -1$

3. a. $3 + 6i$ **b.** $-2 + 14i$ **c.** $-10i$

d. $-1 - i$ **4.** $3 + 7i$

5.

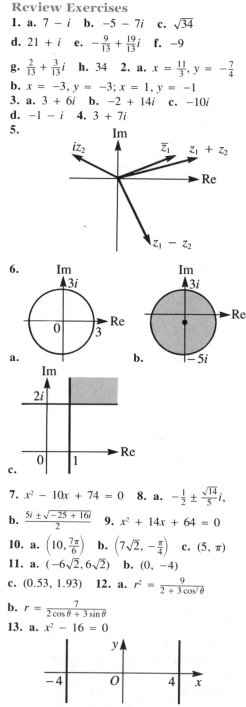

7. $x^2 - 10x + 74 = 0$ **8. a.** $-\frac{1}{2} \pm \frac{\sqrt{14}}{5}i$,

b. $\frac{5i \pm \sqrt{-25 + 16i}}{2}$ **9.** $x^2 + 14x + 64 = 0$

10. a. $\left(10, \frac{7\pi}{6}\right)$ **b.** $\left(7\sqrt{2}, -\frac{\pi}{4}\right)$ **c.** $(5, \pi)$

11. a. $(-6\sqrt{2}, 6\sqrt{2})$ **b.** $(0, -4)$

c. $(0.53, 1.93)$ **12. a.** $r^2 = \frac{9}{2 + 3\cos^2\theta}$

b. $r = \frac{7}{2\cos\theta + 3\sin\theta}$

13. a. $x^2 - 16 = 0$

b. $x^2 + y^2 + 6y = 0$

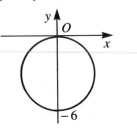

14. a. $4 \text{ cis } \frac{7\pi}{6}, 4e^{\frac{7i\pi}{6}}$ **b.** $3 \text{ cis } \frac{\pi}{2}, 3e^{\frac{i\pi}{2}}$

c. $17 \text{ cis } 2.06, 17e^{2.06i}$ **15. a.** $-\frac{3}{\sqrt{2}} - \frac{3}{\sqrt{2}}i$

b. $2i$ **c.** $-15 - 5\sqrt{3}i$ **d.** $512i$ **e.** -1

f. $-\frac{1}{8}i$ **16. a.** $i, -\frac{\sqrt{3}}{2} - \frac{1}{2}i, \frac{\sqrt{3}}{2} - \frac{1}{2}i$

b. $2 \text{ cis } \left(-\frac{\pi}{15}\right), 2 \text{ cis } \frac{\pi}{3}, 2 \text{ cis } \frac{11\pi}{15},$

$2 \text{ cis } \frac{17\pi}{15}, 2 \text{ cis } \frac{23\pi}{15}$

c. $1, \frac{1}{\sqrt{2}} + \frac{1}{\sqrt{2}}i, i, -\frac{1}{\sqrt{2}} + \frac{1}{\sqrt{2}}i, -1,$

$-\frac{1}{\sqrt{2}} - \frac{1}{\sqrt{2}}i, -i, \frac{1}{\sqrt{2}} - \frac{1}{\sqrt{2}}i$

Index